Springer Series in Computational Mechanics

Edited by S. N. Atluri

D. E. Beskos (Editor)

Boundary Element Analysis of Plates and Shells

With 112 Figures

Springer-Verlag
Berlin Heidelberg New York
London Paris Tokyo
Hong Kong Barcelona Budapest

Editor of the series:

Prof. S. N. Atluri
Center for Computational Machanics
Georgia Institute of Technology
Atlanta, GA 30332-0356
USA

Editors of this volume:

Prof. Dimitri E. Beskos
Department of Civil Engineering
University of Patras
GR-26110 Patras
Greece

ISBN 3-540-54464-X Springer-Verlag Berlin Heidelberg NewYork
ISBN 0-387-54464-X Springer-Verlag NewYork Berlin Heidelberg

Library of Congress Cataloging-in-Publication Data
Boundary element analysis of plates and shells / by D. E. Beskos.
(Springer series in computational mechanics)
1. Plates (Engineering) 2. Shells (Engineering) 3. Boundary element methods.
I. Beskos, D. E. II. Series.
TA660.P6B68 1991
624.1'776'0151535--dc20 91-31928

Typesetting: Camera ready by authors
Printing: Color-Druck Dorfi GmbH, Berlin; Binding: Lüderitz & Bauer, Berlin
61/3020-543210 – Printed on acid-free paper

Preface

Plates and shells constitute a large class of surface type of structures with one of their dimensions, their thickness, much smaller than the other two dimensions. The analysis of the behavior of these structures under static and dynamic loads is of great interest to scientists and engineers both from the theoretical and the practical viewpoint. Indeed, the analysis of these structures represents a very challenging and attractive theoretical problem, as well as a problem of great practical significance, associated with applications in many engineering fields, such as civil, mechanical, aerospace, etc.

It is well known that numberical methods of solution, such as the Finite Difference Method (FDM) and especially the Finite Element Method (FEM) are the only practical means for analysing this class of surface structures under complex boundary and loading conditions and/or realistic material behavior. During the last 20 years the Boundary Element Method (BEM) has emerged as a powerful tool for the numerical solution of various complex problems of mechanics. This method has some distinct advantages over domain type techniques, such as the FDM and the FEM for a wide class of structural analysis problems. Information concerning the application of the BEM to plate and shell analysis can be found in the form of rather short sections or chapters in a number of books devoted to the BEM and its applications to various fields of engineering science and mechanics. These sections or chapters, however, deal mainly with static analysis of plates and shells and do not cover the more recent exciting developments in the area. No specific book dealing exclusively with the analysis of plates and shells by the BEM and covering all the aspects of their behavior up to date exists in the literature.

The present book represents an effort to fill this gap in the literature by combining tutorial and state-of-the-art aspects of the BEM as applied to plates and shells. It aims at informing scientists and engineers engaged in the analysis of surface type of structures, about the use and the advantages of this technique, the most recent developments in the field and the pertinent literature for further study. The reader is expected to have a basic knowledge of plate and shell theory and applied mathematics.

The book is divided into nine chapters, written by persons very well known for their contributions in the field, which cover all the aspects of plate and shell analysis by the BEM existing to this date in the literature. More specifically, chapter one provides a comprehensive treatment of the static analysis of linear elastic Kirchhoff plates and plate systems by the conventional direct BEM and serves as an introduction to the basic concepts and ideas of the method. chapter two considers free and forced vibrations of linear elastic plates and plate systems by the conventional direct BEM and the domain (field) BEM in the time and frequency domains. Static and dynamic analysis of linear elastic Vlasov-Reisner shallow shells by the direct BEM and the domain (field) BEM in the time and frequency domains is the subject of chapter three. Nonlinearities are discussed in the next two chapters. Static and dynamic analysis of plates and shells exhibiting large elastic deformations and inelastic material behavior are discussed in chapter four and five, respectively. Linear and non-linear stability analysis of plates, plate systems and shallow shells is described in chapter six. Chapter seven deals with some special methods for static and dynamic analysis of elastic plates including the indirect BEM, the BEM based on biharmonic analysis and the BEM employing finite domain Green's functions. The special case of Reissner-Mindlin plates under static and dynamic conditions is taken up in chapter eight. Finally, chapter nine discusses two boundary type of methods for analysing elastic plates and shells under static and dynamic conditions, namely the boundary collocation and briefly the edge function method.

The editor would like to express his appreciation to all those who helped him during the course of preparing this book : to Professor S.N. Atluri, the editor of the Springer Series in

Computational Mechanics, for his encouragement and personal participation by writing one of the chapters of the book, to all the authors for their efforts and cooperation, to the publishing house of Springer-Verlag for their prompt cooperation and to his wife Georgia for her patience and understanding.

Patras, Greece 1991

Dimitri E. Beskos
Editor

Contents

Static Analysis of Plates

F. HARTMANN

Department of Civil Engineering
University of Kassel, D-3500 Kassel, Germany

Summary

The direct boundary element method is employed for the static analysis of homogeneous isotropic and linear elastic Kirchhoff plates and plate systems. Using Green's second identity, the plate bending problem is formulated in terms of two singular integral equations involving boundary lateral deflections, normal slopes, normal bending moments and equivalent shear forces.In the numerical implementation of the method use is made of a Hermitian interpolation for the lateral deflection and a piecewise linear interpolation for the other boundary functions.The computation of internal actions, the treatment of sub-domain load integrals, the handling of internal supports and the effect of singularities are discussed. Numerical examples illustrate the method and demonstrate its advantages.

Introduction

The boundary element method is now extensively used for the analysis of linear elastic, homogeneous and isotropic bodies because it offers important advantages over domain type methods, such as the finite element and finite difference methods, since only the discretization of the boundary is needed [1, 2] . In particular, the boundary element method has been successfully applied for the solution of plate bending problems over the past twenty years and has demonstrated its advantages over the finite difference method, which presents many difficulties in treating complicated boundaries,or the finite element method with its serious problems of C' continuity, non-conforming elements, patch test and discontinuous internal actions.

The boundary element method starts with an integral equation formulation of the problem and then proceeds to obtaining an approximate solution by numerically solving these equations. Classical potential theory is concerned with integral equation methods for harmonic functions, $\Delta u = 0$, but not biharmonic functions, $\Delta\Delta u = 0$. Though the results and techniques of classical potential theory easily can be carried over to the biharmonic equation governing plate bending, at the beginning it was Coursat's theorem which provided an inroad to the analysis of plate bending problems with integral equations.Goursat's theorem states that any biharmonic function can be represented as the real part of two analytic (= harmonic) complex-valued functions. This theorem allowed to recast boundary value problems for the Laplacian. Muskhelishivilli [3] made this technique popular by solving boundary value problems for Airy's stress function in the complex plane. Massonet [4] proposed this method for plate bending problems. Jaswon et al [5] applied this technique to plate bending problems and constructed suitable single-layer potentials (harmonic functions). The approach by Maiti and Chakrabarty [6] is also a layer approach. They introduce "bipotentials" which are sums of biharmonic and harmonic potentials.

Altiero and Sikarskie [7] have imbedded the plate in a larger plate for which the Green's functions for a concentrated load and moment are known and created an indirect boundary element method. Irschik and Ziegler [8] work with special regions where the boundary conditions are satisfied exactly at some selected edges while at other edges the densities are unknown. Also other authors have proposed new methods but very often these are suitable only for certain restricted classes of plate bending problems. For more information on these and other methods for plate bending analysis, one should consult the chapter on special methods for plate analysis of this book.

We favor the direct boundary element method, because it is not restricted to certain plate shapes or support or loading conditions and is formulated in terms of physical quantities in plate bending, namely deflection, slope, moment and shear. Forbes and Robinson [9] were the first to apply the direct method to plates with smooth boundaries. Next Bézine [10] and Bézine and Gamby [11] considered plates with corner points, though they did not place collocation points there. This was finally done by Stern [12] who was the first to give a complete description of the basic equations for polygonal domains. Review type of papers on the static analysis of plates by the direct boundary element method were also published by Tottenham [13], Hartmann [14] and Stern [15, 16], while a description of the subject can also be found in the books of Banerjee and Butterfield [17], Brebbia et al [18] and Hartmann [1, 19]. In all the aforementioned papers only very few and very simple examples were treated. Zotemantel [20], Hartmann and Zotemantel [21] and Hartmann [22] emphasized the numerical implementation and programming aspects in their work and presented many complex examples including two-way continuous slabs and plates with very complex planform and boundary conditions.

Use of direct boundary element methods for static analysis of blates has also been done by many other authors, among them, Bézine [23, 24], Gospodinov and Ljutkanov [25], Du et al [26, 27], Costa and Brebbia [28], Tanaka and Miyazaki [29], Stern and Lin [30], Song and Mukherjee [31], Wang et al [32], Kamiya and Sawaki [33], de Paiva and Venturini [34], Moshaiov and Eareckson [35] and Abdel-Akher and Hartley [36, 37]. Static analysis of plates on elastic foundation has been treated by special direct boundary element methods by Katsikadelis and Armenakas [38, 39] and Katsikadelis and Kallivokas [40, 41] and by conventional ones by Puttonen and Varpasuo [42], Costa and Brebbia [43, 44], Kamiya and Sawaki [45] and Bézine [46]. Bending analysis of anisotropic plates under static loading has been reported in Kamiya and Sawaki [47], Zastrow [48] and Shi and Bézine [49].

The present review briefly describes the direct boundary element method as applied to static plate bending problems and is based on the works of Hartmann [1] and Hartmann and Zotemantel [21] where the interested reader can look for more details.

Basic and Governing Equations

We consider a homogeneous, isotropic and linear elastic Kirchhoff plate under lateral loading p. In static equilibrium, the deflection w, the curvatures $\varkappa_{ij}$ and the bending moments M_{ij} of the plate satisfy the equations

$$\varkappa_{ij} - w,_{ij} = 0 \,, \qquad \text{(3 eqs)}$$

$$K[(1-\nu)\varkappa_{ij} + \nu\varkappa_{kk}\,\delta_{ij}] + M_{ij} = 0 \qquad \text{(3 eqs)}$$

$$-M_{ij,ji} = p \,, \qquad \text{(1 eq.)}$$

where

$$K = \frac{Eh^3}{12(1-\nu^2)}$$

is the bending stiffness of the plate with h being the plate thickness and E and ν the elastic modulus and Poisson's ratio, respectively. In the above i, j, k receive the values 1 and 2, summation convention is assumed over replated indices, commas indicate spatial differentiation and δ_{ij} is Kronecker's delta.

This set of basic equations is equivalent to a governing fourth-order differential equation for the deflection w, i.e..

$$K(w,_{1111} + 2w,_{1122} + w,_{2222}) = K\Delta\Delta w = p$$

alone, where Δ is the Laplacian operator. The displacement terms on the boundary are the deflection and the slope

$$w \,, \quad \frac{\partial w}{\partial n} = w_{,1}\, n_1 + w_{,2}\, n_2 \,,$$

where n is the unit outward normal vector and the force terms are the bending moment and the equicalent (Kirchhoff) shear

$$M_n(w) = M_{ij} n_i n_j \,, \quad V_n(w) = \frac{d}{ds} M_{nt} + Q_n$$

where s denotes the tangential direction. The Kirchhoff shear is the sum of the tangential derivative of the twisting moment M_{nt} and the shear force Q_n,

$$M_{nt} = M_{ij}\, n_i\, t_j \,, \quad Q_n = Q_1 n_1 + Q_2 n_2 \,,$$

where

$$M_{11} = -K(w_{,11} + v w_{,22}) \,, \quad M_{22} = -K(w_{,22} + v w_{,11})$$

$$M_{12} = -(1-v) K w_{,12}$$

$$Q_1 = -K(w_{,111} + w_{,221}) \,, \quad Q_2 = -K(w_{,112} + w_{,222})$$

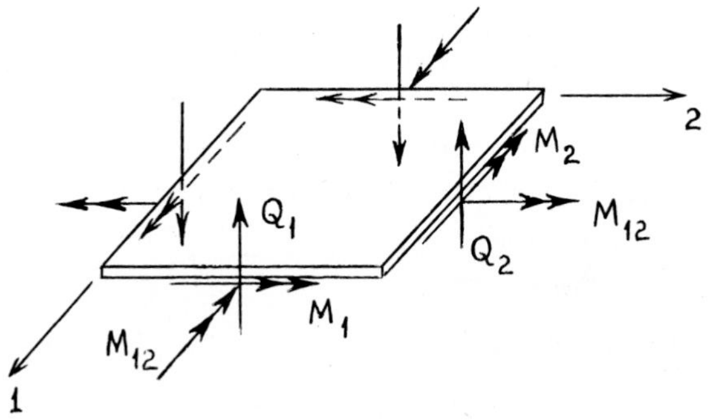

Plate forces and moments

The Direct Method

The basis of the direct boundary element method is Betti's principle or Green's second identity.

$$\text{p: } \hat{w}, w \in C^4(\bar{\Omega}),$$

$$\text{q: } B(\hat{w}, w) = \int_\Omega K\Delta\Delta\hat{w}\, w\, d\Omega + \int_\Gamma (\hat{V}_n w - \hat{M}_n \frac{\partial w}{\partial n} + \frac{\partial \hat{w}}{\partial n} M_n - \hat{w} V_n) ds$$

$$+ \sum_c [F(\hat{w})(\boldsymbol{x}^c) w(\boldsymbol{x}^c) - \hat{w}(\boldsymbol{x}^c) F(w)(\boldsymbol{x}^c)]$$

$$- \int_\Omega \hat{w} K \Delta\Delta w\, d\Omega = 0 \qquad (1)$$

where

$$\hat{V}_n = V_n(\hat{w}) \qquad \hat{M}_n = M_n(\hat{w})$$

$$V_n = V_n(w) \qquad M_n = M_n(w)$$

The term

$$F(\hat{w})(\boldsymbol{x}^c) = M_{nt}(\hat{w})(\boldsymbol{x}^c_+) - M_{nt}(\hat{w})(\boldsymbol{x}^c_-)$$

is the corner force at a corner point $\boldsymbol{x}^c$. The notation $F(\hat{w})$ (as also $M_{nt}(\hat{w})$ etc.) is to denote that F is associated with the deflection $\hat{w}$. The sum $\sum$ in Eq.(1) is to be taken over all corner points $\boldsymbol{x}^c$ of the plate.

The fundamental solution of the biharmonic operator $K\Delta\Delta$

$$g_0(\boldsymbol{y}, \boldsymbol{x}) = \frac{1}{8\pi K} r(1 + 2\ln r) r_n$$

gives the deflection at a point $\boldsymbol{y} = (y_1, y_2)$ if an infinite plate is loaded at some distant point $\boldsymbol{x} = (x_1, x_2)$ with a concentrated unit force $P = 1$. The distance between the two points

$$r = [(y_1 - x_1)^2 + (y_2 - x_2)^2]^{\frac{1}{2}},$$

is a function of both coordinates and it therefore can be differentiated with respect to y_i and x_i:

$$r_{,y_i} = \frac{y_i - x_i}{r}, \qquad r_{,x_i} = \frac{x_i - y_i}{r} = -r_{,y_i}$$

In the following we shall denote by

$$r_{,i} = r_{,y_i}$$

the derivate with respect to the coordinates y_i.

If the source point $\boldsymbol{x}$ lies on the boundary then we denote the normal vector and the tangent vector at $\boldsymbol{x}$ by $\boldsymbol{n}$ and $\boldsymbol{t}$,

$$\boldsymbol{n} = \{n_1, n_2\}^T, \qquad \boldsymbol{t} = \{t_1, t_2\}^T = \{-n_2, n_1\}^T,$$

and at an integration point $\boldsymbol{y}$ by $\boldsymbol{\nu}$ and $\boldsymbol{\tau}$

$$\boldsymbol{\nu} = \{\nu_1, \nu_2\}^T, \qquad \boldsymbol{\tau} = \{\tau_1, \tau_2\}^T = \{-\nu_2, \nu_1\}^T$$

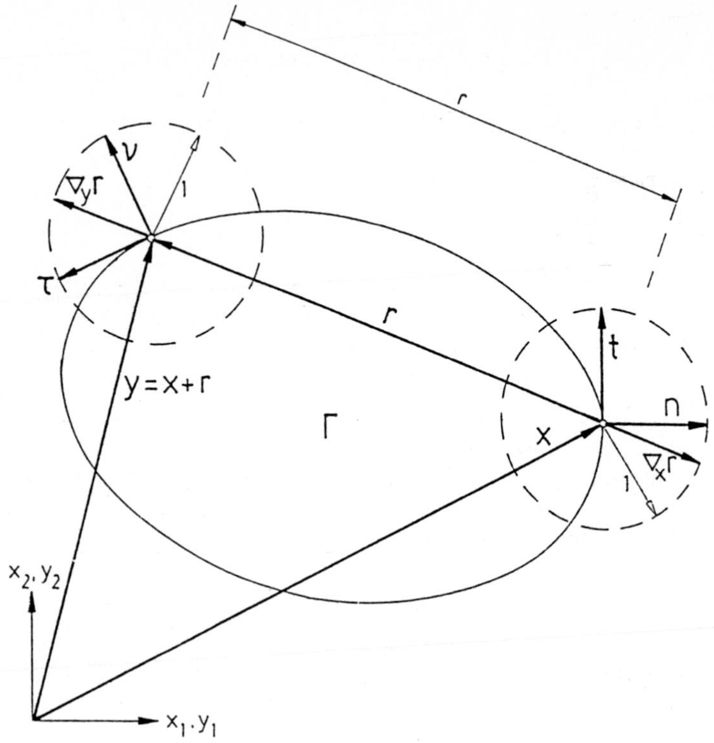

Figure 1 The source point $\boldsymbol{x}$ and the integration point $\boldsymbol{y}$

The directional derivatives

$$r_n = \frac{\partial r}{\partial n} = r_{,x_1} n_1 + r_{,x_2} n_2 = -r_{,1} n_1 - r_{,2} n_2 \,,$$

$$r_t = \frac{\partial r}{\partial t} = r_{,x_1} t_1 + r_{,x_2} t_2 = +r_{,1} n_2 - r_{,2} n_1 \,,$$

$$r_\nu = \frac{\partial r}{\partial \nu} = r_{,y_1} \nu_1 + r_{,y_2} \nu_2 = +r_{,1} \nu_1 + r_{,2} \nu_2 \,,$$

$$r_\tau = \frac{\partial r}{\partial \tau} = r_{,y_1} \tau_1 + r_{,y_2} \tau_2 = -r_{,1} \nu_2 + r_{,2} \nu_1 \,,$$

measure the rate of change of the distance r if the point $\boldsymbol{x}$ or $\boldsymbol{y}$ respectively moves into the direction of the normal or tangent vector. These directional derivatives are the scalar product between the gradients ∇r

$$\nabla_{\boldsymbol{x}}\, r = \{r_{,x_i}\}\,, \qquad \nabla_{\boldsymbol{y}}\, r = \{r_{,y_i}\}$$

and the pertinent directions. As all the vectors involved are unit vectors the values of these directional derivatives range from -1 to $+1$.

To derive an integral representation of the plate deflection we formulate Betti's principle $B(\hat{w}, w) = 0$ in terms of the fundamental solution $\hat{w} = g_0$ and the plate deflection w over the punctured plate Ω_ε and take the limit

$$\lim_{\varepsilon \to 0} B(g_0, w)_{\Omega_\varepsilon} =: B(g_0, w) = 0$$

This renders

$$c(\boldsymbol{x})w(\boldsymbol{x}) = \int_\Gamma [\, g_0(\boldsymbol{y},\boldsymbol{x})V_\nu(w)(\boldsymbol{y}) - \frac{\partial}{\partial \nu} g_0(\boldsymbol{y},\boldsymbol{x}) M_\nu(w)(\boldsymbol{y}) - V_\nu(g_0(\boldsymbol{y},\boldsymbol{x}))w(\boldsymbol{y})$$

$$+ M_\nu(g_0(\boldsymbol{y},\boldsymbol{x}))\frac{\partial w}{\partial \nu}(\boldsymbol{y})]\, ds_{\boldsymbol{y}} + \int_\Omega g_0(\boldsymbol{y},\boldsymbol{x})p(\boldsymbol{y})\, d\Omega_{\boldsymbol{y}}$$

$$+ \sum_c [\, g_0(\boldsymbol{y}^c,\boldsymbol{x})F(w)(\boldsymbol{y}^c) - w(\boldsymbol{y}^c)F(g_0)(\boldsymbol{y}^c,\boldsymbol{x})] \tag{2}$$

where the sum $\sum$ is to be taken over all corner points $\boldsymbol{y}^c$ of the plate. If the source point $\boldsymbol{x}$ coincides with one of the corner points, $\boldsymbol{x} = \boldsymbol{y}^c$, then the contribution of this point to the sum is neglected. The characteristic function in Eq(2) is

$$c(\boldsymbol{x}) = \begin{cases} 1\,, & \boldsymbol{x} \in \Omega\,, \\ \Delta\varphi/2\pi\,, & \boldsymbol{x} \in \Gamma\,, \\ 0\,, & \boldsymbol{x} \in \Omega^c\,, \qquad \text{(complement)}\,, \end{cases}$$

and the kernel functions are defined as

$$\frac{\partial}{\partial \nu} g_0(\boldsymbol{y},\boldsymbol{x}) = \frac{1}{8\pi K} r r_\nu (1 + 2\ln\, r)\,,$$

$$M_\nu(g_0(\boldsymbol{y},\boldsymbol{x})) = -\frac{1}{8\pi}[2(1+\nu)\ln\, r + (3+\nu)r_\nu^2 + (1+3\nu)r_\tau^2]\,,$$

$$V_\nu(g_0(\boldsymbol{y},\boldsymbol{x})) = -\frac{2}{8\pi r}[2r_\nu + (1-\nu)(r_\nu - \kappa r)(r_\nu^2 - r_\tau^2)]\,,$$

$$M_{\nu\tau}(g_0(\boldsymbol{y},\boldsymbol{x})) = -\frac{1}{4\pi}(1-\nu)r_\nu r_\tau$$

If we take the directional derivative of the fundamental solution g_0 with respect to a vector $\boldsymbol{n} = (n_1, n_2)$

$$g_1(\boldsymbol{y},\boldsymbol{x}) = \frac{\partial}{\partial n_{\boldsymbol{x}}} g_0(\boldsymbol{y},\boldsymbol{x}) = \frac{1}{8\pi K} r(1 + 2\ln r) r_n$$

and formulate Betti's principle over a punctured domain and then take the limit, [1] p. 355,

$$\lim_{\varepsilon \to 0} B(g_1[\boldsymbol{x}], w - w(\boldsymbol{x}))_{\Omega_\varepsilon} = \lim_{\varepsilon \to 0} \{ \int_{\Gamma_\varepsilon} [V_\nu(g_1(\boldsymbol{y},\boldsymbol{x}))(w(\boldsymbol{y}) - w(\boldsymbol{x}))$$

$$- M_\nu(g_1(\boldsymbol{y},\boldsymbol{x}))\frac{\partial w}{\partial \nu}(\boldsymbol{y}) - g_1(\boldsymbol{y},\boldsymbol{x}) V_\nu(w)(\boldsymbol{y})$$

$$+ \frac{\partial}{\partial \nu} g_1(\boldsymbol{y},\boldsymbol{x}) M_\nu(w)(\boldsymbol{y})] \, ds_{\boldsymbol{y}} - \int_{\Omega_\varepsilon} g_1(\boldsymbol{y},\boldsymbol{x}) p(\boldsymbol{y}) \, d\Omega_{\boldsymbol{y}}$$

$$+ \sum_c [(w(\boldsymbol{y}^c) - w(\boldsymbol{x}))F(g_1)(\boldsymbol{y}^c,\boldsymbol{x}) - g_1(\boldsymbol{y}^c,\boldsymbol{x})F(w)(\boldsymbol{y}^c)]\} = 0 .$$

we obtain an integral-representation for the normal derivative

$$c_1(\boldsymbol{x}) w_{,1}(\boldsymbol{x}) + c_2(\boldsymbol{x}) w_{,2}(\boldsymbol{x}) = \int_{\Gamma} [\, g_1(\boldsymbol{y},\boldsymbol{x}) V_\nu(w)(\boldsymbol{y})$$

$$- \frac{\partial}{\partial \nu} g_1(\boldsymbol{y},\boldsymbol{x}) M_\nu(w)(\boldsymbol{y}) - V_\nu(g_1(\boldsymbol{y},\boldsymbol{x}))[w(\boldsymbol{y}) - w(\boldsymbol{x})]$$

$$+ M_\nu(g_1(\boldsymbol{y},\boldsymbol{x}))\frac{\partial w}{\partial \nu}(\boldsymbol{y})] \, ds_{\boldsymbol{y}} + \int_{\Omega} g_1(\boldsymbol{y},\boldsymbol{x}) p(\boldsymbol{y}) \, d\Omega_{\boldsymbol{y}}$$

$$+ \sum_c [\, g_1(\boldsymbol{y}^c,\boldsymbol{x}) F(w)(\boldsymbol{y}^c) - [w(\boldsymbol{y}^c) - w(\boldsymbol{x})] F(g_1)(\boldsymbol{y}^c,\boldsymbol{x})] \tag{3}$$

where

$$\frac{\partial}{\partial \nu} g_1(\boldsymbol{y},\boldsymbol{x}) = \frac{1}{8\pi K}[2(r_\nu r_n + r_t r_\tau)\ln r + 3 r_\nu r_n + r_t r_\tau] \,,$$

$$M_\nu(g_1(\boldsymbol{y},\boldsymbol{x})) = - \frac{1}{4\pi r}[(1+\nu) r_n + 2(1-\nu) r_\nu r_\tau r_t] \,,$$

$$V_\nu(g_1(\boldsymbol{y},\boldsymbol{x})) = - \frac{1}{4\pi r^2}[\{3 - \nu - 2(1-\nu) r_\tau^2\}(r_\tau r_t - r_\nu r_n)$$

$$+ 4(1-\nu)(r_\nu - \kappa r) r_\nu r_\tau r_t] \,,$$

$$M_{\nu\tau}(g_1(\boldsymbol{y},\boldsymbol{x})) = - \frac{(1-\nu)}{4\pi r}(r_\tau^2 - r_\nu^2) r_t$$

and the c-functions are defined as

$$c_1(\boldsymbol{x}) = \begin{cases} n_1\,, \\ \dot{c}_1(\boldsymbol{x})\,, \\ 0\,, \end{cases} \qquad c_2(\boldsymbol{x}) = \begin{cases} n_2\,, & \boldsymbol{x} \in \Omega\,, \\ \dot{c}_2(\boldsymbol{x})\,, & \boldsymbol{x} \in \Gamma\,, \\ 0\,, & \boldsymbol{x} \in \Omega^c \end{cases}$$

Their boundary values

$$\dot{c}_1(\boldsymbol{x}) = \frac{\Delta\varphi}{2\pi} n_1 + \frac{\nu}{2\pi}[\frac{1}{2}\sin 2\varphi\, n_1 + \sin^2\varphi\, n_2]_{\varphi_2}^{\varphi_1}\,, \tag{4}$$

$$\dot{c}_2(\boldsymbol{x}) = \frac{\Delta\varphi}{2\pi} n_2 + \frac{\nu}{2\pi}[\sin^2\varphi\, n_1 - \frac{1}{2}\sin 2\varphi\, n_2]_{\varphi_2}^{\varphi_1} \tag{5}$$

depend on the angles φ_1 and φ_2 which the two tangents at the boundary point form with the x_1-axis. At smooth points, where $\Delta\varphi = \varphi_1 - \varphi_2$ is $180° = \pi$ the brackets in Eqs.(4) and (5) vanish,

$$[\sin 2\varphi]_{\varphi_2}^{\varphi_1} = \sin 2\varphi_1 - \sin 2\varphi_2 = 0\,,$$

$$[\sin^2\varphi]_{\varphi_2}^{\varphi_1} = \sin^2\varphi_1 - \sin^2\varphi_2 = 0$$

so that at such points

$$\dot{c}_1(\boldsymbol{x}) w_{,1}(\boldsymbol{x}) + \dot{c}_2(\boldsymbol{x}) w_{,2}(\boldsymbol{x}) = \frac{1}{2}\frac{\partial w}{\partial n}(\boldsymbol{x})$$

Note that in formulating

$$B(g_1[\boldsymbol{x}], w - w(\boldsymbol{x}))_{\Omega_\epsilon}$$

we subtracted the zero-order term of the Taylor expansion of w at $\boldsymbol{x}$, the constant term $w(\boldsymbol{x})$, from the deflection w. This is admissible because the normal derivative of a constant function is zero. If we seek the influence function for the bending moment $M_n(w)$ ('the second derivative') then we can subtract also the first-order (linear) terms of the Taylor expansion

$$B(g_2[\boldsymbol{x}], w - w(\boldsymbol{x}) - \nabla^T w(\boldsymbol{x})(\boldsymbol{y} - \boldsymbol{x}))_{\Omega_\epsilon}$$

$$g_2[\boldsymbol{x}] = M_n(g_0(\boldsymbol{y}, \boldsymbol{x}))$$

and if we seek the the influence function for the Kirchhoff shear $V_n(w)$ ('the third derivative') then we can subtract all terms up to the second-order (quadratic) terms of the Taylor expansion

$$B(g_3[\boldsymbol{x}], w - w(\boldsymbol{x}) - \nabla w^T(\boldsymbol{x})(\boldsymbol{y} - \boldsymbol{x}) - \frac{1}{2}(\boldsymbol{y} - \boldsymbol{x})^T \nabla\nabla w(\boldsymbol{x})(\boldsymbol{y} - \boldsymbol{x}))_{\Omega_\epsilon}$$

$$g_3[\boldsymbol{x}] = V_n(g_0(\boldsymbol{y}, \boldsymbol{x}))$$

This should be evident. You need to do this Taylor expansions also to calculate the Cauchy principal values of the hyper-singular integrals. The first terms of the Taylor

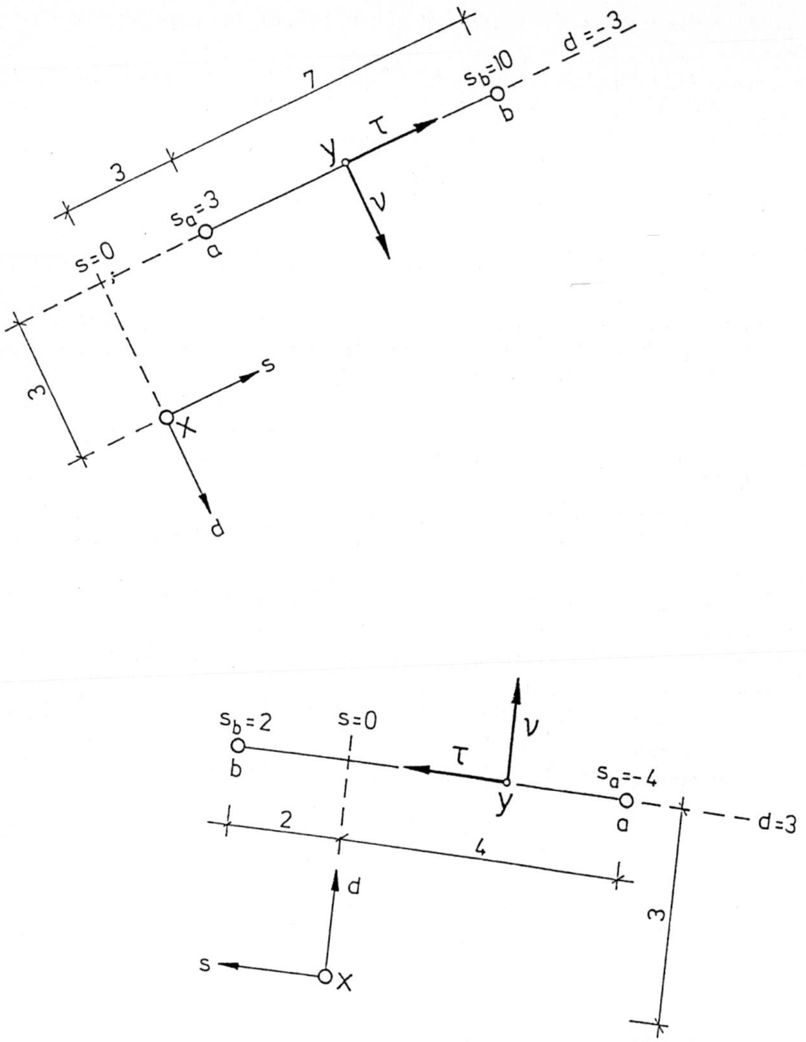

Figure 2 Orientation of coordinate system s, d

expansion power series are just the terms that counterbalance the negative powers of the hyper-singular kernels.

If we place the point $\boldsymbol{x}$ on the boundary then Eqs(1) and (3) constitute two integral equations for the four boundary values

$$w \qquad \frac{\partial w}{\partial n} \qquad M_n(w) \qquad V_n(w)$$

and the corner terms

$$w(\boldsymbol{x}_c) \qquad F(\boldsymbol{x}_c)$$

of a Kirchhoff plate. As two of the four boundary functions and one of the two conjugated corner terms are determined by support and loading conditions the two integral equations can be solved for the two unspecified functions.

Discretization

To solve these integral equations approximately we interpolate the boundary functions by polynomials which are defined piecewise over subregions of the boundary called boundary elements.

The unknown nodal values of these piecewise polynomials are determined by collocating the two integral equations (1.3) at K points $\boldsymbol{x}^k$ on the boundary.

Now for the boundary integrals to exist, the piecewise polynomial basis functions must be sufficiently smooth at the collocation points. The approximation of the deflection must be C^1 at the node (the tangential derivative must be continuous) and the approximation of the slope must be C^0, i.e. continuous.

Therefore we approximate the deflection w along the boundary by Hermite-polynomials,

$$w(\boldsymbol{x}) = w_i \psi_i(\boldsymbol{x}) + w_i' \chi_i(\boldsymbol{x}) \,, \qquad w' = \frac{dw}{ds} \,,$$

that is, C^1-functions with the interpolation properties

$$\psi_i(\boldsymbol{x}^j) = \delta_{ij} \,, \qquad \psi_i'(\boldsymbol{x}^j) = 0 \,, \qquad (\;)' = \frac{d}{ds} \,,$$

$$\chi_i(\boldsymbol{x}^j) = 0 \,, \qquad \chi_i'(\boldsymbol{x}^j) = \delta_{ij} \,,$$

and the other boundary functions by piecewise linear polynomials.

With respect to the coordinate ξ of the master element $0 \le \xi \le 1$ the functions ψ_i and χ_i are given as

$$\psi_i(\boldsymbol{x}) = \begin{cases} \xi^2(3-2\xi) \,, & \boldsymbol{x} \in \Gamma_{i-1} \,, \\ (\xi-1)^2(1+2\xi) \,, & \boldsymbol{x} \in \Gamma_i \,, \\ 0 \,, & \text{otherwise} \,, \end{cases}$$

$$\chi_i(\boldsymbol{x}) = \begin{cases} \xi^2(\xi-1) l_{i-1} \,, & \boldsymbol{x} \in \Gamma_{i-1} \,, \\ \xi(\xi-1)^2 l_i \,, & \boldsymbol{x} \in \Gamma_i \,, \\ 0 \,, & \text{otherwise} \,, \end{cases}$$

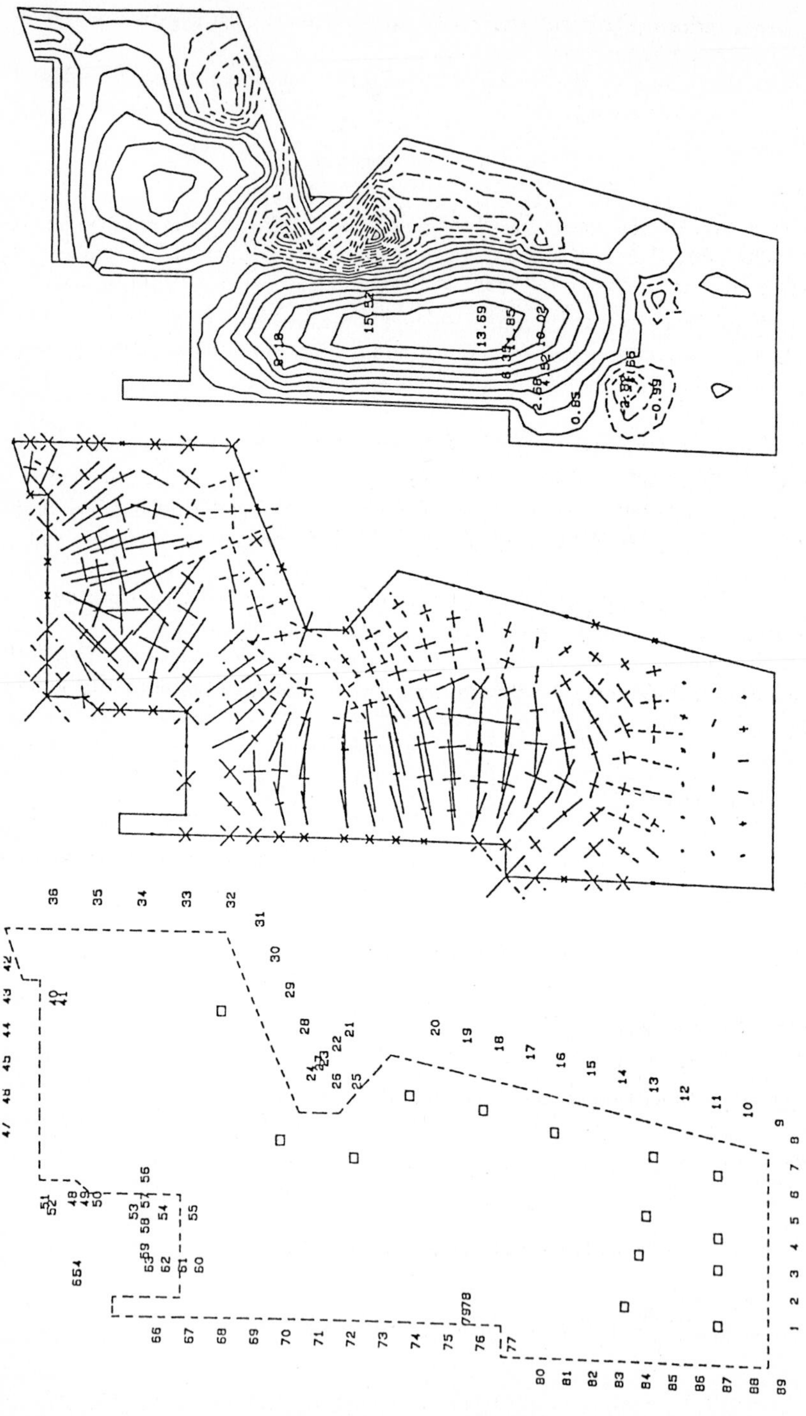

Figure 3 Plate analysis with boundary elements

and the linear functions $\varphi_i(\boldsymbol{x})$ are given as

$$\varphi_i(\boldsymbol{x}) = \begin{cases} \xi, & \boldsymbol{x} \in \Gamma_{i-1}, \\ 1-\xi, & \boldsymbol{x} \in \Gamma_i, \\ 0, & \text{otherwise.} \end{cases}$$

All boundary functions of a plate, except the deflection w, depend on the normal vector on the boundary, and therefore become discontinuous at corner points. To handle such discontinuities we assign to each function at each node two nodal values so that the approximation of, say, the Kirchhoff shear looks like

$$V_n(\boldsymbol{x}) = \varphi_1^i(\boldsymbol{x})V_1^i + \varphi_2^i(\boldsymbol{x})V_2^i,$$

where φ_1^i and φ_2^i are the restrictions of the hat-function φ_i onto the element to left of the node, Γ_{i-1} and to the right of the node, Γ_i.

The tangential derivative w' is eliminated when we assemble the element matrices. We replace it by finite differences of the nodal deflections w^i,

$$w'^i = \frac{1}{2}\left(\frac{w^{i+1}-w^i}{l_i} + \frac{w^i - w^{i-1}}{l_{i-1}}\right)$$

This substitution is done when the element matrices $\boldsymbol{H}^e$ are stored in the global matrix $\boldsymbol{H}$, see [1].

Singular Integrals

The integrals over the two elements Γ_{i-1} and Γ_i which enclose the collocation point $\boldsymbol{x}^i$ are Cauchy principal values. Employing the notations

$$l_i = \text{length of element } i, \qquad \lambda_i = \ln\, l_i$$

for the integrals over $\Gamma_{i-1} \cup \Gamma_i$ we obtain

$$\int g_0(\boldsymbol{y},\boldsymbol{x}^i)V_\nu(w)(\boldsymbol{y})\,ds_{\boldsymbol{y}} = \{[\frac{1}{4}(\lambda_{i-1} - \frac{1}{4})V_2^{i-1}$$

$$+\frac{1}{12}(\lambda_{i-1} - \frac{7}{12})V_1^i]l_{i-1}^3 + [\frac{1}{12}(\lambda_i - \frac{7}{12})V_2^i + \frac{1}{4}(\lambda_i - \frac{1}{4})V_1^{i+1}]l_i^3\}\frac{1}{8\pi K},$$

$$\int \frac{\partial}{\partial\nu} g_0(\boldsymbol{y},\boldsymbol{x}^i)M_\nu(w)(\boldsymbol{y})\,ds_{\boldsymbol{y}} = \int V_\nu(g_0(\boldsymbol{y},\boldsymbol{x}^i))w(\boldsymbol{y})\,ds_{\boldsymbol{y}} = 0,$$

$$\int M_\nu(g_0(\boldsymbol{y},\boldsymbol{x}^i))\frac{\partial w}{\partial\nu}(\boldsymbol{y})\,ds_{\boldsymbol{y}} = -\{[(\lambda_{i-1}(1+\nu)+\nu)w_{\nu_2}^{i-1}$$

$$+(\lambda_{i-1}(1+\nu)-1)w_{\nu_1}^i]l_{i-1} + [(\lambda_i(1+\nu)-1)w_{\nu_2}^i + (\lambda_i(1+\nu)+\nu)w_{\nu_1}^{i+1}]l_i\}\frac{1}{8\pi}$$

$$\int g_1(\boldsymbol{y},\boldsymbol{x}^i)V_\nu(w)(\boldsymbol{y})\,ds_{\boldsymbol{y}} = \frac{1}{3}\{\boldsymbol{\tau}^{i-1}\cdot\boldsymbol{n}\,l_{i-1}^2[(2\lambda_{i-1}+\frac{1}{3})V_2^{i-1}$$

$$+(\lambda_{i-1}-\frac{1}{3})V_1^i] - \boldsymbol{\tau}^i\cdot\boldsymbol{n}\,l_i^2[(\lambda_i-\frac{1}{3})V_2^i+(2\lambda_i+\frac{1}{3})V_1^{i+1}]\}\frac{1}{8\pi K}$$

$$\int\frac{\partial}{\partial\nu}g_1(\boldsymbol{y},\boldsymbol{x}^i)M_\nu(w)(\boldsymbol{y})\,ds_{\boldsymbol{y}} = \{\boldsymbol{\tau}^{i-1}\cdot\boldsymbol{t}\,l_{i-1}[-\lambda_{i-1}M_2^{i-1}$$

$$+(1-\lambda_{i-1})M_1^i]+\boldsymbol{\tau}^i\cdot\boldsymbol{t}\,l_i[(1-\lambda_i)M_2^i-\lambda_i M_1^{i+1}]\}\frac{1}{8\pi K},$$

and

$$\int V_\nu(g_1(\boldsymbol{y},\boldsymbol{x}^i))[w(\boldsymbol{y})-w(\boldsymbol{x}^i)]\,ds_{\boldsymbol{y}} - \int M_\nu(g_1(\boldsymbol{y},\boldsymbol{x}^i))\frac{\partial w}{\partial\nu}\,ds_{\boldsymbol{y}}$$

$$=2(1+\nu)\{\frac{2}{l_{i-1}}\boldsymbol{\tau}^{i-1}\cdot\boldsymbol{t}\,w^{i-1}+2(-\frac{1}{l_i}\boldsymbol{\tau}^i\cdot\boldsymbol{t}-\frac{1}{l_{i-1}}\boldsymbol{\tau}^{i-1}\cdot\boldsymbol{t})w^i$$

$$+\frac{2}{l_i}\boldsymbol{\tau}^i\cdot\boldsymbol{t}\,w^{i+1}+(\frac{3}{2}-\lambda_{i-1})\boldsymbol{\tau}^{i-1}\cdot\boldsymbol{t}\,w_1'^{\,i}-\frac{1}{2}\boldsymbol{\tau}^i\cdot\boldsymbol{t}\,w_1'^{\,i+1}$$

$$+\frac{1}{2}\boldsymbol{\tau}^{i-1}\cdot\boldsymbol{t}\,w_2'^{\,i-1}-(\frac{3}{2}-\lambda_i)\boldsymbol{\tau}^i\cdot\boldsymbol{t}\,w_2'^{\,i}+(\lambda_{i-1}-1)\boldsymbol{\tau}^{i-1}\cdot\boldsymbol{n}\,w_{\nu_1}^i$$

$$-\boldsymbol{\tau}^i\cdot\boldsymbol{n}\,w_{\nu_1}^{i+1}+\boldsymbol{\tau}^{i-1}\cdot\boldsymbol{n}\,w_{\nu_2}^{i-1}-(\lambda_i-1)\boldsymbol{\tau}^i\cdot\boldsymbol{n}\,w_{\nu_2}^i\}\frac{1}{8\pi},$$

$$w_\nu = \text{normal derivative}$$

The expressions

$$\boldsymbol{\tau}^i\cdot\boldsymbol{n}, \qquad \boldsymbol{\tau}^i\cdot\boldsymbol{t}$$

denote the scalar product between the tangent vector $\boldsymbol{\tau}^i$ of element Γ_i and the vector $\boldsymbol{n}$ in the fundamental solution g_1 or the associated tangent vector $\boldsymbol{t} = (t_1,t_2)^T = (-n_2,n_1)^T$.

Regular Integrals

Over straight boundary elements the product of kernel function times boundary layer can be integrated easily analytically if we switch to a system of coordinates s, d that is centered at the source point $\boldsymbol{x}$ and whose axis run parallel (s) and orthogonal (d) respectively to the element, s. Fig. 2.

In this system of coordinates the distance

$$r = [d^2+s^2]^{\frac{1}{2}},$$

varies only with the variable s (which is up to a constant 'translational' term the arc-length s on the element). The normal and tangential derivative of the distance r become

$$r_\nu = \frac{d}{r} \qquad r_T = \frac{s}{r} \qquad d = \text{fixed}$$

so that the kernel functions can be written as

$$\frac{\partial}{\partial \nu} g_0(\boldsymbol{y},\boldsymbol{x}) = \frac{1}{8\pi K} d(1+2\ln r),$$

$$M_\nu(g_0(\boldsymbol{y},\boldsymbol{x})) = -\frac{1}{8\pi}[2(1+\nu)\ln r + (1+3\nu) + 2(1+-\nu)\frac{d}{r^2}],$$

$$V_\nu(g_0(\boldsymbol{y},\boldsymbol{x})) = -\frac{1}{8\pi}[2(1+\nu)\frac{d}{r^2} + 4(1-\nu)\frac{d^3}{r^4}]$$

and

$$g_1(\boldsymbol{y},\boldsymbol{x}) = -\boldsymbol{n}\cdot\boldsymbol{\nu}\frac{1}{8\pi K} d(1+2\ln r) - \boldsymbol{n}\cdot\boldsymbol{\tau}\frac{1}{8\pi K} s(1+\ln r)$$

$$\frac{\partial}{\partial \nu} g_1(\boldsymbol{y},\boldsymbol{x}) = -\boldsymbol{n}\cdot\boldsymbol{\nu}\frac{1}{8\pi K}[1+2\ln r + 2\frac{d^2}{r^2}] - \boldsymbol{n}\cdot\boldsymbol{\tau}\frac{1}{4\pi K}\frac{ds}{r^2},$$

$$M_\nu(g_1(\boldsymbol{y},\boldsymbol{x})) = \boldsymbol{n}\cdot\boldsymbol{\nu}\frac{1}{4\pi}[(1+\nu)\frac{d}{r^2} + 2(1-\nu)\frac{ds^2}{r^4}]$$

$$+\boldsymbol{n}\cdot\boldsymbol{\tau}\frac{1}{4\pi}[(1+\nu)\frac{s}{r^2} - 2(1-\nu)\frac{d^2 s}{r^4}],$$

$$V_\nu(g_1(\boldsymbol{y},\boldsymbol{x})) = \boldsymbol{n}\cdot\boldsymbol{\nu}\frac{1}{4\pi}[4(2\nu-1)\frac{d^2}{r^4} + 8(1-\nu)\frac{d^4}{r^6}] - (1+\nu)\frac{1}{r^2}$$

$$+\boldsymbol{n}\cdot\boldsymbol{\tau}\frac{1}{4\pi}[2(1+\nu)\frac{ds}{r^4} + 8(1-\nu)\frac{d^3 s}{r^6}]$$

The polynomial basis functions defined on an element Γ_i can be expressed in terms of s as well

$$\psi_a = (\xi-1)^2(1+2\xi)$$

$$= \frac{1}{l^3}[2s^3 - 3(2s_a - l)s^2 + 6s_a(s_a+l)s - (-2s_a^3 - 3ls_a^2 + l^3)]$$

$$\psi_b = \xi^2(3-2\xi)$$

$$= \frac{1}{l^3}[-2s^3 + 3(l+2s_a)s^2 - 6s_a(l+s_a)s + s_a^2(3l+2s)]$$

$$\chi_a = \xi(\xi-1)^2 l$$

$$= \frac{1}{l^2}[s^3 - (3s_a+2l)s^2 + (3s_a^2 + 4ls_a + l^2)s - s_a^3 - 2ls_a^2 - l^2 s_a]$$

$$\chi_b = \xi^2(\xi-1)l$$

$$= \frac{1}{l^2}[s^3 - (3s_a+l)s^2 + s_a(3s_a^2+2l)s - s_a^2(s_a+l)]$$

$$\phi_a = 1-\xi = \frac{s_b - s}{s_b - s_a}$$

$$\phi_b = \xi = \frac{s - s_a}{s_b - s_a}$$

where

$$l = \text{length of element } \Gamma_i \qquad s_a\,, s_b = \text{coordinates of the endpoints}$$

– and an index a signals that the function is centered at the node $s = s_a$ and index b signals that it is centered at the node $s = s_b$. If we multiply these boundary layers with the kernel functions then all the boundary integrals can be expressed in terms of the following five integrals, [36],

$$I^k = \int s^k \ln r ds = \frac{1}{k+1}[s^{k+1} \ln r - J^{k+2}]$$

$$J^k = \int \frac{s^k}{r^2} ds = \begin{cases} [\frac{s^{k-1}}{k-1} - d^2 J^{k-2}], & k \geq 2, \\ \ln r, & k = 1, \\ \frac{1}{d} \tan^{-1} \frac{s}{d} & k = 0, \end{cases}$$

$$K^k = \int \frac{ds^k}{r^4} ds = \begin{cases} \frac{d}{2}[-\frac{s^{k-1}}{r^2} + (k-1) J^{k-2}], & k \geq 2, \\ \frac{d}{2r^2}, & k = 1, \\ \frac{1}{2d^2}[\frac{ds}{r^2} + \tan^{-1} \frac{s}{d}] & k = 0, \end{cases}$$

$$L^k = \int \frac{d^3 s^k}{r^6} ds = \begin{cases} \frac{d^2}{4}[-\frac{ds^{k-1}}{r^4} + (k-1) K^{k-2}], & k \geq 2, \\ \frac{d^3}{4r^4}, & k = 1, \\ \frac{1}{4}[\frac{ds}{r^4} + 3K^0] & k = 0, \end{cases}$$

$$M^k = \int \frac{d^5 s^k}{r^8} ds = \begin{cases} \frac{d^2}{6}[-\frac{d^3 s^{k-1}}{r^6} + (k-1) L^{k-2}], & k \geq 2, \\ \frac{d^5}{6r^6}, & k = 1, \\ \frac{1}{6}[\frac{d^3 s}{r^6} + 5L^0] & k = 0, \end{cases}$$

All these integrals are indefinite integrals. To apply these formulas to an integral over a given elment $\Gamma_i = [s_a, s_b]$ you, naturally, have to substitute the integration limits as in

$$I^2 = \int_{s_a}^{s_b} s^2 \ln r \, ds = \frac{1}{3}[s^3 \ln r - J^4]_{s_a}^{s_b} \qquad \text{etc.}$$

With these formulas an analytical integration of the regular boundary integrals for any given order n of polynomial shape functions (adaptive boundary elements !) can be carried out.

Results obtained with standard Gaussian quadrature show that there is no measurable gain of accuracy in the boundary values. Analytical integration and numerical quadrature render nearly identical results. But the gain in accuracy is remarkable if we calculate the internal actions at points close to the boundary. In Fig. 4 you see the distribution of the principal moments for a slightly skwe-angled plate. The stress-lines run parallel to the x-axis and so at the upper and lower edge the stress-points (these are the points at which we calculate the internal actions, compare these with the nodes of a finite element mesh) come close to the boundary. Gaussian quadrature with ten points over the boundary elements closest to the stress-points renders totally unreliable results. Figure. 5 shows the same results obtained with analytical integration. The gain in accuracy is remarkable. How we obtained these results will be explained next.

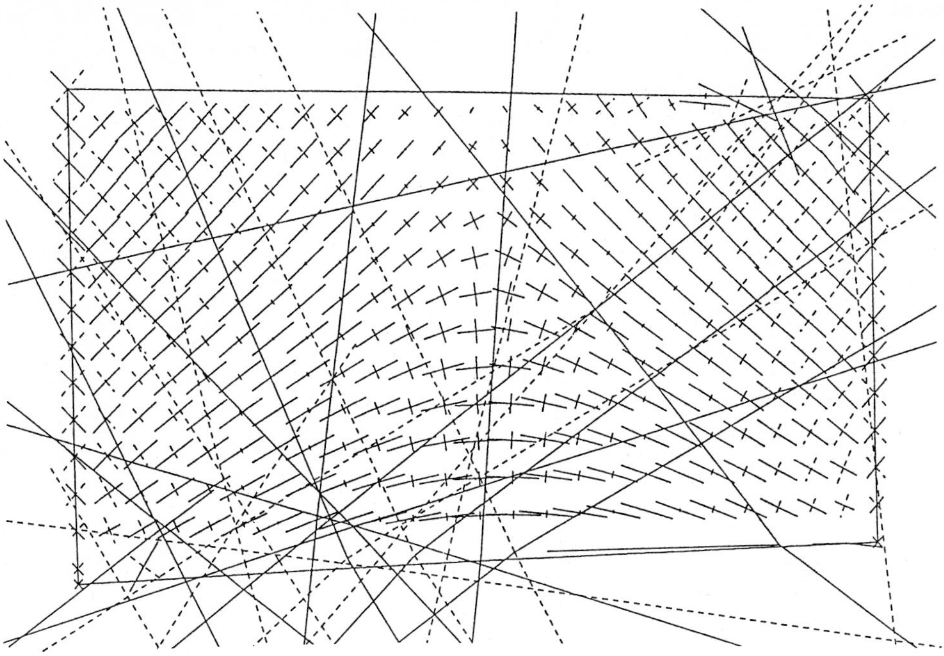

Figure 4 Numerical integration

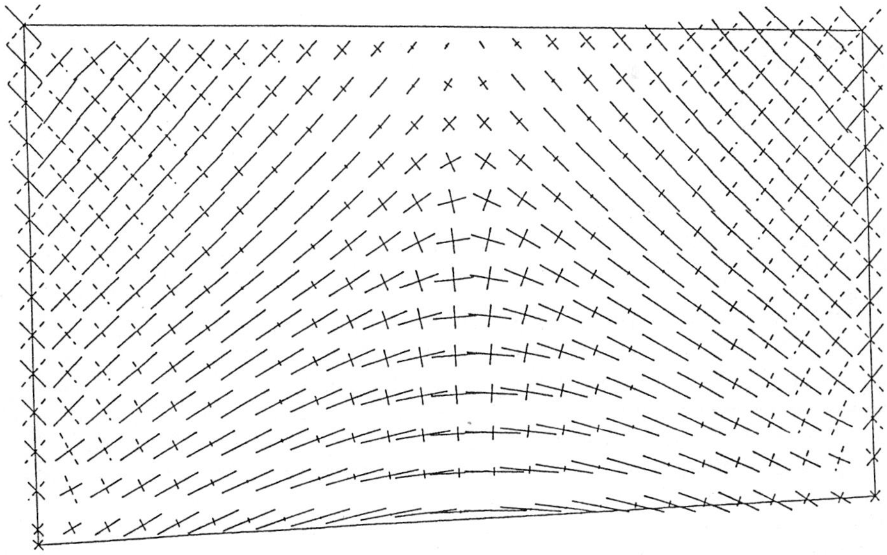

Figure 5 Analytical integration

Internal Actions

To calculate the bending moments

$$M_{11} = -K(w_{,11} + \nu w_{,22}), \qquad M_{12} = -K(1-\nu) w_{,12} ,$$

$$M_{22} = -K(w_{,22} + \nu w_{,11}),$$

which are linear combinations of the second order derivatives

$$w_{,11} , \quad w_{,12} , \quad w_{,22}$$

we have to apply the operator

$$\frac{\partial}{\partial m} \frac{\partial}{\partial n} w$$

to the kernel functions. These differentiated kernel functions consist basically of negative powers of r times the directional derivatives, see [1] Equ.(6.10),

$$r_n , \quad r_t , \quad r_m , \quad r_p , \quad r_\nu , \quad r_\tau$$

The two linearly independent vectors $\boldsymbol{\nu}, \boldsymbol{\tau}$ form a basis in the plane and therefore any directional derivative can be expressed in terms of the directional derivatives r_ν, r_τ as well. If we let the angles α, β, γ denote the orientati- on of the directions $\boldsymbol{\nu}, \boldsymbol{n}, \boldsymbol{m}$

$$\nu_1 = \cos\alpha , \qquad \nu_2 = \sin\alpha$$

$$m_1 = \cos\beta , \qquad m_2 = \sin\beta$$

$$n_1 = \cos\gamma , \qquad n_2 = \sin\gamma$$

then we can express the derivatives

$$r_n = -\cos(\gamma - \alpha) r_\nu - \sin(\gamma - \alpha) r_\tau$$

$$r_t = +\sin(\gamma - \alpha) r_\nu - \cos(\gamma - \alpha) r_\tau$$

and also

$$r_m = -\cos(\beta - \alpha) r_\nu - \sin(\beta - \alpha) r_\tau$$

$$r_p = +\sin(\beta - \alpha) r_\nu - \cos(\beta - \alpha) r_\tau$$

in that basis. Making these substitutions the kernel functions will contain only powers of r, r_ν and r_τ and consequently the boundary integrals can be written as linear combinations of the exact integrals I^k, J^k, L^k, M^k. This is the trick.

Now let us streamline this process a little bit. We can avoid the tedious elimination of the derivatives r_n, r_t, r_m, r_p if we begin the substitution process with the differential operators and express these operators in terms of the 'element intrinsic operators' $\partial / \partial \nu$ and $\partial / \partial \tau$ operators as in

$$\frac{\partial^2}{\partial m \partial n} = \cos(\beta - \alpha) \cos(\gamma - \alpha) \frac{\partial^2}{\partial \nu^2}$$

$$+ \sin(\beta + \gamma - 2\alpha) \frac{\partial^2}{\partial \nu \partial \tau} + \sin(\beta - \alpha) \sin(\gamma - \alpha) \frac{\partial^2}{\partial \tau^2}$$

Note that

$$r_{\nu\nu} = \frac{1}{r} r_\tau^2, \qquad r_{\nu\tau} = -\frac{1}{r} r_\nu r_\tau, \qquad r_{\tau\tau} = \frac{1}{r} r_\nu^2,$$

Hence we need a list of the derivatives

$$\frac{\partial^2}{\partial\nu^2}, \qquad \frac{\partial^2}{\partial\nu\tau}, \qquad \frac{\partial^2}{\partial\tau^2}$$

of the kernel functions. To this end we use the results Equ.(6.10) in [**1**] which lists the second order derivatives

$$\frac{\partial^2}{\partial n \partial m}(\,)$$

of the kernel functions in terms of $\boldsymbol{n}$ and $\boldsymbol{m}$. By making the substitutions

$$\begin{array}{llllll} \boldsymbol{n} = \boldsymbol{\nu} & \boldsymbol{m} = \boldsymbol{\nu} & r_n = -r_\nu & r_t = -r_\tau & r_m = -r_\nu & r_p = -r_\tau \\ \boldsymbol{n} = \boldsymbol{\nu} & \boldsymbol{m} = \boldsymbol{\tau} & r_n = -r_\nu & r_t = -r_\tau & r_m = -r_\tau & r_p = r_\nu \\ \boldsymbol{n} = \boldsymbol{\tau} & \boldsymbol{m} = \boldsymbol{\tau} & r_n = -r_\tau & r_t = r_\nu & r_m = -r_\tau & r_p = r_\nu \end{array}$$

we obtain the following results

$$\frac{\partial^2}{\partial\nu^2} g_0(\boldsymbol{y}, \boldsymbol{x}) = \frac{1}{8\pi K}(1 + 2\ln r + 2r_\nu^2)$$

$$\frac{\partial^2}{\partial\tau^2} g_0(\boldsymbol{y}, \boldsymbol{x}) = \frac{1}{8\pi K}(1 + 2\ln r + 2r_\tau^2)$$

$$\frac{\partial^2}{\partial\nu\partial\tau} g_0(\boldsymbol{y}, \boldsymbol{x}) = \frac{1}{4\pi K} r_\nu r_\tau$$

$$\frac{\partial^2}{\partial\nu^2}\frac{\partial}{\partial\nu}(g_0(\boldsymbol{y}, \boldsymbol{x})) = \frac{1}{4\pi K r}[r_\nu + 2r_\tau^2 r_\nu]$$

$$\frac{\partial^2}{\partial\tau^2}\frac{\partial}{\partial\nu}(g_0(\boldsymbol{y}, \boldsymbol{x})) = \frac{1}{4\pi K r}[r_\nu - 2r_\tau^2 r_\nu]$$

$$\frac{\partial^2}{\partial\nu\partial\tau}\frac{\partial}{\partial\nu}(g_0(\boldsymbol{y}, \boldsymbol{x})) = \frac{1}{4\pi K r}[r_\tau - 2r_\nu^2 r_\tau]$$

$$\begin{aligned}\frac{\partial^2}{\partial\nu^2} M_\nu(g_0(\boldsymbol{y}, \boldsymbol{x})) = &\frac{1}{4\pi r^2}([(1+\nu) + 2(1-\nu)r_\tau^2](r_\nu^2 - r_\tau^2) \\ &+ 4(1-\nu)r_\nu^2 r_\tau^2)\end{aligned}$$

$$\frac{\partial^2}{\partial\nu\partial\tau} M_\nu(g_0(\boldsymbol{y}, \boldsymbol{x})) = \frac{1}{4\pi r^2}[2(1+\nu) + 4(1-\nu)(r_\tau^2 - r_\nu^2)] r_\nu r_\tau$$

$$\begin{aligned}\frac{\partial^2}{\partial\tau^2} M_\nu(g_0(\boldsymbol{y}, \boldsymbol{x})) = &\frac{1}{4\pi r^2}([(1+\nu) - 2(1-\nu)r_\nu^2](r_\tau^2 - r_\nu^2) \\ &+ 4(1-\nu)r_\nu^2 r_\tau^2)\end{aligned}$$

$$\frac{\partial^2}{\partial\nu^2}(V_\nu(g_0(\boldsymbol{y},\boldsymbol{x}))) = \frac{1}{4\pi r^3}\{2r_\nu\{[3-\nu-2(1-\nu)r_\tau^2](r_\tau^2-r_\nu^2)$$
$$+4(1-\nu)r_\nu^2r_\tau^2\} - r_\tau\{12(1-\nu)r_\nu r_\tau(r_\tau^2-r_\nu^2)$$
$$-4[3-\nu-2(1-\nu)r_\tau^2]r_\nu r_\tau\}\},$$

$$\frac{\partial^2}{\partial\tau^2}(V_\nu(g_0(\boldsymbol{y},\boldsymbol{x}))) = \frac{1}{4\pi r^3}\{2r_\tau\{-2[3-\nu-2(1-\nu)r_\tau^2]2r_\nu r_\tau$$
$$-4(1-\nu)r_\nu^3r_\tau\} + r_\nu\{-8(1-\nu)r_\nu^2r_\tau^2$$
$$-2[3-\nu-2(1-\nu)r_\tau^2](r_\tau^2-r_\nu^2)$$
$$+4(1-\nu)r_\nu^2(r_\nu^2-3r_\tau^2)\}\},$$

$$\frac{\partial^2}{\partial\nu\partial\tau}(V_\nu(g_0(\boldsymbol{y},\boldsymbol{x}))) = \frac{1}{4\pi r^3}\{2r_\tau\{[3-\nu-2(1-\nu)r_\tau^2](r_\tau^2-r_\nu^2)$$
$$+4(1-\nu)r_\nu^2r_\tau^2\} + r_\nu\{4(1-\nu)r_\nu r_\tau(r_\tau^2-r_\nu^2)$$
$$-2[3-\nu-2(1-\nu)r_\tau^2]2r_\nu r_\tau$$
$$+4(1-\nu)(2r_\nu r_\tau^3-r_\nu^3r_\tau-r_\nu^3r_\tau)\}\},$$

The same technique can be applied to the third order directional derivative

$$\frac{\partial}{\partial l}\frac{\partial}{\partial m}\frac{\partial}{\partial n}w$$

It can be expressed as

$$\frac{\partial}{\partial l}\frac{\partial}{\partial m}\frac{\partial}{\partial n} = -\cos(\gamma-\alpha)\cos(\beta-\alpha)\cos(\gamma-\alpha)\frac{\partial^3}{\partial\nu^3}$$
$$-[\cos(\gamma-\alpha)\sin(\beta-\alpha)\cos(\gamma-\alpha)$$
$$+\cos(\gamma-\alpha)\cos(\beta-\alpha)\sin(\gamma-\alpha)$$
$$+\sin(\gamma-\alpha)\cos(\beta-\alpha)\cos(\gamma-\alpha)]\frac{\partial^3}{\partial\nu^2\partial\tau}$$
$$-[\cos(\gamma-\alpha)\sin(\beta-\alpha)\sin(\gamma-\alpha)$$
$$+\cos(\gamma-\alpha)\cos(\beta-\alpha)\cos(\gamma-\alpha)$$
$$+\sin(\gamma-\alpha)\cos(\beta-\alpha)\sin(\gamma-\alpha)]\frac{\partial^3}{\partial\nu\partial\tau^2}$$
$$-\sin(\gamma-\alpha)\sin(\beta-\alpha)\sin(\gamma-\alpha)\frac{\partial^3}{\partial\tau^3}$$

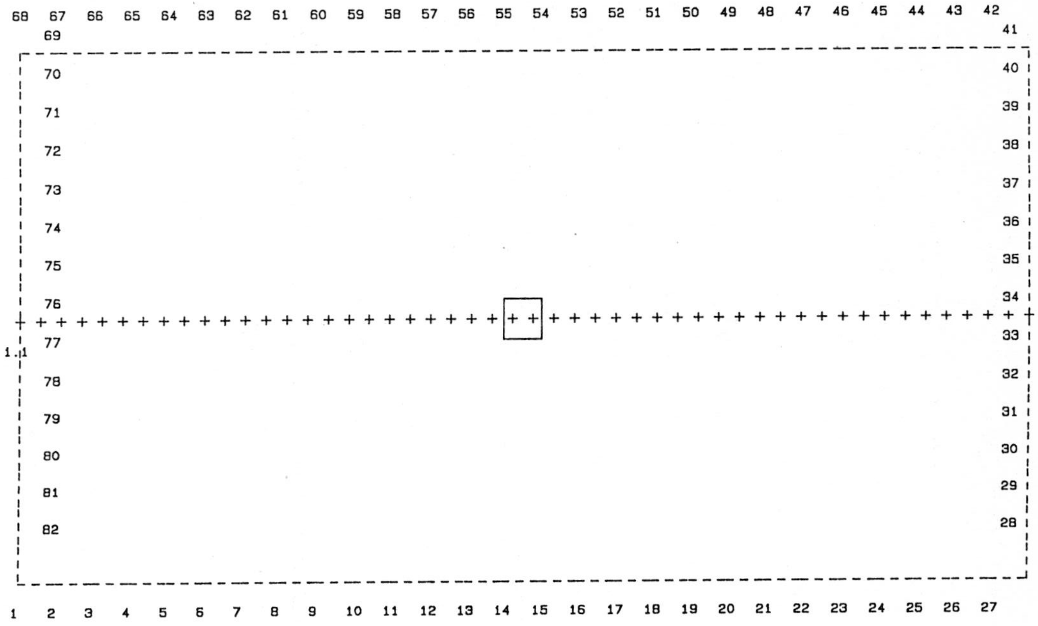

Figure 6 Rectangular plate with point support at the centre

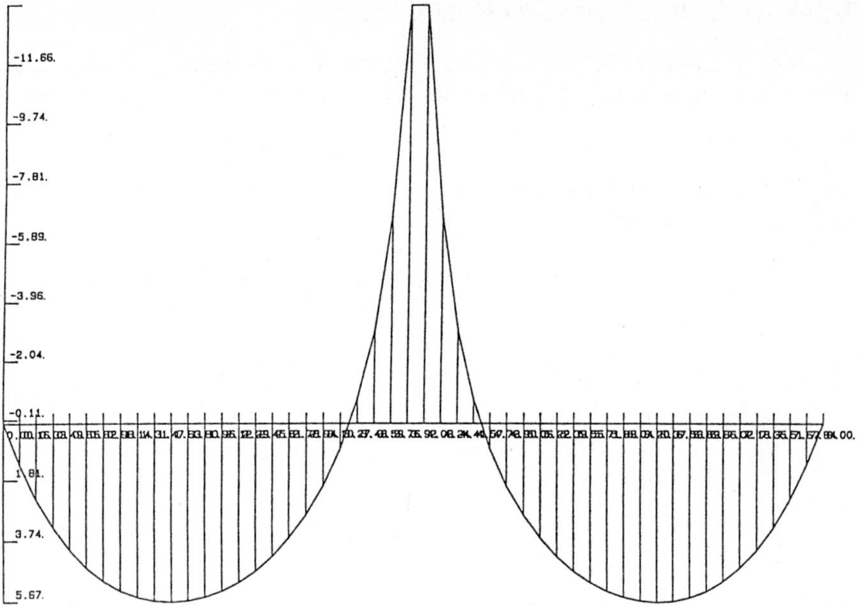

POS T3: VERLAUF VON Momenten mx [kNm/m] LAENGS LINIE 1.1

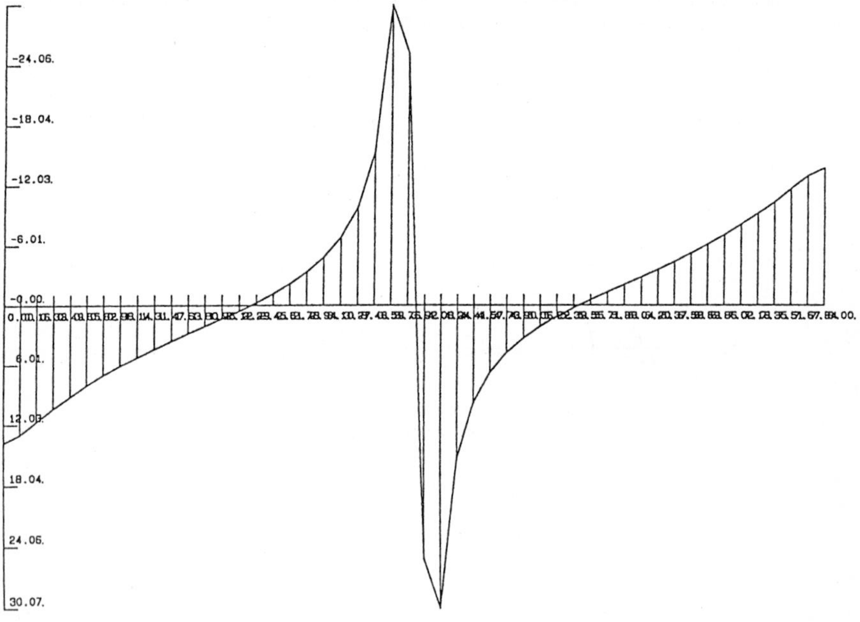

Figure 7 Distribution of bending moments m_x and shear forces q_x along the centre line

Internal Supports and Subdomain Loads

The influence of a single point support at a point $\boldsymbol{x}^P$ is considered by supplementing the influence functions for the deflection and the slope respectively with the functions

$$g_i(\boldsymbol{x}^P, \boldsymbol{x})P\,, \qquad i = 0 \quad , \qquad i = 1$$

where P is the unknown support reaction which is subject to the condition that the deflection is zero at $\boldsymbol{x}^P$,

$$w(\boldsymbol{x}^P) = 0 = \int\limits_{\Gamma} [\, g_0(\boldsymbol{y}, \boldsymbol{x}^P)V_\nu(w)(\boldsymbol{y}) - \frac{\partial}{\partial \nu} g_0(\boldsymbol{y}, \boldsymbol{x}^P)M_\nu(w)(\boldsymbol{y})$$

$$- V_\nu(g_0(\boldsymbol{y}, \boldsymbol{x}^P))w(\boldsymbol{y}) + M_\nu(g_0(\boldsymbol{y}, \boldsymbol{x}^P))\frac{\partial w}{\partial \nu}(\boldsymbol{y})]\, ds_{\boldsymbol{y}}$$

$$+ \int\limits_{\Omega} g_0(\boldsymbol{y}, \boldsymbol{x}^P)p(\boldsymbol{y})\, d\Omega_{\boldsymbol{y}} + g_0(\boldsymbol{x}^P, \boldsymbol{x}^P)P$$

$$+ \sum_{c} \{g_0(\boldsymbol{y}^c, \boldsymbol{x}^P)F(w)(\boldsymbol{y}^c) - w(\boldsymbol{y}^c)F(g_0)(\boldsymbol{y}^c, \boldsymbol{x}^P)\}$$

Because the bending moments become singular at the source point $\boldsymbol{x}$ the point load P later is spread over a small square which corresponds to the cross-section of the point support. By this technique we obtain a very accurate distribution of the bending moments and shear-forces near point supports, see Figs. 6 and 7.

Line supports γ are modelled by a series of elements Γ_i and the unknown support reactions are approximated by a series of linear functions

$$p_s(\boldsymbol{x}) = p_s(\boldsymbol{x}^j)\varphi_j(\boldsymbol{x})$$

and the influence of the support reactions $p_s(\boldsymbol{y})$ is represented by a line integral

$$\int\limits_{\gamma} g_0(\boldsymbol{y}, \boldsymbol{x})p_s(\boldsymbol{y})\, ds_{\boldsymbol{y}}$$

The domain integral of a (constant) subdomain load can be transformed into an equivalent boundary integral [50]

$$\frac{p}{8\pi K}\int\limits_{\Omega_p} r^2 \ln r \; d\Omega_{\boldsymbol{y}} = \frac{p}{64\pi K}\int\limits_{\Gamma_p} r^3(2\ln r - \frac{1}{2})r_\nu \, ds_{\boldsymbol{y}}$$

where Γ_p is the boundary of the subdomain Ω_p.

Applications

In this section we present a small selection of results obtained with a professional code, the program BE-PLATE-BENDING [22, 51]. The numerical details outlined above are implemented into this program, which can easily run on personal computers. Additional examples can be found in Hartmann and Zotemantel [21] and Hartmann [1, 22, 51]. All these examples are characterized by high complexicity of plate geometry and boundary and loading conditions and correspond to real civil engineering applications involving floor plates, slabs and bridge structures.

The first example deals with the analysis of the plate structure of Fig. 8. Results of a static analysis of this plate subjected to a uniform load are shown in Fig.9 in the form of principal moments and contour lines of the deflection. Figure 10 depicts the influence of a subdomain load onto the deflection near the free edge of the plate, while Fig. 11 the principal moments and contour lines for the moment m_x of the plate under the subdomain load. The second example deals with a floor plate with internal line supports as shown in Fig. 12. The same figure also shows the principal moments in the plate under dead weight.Finally the third example has to do with the floor plate of Fig. 13, which also shows its principal moments under dead weight. Figure 14 portrays the principal moments of the same plate for two additional load cases.

Conclusions

We close this chapter with a presentation of the most important conclusions resulting from the previous sections.

A general and advanced direct boundary element method for the static analysis of elastic Kirchhoff plates and plate systems of arbitrary geometry under arbitrary boundary and loading conditions has been presented. This method employs linear boundary elements and a Hermitian interpolation for the lateral deflection. Possible loading conditions are evenly distributed loads, discontinuous loads and concentrated forces or couples. The plate may be multiply connected and internal supports can be considered. The method does not require internal discretization and no mesh refinement is necessary at point supports.

The boundary element solution satisfies the equilibrium conditions, $K\Delta\Delta w = p$, exactly and the boundary conditions approximately. The solution is infinitely smooth if the distributed load p is in C^{∞} (p being a polynomial suffices to this end) so that, unlike finite element methods, the internal actions are also smooth. The typical jumps between elements are absent and good results are obtained not only at the Gauss points, but at any point, in contrast to the finite element method. The load area must not coincide with a patch of elements as in the case of finite elements and exact modelling of the singular stresses at point supports is possible. Whereas the equivalent nodal forces of finite element solutions are pseudo-concentrated forces, the boundary element method has no trouble in modelling the action of such forces or of higher singularities. This renders the method also an ideal tool to calculate influence surfaces. In conclusion, we think that the boundary element method outperforms the finite element method in this important area of static analysis of elastic plates.

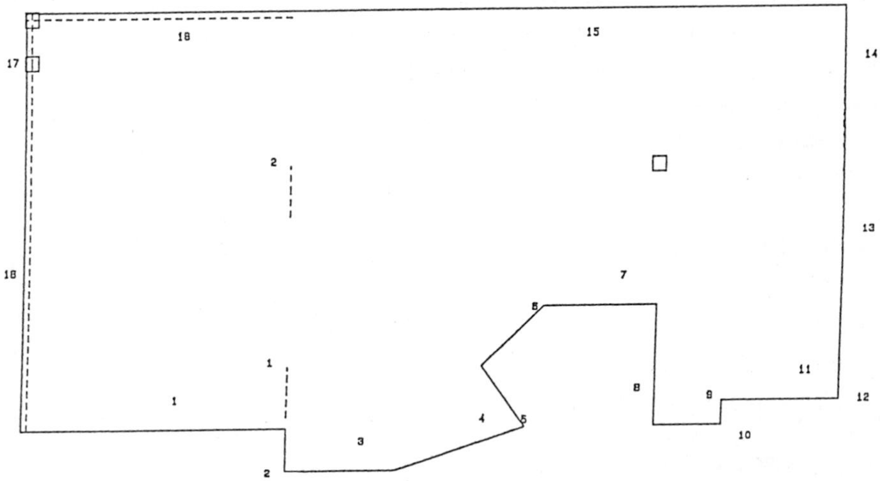

Figure 8 Subdivision of the edge into macro elements

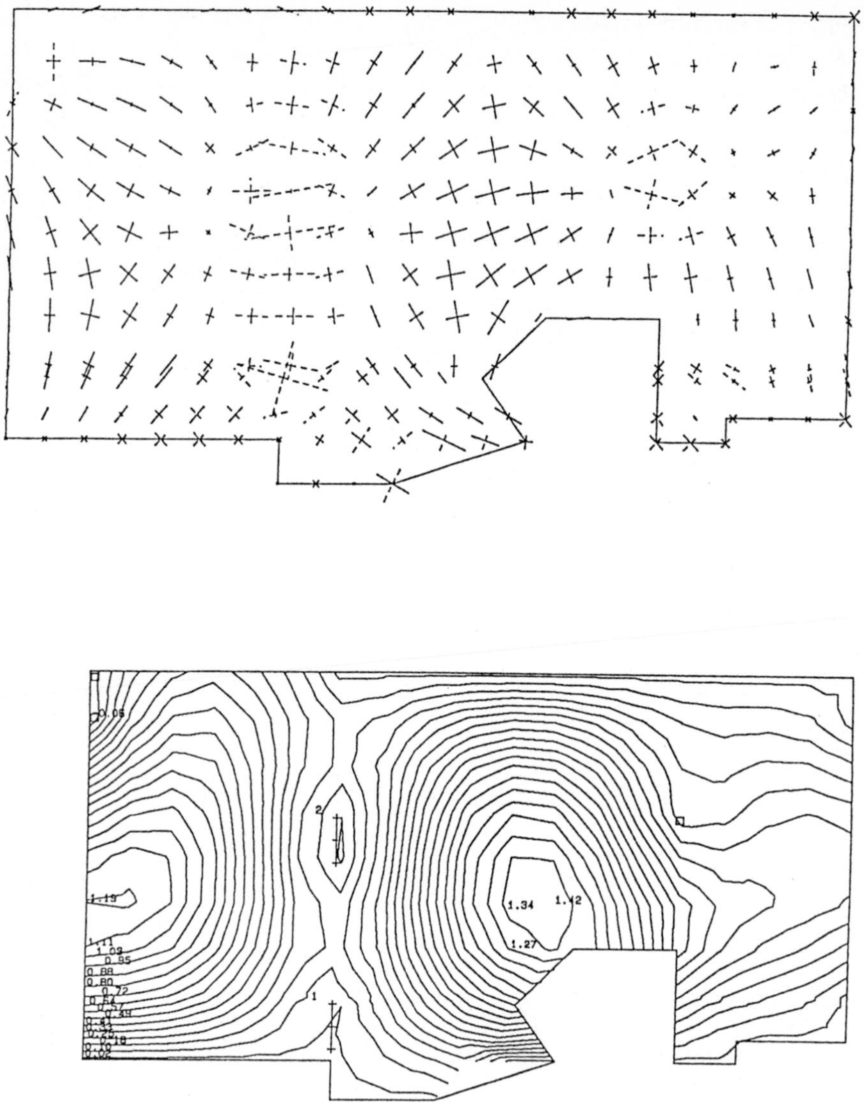

Figure 9 Results for a uniform load: principal moments and contour lines of the deflection

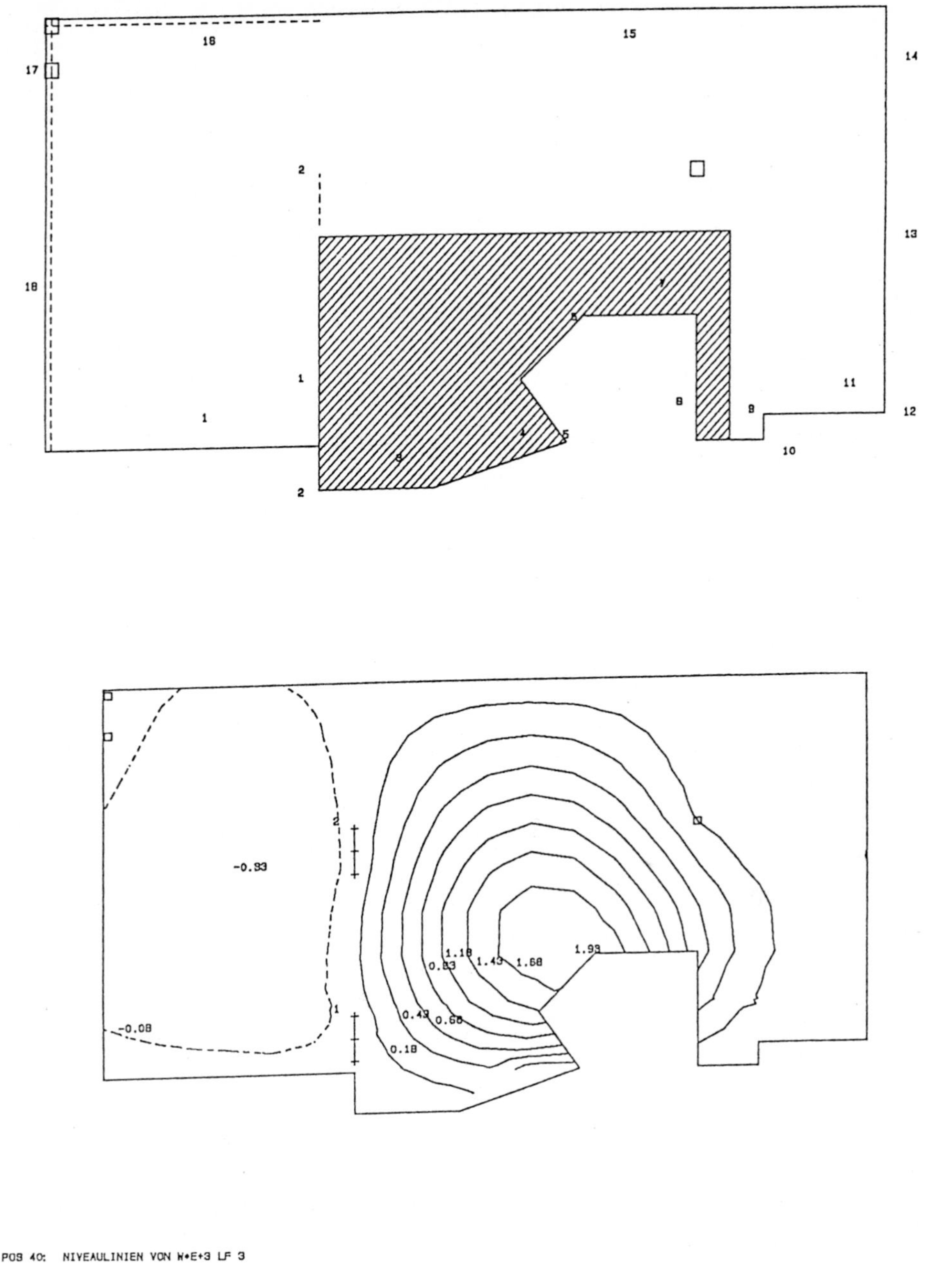

Figure 10 Influence of a subdomain load onto the deflection near the free edge

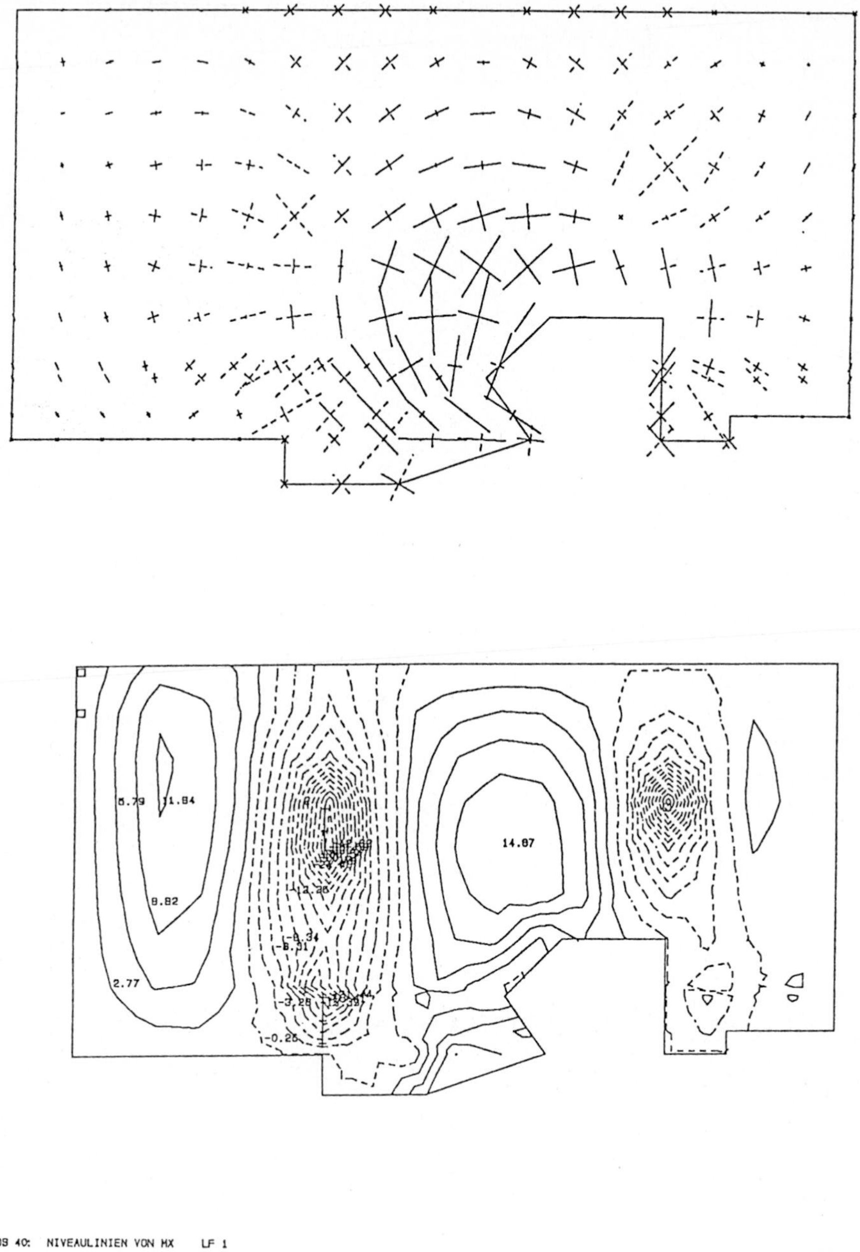

Figure 11 Principal moments and contour lines for m_x under the influence of the subdomain load

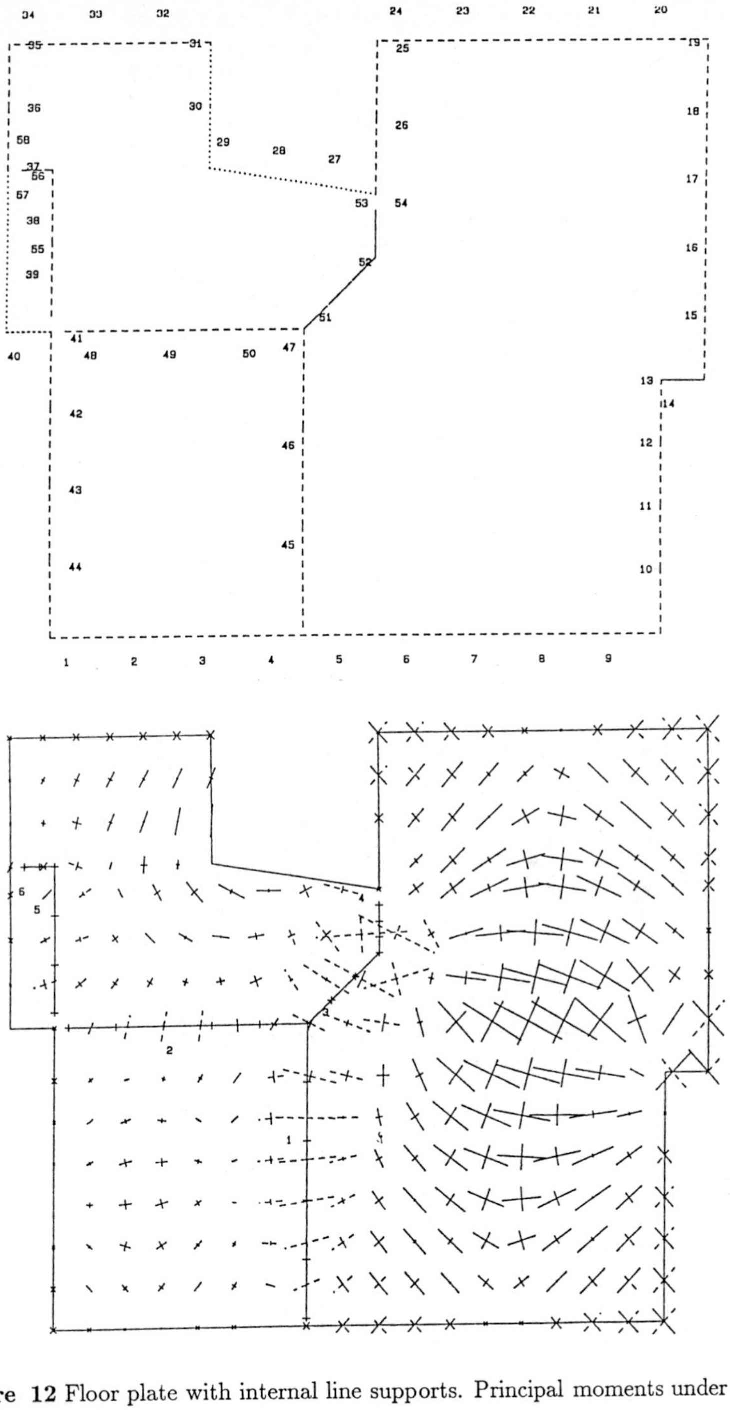

Figure 12 Floor plate with internal line supports. Principal moments under dead weight

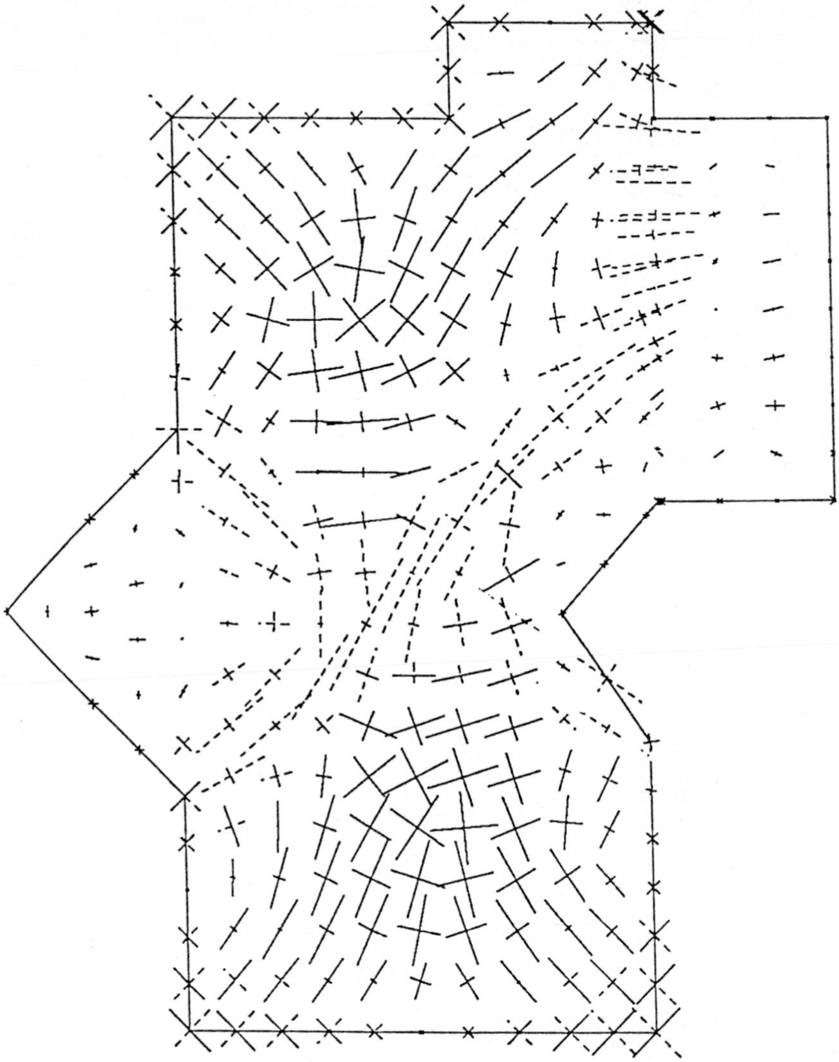

Figure 13 Principal moments of a floor plate under dead weight

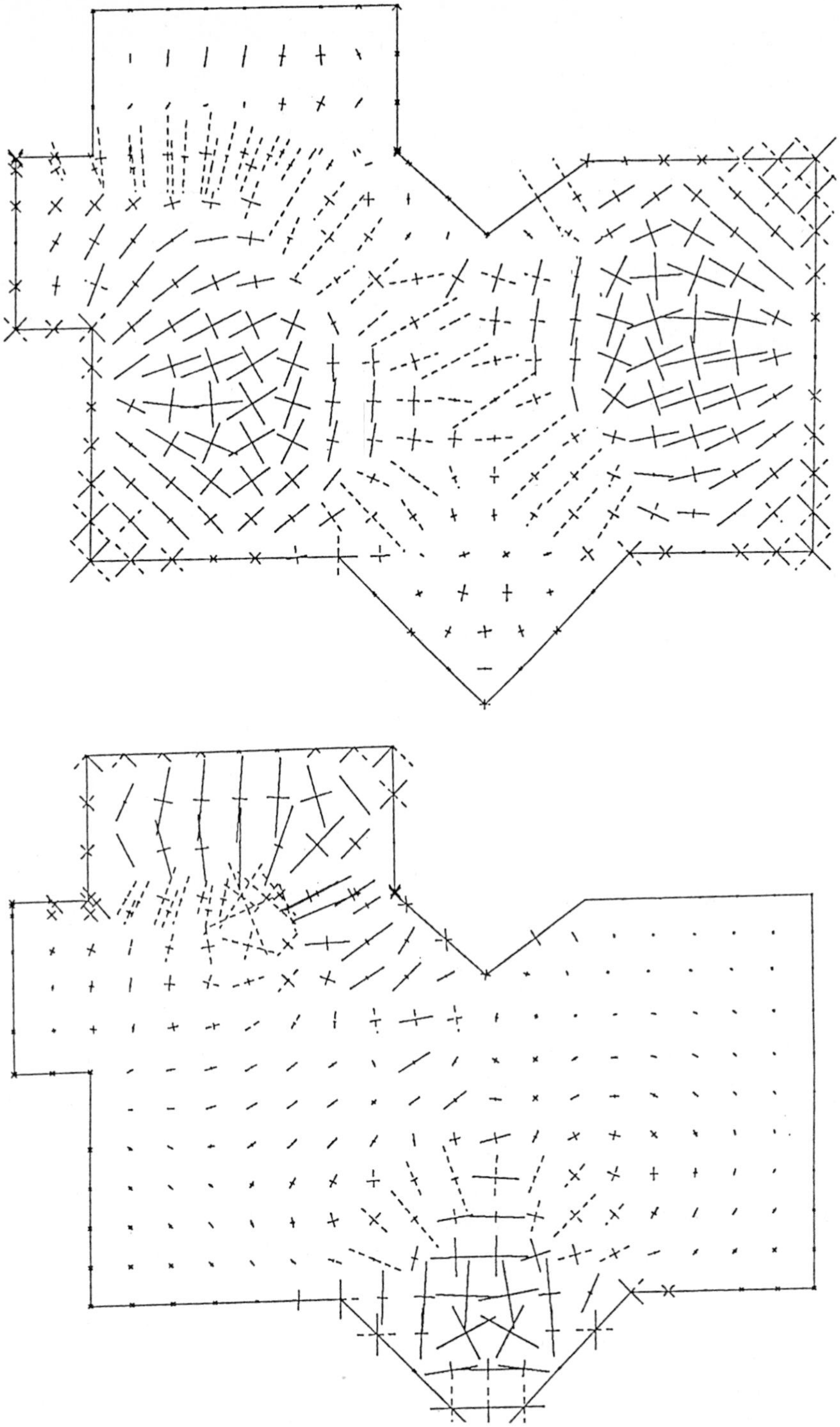

Figure 14 Principal moments for two additional loadcases

References

1. Hartmann, F.: Introduction to boundary elements. Berlin: Springer-Verlag 1989.

2. Brebbia, C.A.; Dominguez, J.: Boundary elements. An introductory course. Southampton: Computational Mechanics Publications 1989.

3. Muskhelishivili, N.I.: Singular intergral equations. Groningen: Noordhoff 1953.

4. Massonet, C.: Résolution graphomécanique des problems généraux de l' élasticité plane. Bull. Centre Et. Rech. Essais Sc. Génie Civil. 4, 169-180.

5. Jaswon, M.A.; Maiti, M.; Symm, G.T.: Numerical biharmonic analysis and some applications. Int. J. Solids Struct. 3 (1967) 309-332.

6. Maiti, M.; Chakrabarty, S.K.: Integral equation solutions for simply supported polygonal plates. Int. J. Engng. Sci. 12 (1974) 793-806.

7. Altiero, N.; Sikarskie, D.: A boundary integral method applied to plates of arbitrary plane form. Comput. Struct. 9 (1978) 163-168.

8. Irschik, H.; Ziegler, F.: Application of the Green's function method to thin elastic polygonal plates. Acta Mech. 39 (1981) 155-169.

9. Forbes, D.J.; Robinson, A.R.: Numerical analysis of elastic plates and shallow shells by an integral equation method. Struct. Res. Ser. Rept. 345. Urbana: University of Illinois 1969.

10. Bézine, G.: Boundary integral formulation for plate flexure with arbitrary boundary conditions. Mech. Res. Comm. 5 (1978) 197-206.

11. Bézine, G.P.; Gamby, D.A.: A new integral equation formulation for plate bending problems, in: Recent advances in boundary element methods. C. A. Brebbia (ed.). London: Pentech Press 1978. pp. 327-342.

12. Stern, M.: A general boundary integral formulation for the numerical solution of plate bending problems. Int. J. Solids Struct. 15 (1979) 769-782.

13. Tottenham, H.: The boundary element method for plates and shells, in : Developments in boundary element methods - 1, P.K. Banerjee and R. Butterfield (eds.). London: Applied Science Publishers 1979. pp. 173-205.

14. Hartmann, F.; Elastostatics, in: Progress in boundary element methods - Vol. 1. C.A. Brebbia (ed.). New York: John Wiley & Sons 1981. pp. 84-167.

15. Stern, M.: Boundary integral equations for bending of thin plates, in: Progress in boundary element methods - Vol. 2. C.A. Brebbia (ed.). London: Pentech Press 1983. pp. 158-181.

16. Stern, M.: Static analysis of beams, plates and shells, in: Boundary element methods in structural analysis. D.E. Beskos (Ed.). New York: ASCE 1989. pp. 41-64.

17. Banerjee, P.K.; Butterfield, R.: Boundary element methods in engineering science. London: Mc Graw-Hill 1981.

18. Brebbia, C.A.; Telles, J.C.F.; Wrobel, L.C.: Boundary element techniques. Berlin: Springer-Verlag 1984.

19. Hartmann, F.: The mathematical foundation of structural mechanics. Berlin: Springer-Verlag 1985.

20. Zotemantel, R.: Numerical solution of plate bending problems using the boundary element method, in: Boundary elements VII-Vol. 1. C.A. Brebbia and G. Maier (eds). Berlin: Springer-Verlag 1985. pp. 4.81 - 4.91.

21. Hartmann, F.; Zotemantel, R.: The direct boundary element method in plate bending. Int. J. Num. Meth. Engng. 23 (1986) 2049-2069.

22. Hartmann, F.: Kirchhoff plates, in: Boundary elements X - Vol. 3. C.A. Brebbia (ed.). Berlin: Springer-Verlag 1988. pp. 409-423.

23. Bézine, G.: A boundary integral equation method for plate flexure with conditions inside the domain. Int. J. Num. Meth. Engng. 17 (1981) 1647-1657.

24. Bézine, G.: Application of similarity to research of new boundary integral equations for plate flexure problems. Appl. Math. Modelling. 5 (1981) 66--70.

25. Gospodinov, G.; Ljutskanov, D.: The boundary element method applied to plates. Appl. Math. Modelling. 6 (1982) 237-244.

26. Du, Q.; Yao, Z.; Song, G.: Solution of some plate bending problems using the boundary element method. Appl. Math. Modelling 8 (1984) 15-22.

27. Du, Q.H.; Lu, X.L.: Some further works for the Kirchhoff plate bending problems by highly conforming boundary element method, in: Boundary elements VIII - Vol. 1. M. Tanaka and C.A. Brebbia (eds.). Berlin: Springer-Verlag 1986. pp. 475-485.

28. Costa, Jr., J.A.; Brebbia, C.A.: Plate bending problems using B.E.M., in : Boundary elements VI. C.A. Brebbia (ed.). Berlin: Springer-Verlag 1984, pp. 3.43 - 3.63.

29. Tanaka, M.; Miyazaki, K.: A direct BEM for elastic plate structures subjected to arbitrary loadings, in: Boundary elements VII. C.A. Brebbia and G. Maier (eds.). Berlin: Springer-Verlag 1985. pp. 4.3 - 4.16.

30. Stern, M.; Lin, T.L.: Thin elastic plates in bending, in: Developments in boundary element methods - 4. P.K. Banerjee and J.O. Watson (eds.). London: Elsevier Applied Science Publishers 1986. pp. 91-119.

31. Song, G.S.; Mukherjee, S.: Boundary element method analysis of bending of elastic plates of arbitrary shape with general boundary conditions. Engng. Anal. 3 (1986) 36-44.

32. Wang, Y.C.; Jiang, L.Z.; Li, J.; Wang, Z.H.: Spline boundary element method for plate bending problems, in: Boundary elements. Q. Du (ed.). Oxford: Pergamon Press 1986. pp. 427-436.

33. Kamiya, N.; Sawaki, Y.: Boundary element analysis of plate bending problem with nonlinear boundary conditions, in: Boundary elements. Q. Du (ed.). Oxford: Pergamon Press 1986. pp. 383-392.

34. de Paiva, J.B.; Venturini, W.S.: Analysis of building structures considerning plate-beam-column interactions, in: Boundary element techniques: applica-

tions in stress analysis and heat transfer. C.A. Brebbia and W.S. Venturini (eds.). Southampton: Computational Mechanics Publications 1987. pp. 209-219.

35. Moshaiov, A.; Eareckson, P.D.: Analysis of axisummetrically loaded annular plates using Green's functions. Comput. Struct. 28 (1988) 59-66.

36. Abdel-Akher, A.; Hartley, G.A.: Evaluation of boundary integrals for plate bending. Int. J. Num. Meth. Engng. 28 (1989) 75-93.

37. Abdel-Akher, A.: Hartley, G.A.: Boundary integration and interpolation procedures for plate bending. Int. J. Num. Meth. Engng. 28 (1989) 1389-1408.

38. Katsikadelis, J.T.; Armenakas, A.E.: Analysis of clamped plates on elastic foundation by the boundary integral equation method. J. Appl. Mech.ASME, 51 (1984) 574-580.

39. Katsikadelis, J.T.; Armenakas, A.E.: Plates onf elastic foundation by BIE method. J. Engng. Mech. ASCE. 110 (1984) 1086-1105.

40. Katsikadelis, J.T.: Kallivokas, L.F.: Clamped plates on Pasternak-type elastic foundation by the boundary element method. J. Appl. Mech. ASME 53 (1986) 909-917.

41. Katsikadellis, J.T.: Kallivokas, L.F.: Plates on biparametric elastic foundation by BDIE method. J. Engng. Mech. ASCE. 114 (1988) 847-875.

42. Puttonen, J.; Varpasuo, P.: Boundary element analysis of a plate on elastic foundations. Int. J. Num. Meth. Engng. 23 (1986) 287-303.

43. Costa, Jr., J.A.,; Brebbia, C.A.: Bending of plates on elastic foundations using the boundary element method, in: Variational methods in engineering. C.A. Brebbia (ed.). Berrlin: Springer-Verlag 1985. pp. 5.23-5.33.

44. Costa, Jr., J.A.; Brebbia, C.A.: On the reduction of domain integrals to the boundary for the BEM formulation of plates on elastic foundation. Engng. Anal. 3 (1986) 123-126.

45. Kamiya, N.; Sawaki, Y.; An alternative boundary element analysis of plates resting on elastic foundation, in: Boundary elements VIII - Vol. 2. M. Tanaka and C.A. Brebbia (eds.). Berlin: Springer-Verlag 1986. pp. 561-570.

46. Bézine, G.: A new boundary element method for bending of plates on elastic foundations. Int. J. Solids Struct. 24 (1988) 557-565.

47. Kamiya, N.; Sawaki, Y.: A general boundary element method for bending analysis of orthotropic elastic plates. Res Mech. 5 (1982) 329-334.

48. Zastrow, U.: A boundary integral equation for anisotropic plates with simly-supported smooth edges, in: Boundary elements. Q. Du (ed.). Oxford : Pergamon Press 1986. pp. 393-402.

49. Shi, G.; Bézine, G.: A general boundary integral formulation for the anisotropic plate bending problems. J. Compos. Matls. 22 (1988) 694-716.

50. Hartmann, F.: A note on the domain force integral of Kirchhoff plates. Engng. Anal. 2 (1985) 111-112.

51. Hartmann, F.: Methode der randelemente. Boundary elements in der mechanik auf dem PC. Berlin: Springer-Verlag 1987.

Dynamic Analysis of Plates

D.E. BESKOS

Department of Civil Engineering
University of Patras, GR-261 10 Patras, Greece

Summary

Free and forced flexural vibrations of homogeneous, isotropic and linear elastic Kirchhoff plates and plate systems are studied numerically. The conventional direct boundary element method, which employs the dynamic fundamental solution of the problem, and the direct domain/boundary element method, which employs the static fundamental solution of the problem are employed in both the time and the frequency domain. The former is essentially associated with boundary integrals only, while the latter with boundary as well as domain integrals accommodating the inertia terms. Thus, while only a boundary discretization is necessary in the former method, a boundary as well as an interior discretization is required in the latter one. However, the latter method deals with a much simpler fundamental solution and is computationally more efficient. Transient forced vibrations are treated with the aid of a time marching scheme in the time domain or Laplace transform with respect to time, in which case a numerical inversion of the transformed solution is required to obtain the time domain response. The effect of external viscous damping or internal viscoelastic damping as well as of in-plane forces on the response is also studied. Various numerical examples are presented for illustrating the two aforementioned boundary element approaches and comparisons against the finite element method are also made to demonstrate their merits.

Introduction

Linear elastic dynamic analysis of flat flexural plates involving complex geometries, loading and boundary conditions can only be done by numerical methods. The most widely used numerical methods for this type of problems are the Finite Difference Method (FDM) and especially the Finite Element Method (FEM).

During the last decade the Boundary Element Method (BEM) has emerged as an accurate and efficient numerical method for plate dynamic analysis as it is evident, e.g., in the recent articles of Beskos [1,2] and Hutchinson [3] and the book of Manolis and Beskos [4]. There are basically three approaches for treating plate dynamic problems by the BEM and its variations. These are the indirect or direct BEM that employs the dynamic fundamental solution of the problem, the direct BEM that employs the static fundamental solution of the problem and various boundary methods.

The conventional BEM, in its direct or indirect form, employs the dynamic fundamental solution of the problem in its formulation and this results in an integral representation involving only boundary integrals apart, of course, from domain integrals containing the applied load, which, however, have known integrands and thus do not essentially affect the basic character of the representation. Thus, such a formulation requires essentially only a discretization of the perimeter of the plate. However, the efficiency of the method is greatly hampered by the complicated form of the dynamic fundamental solution, which involves Hankel functions and complex arithmetic. As a result of that, the free vibration problem involves frequency dependent complex matrices and the computation of the natural frequencies, based on the determinant method, is not very efficient. Computational difficulties are also encountered in connection with the forced vibration problem in the time or the frequency domain. The accuracy of the method, however, is very high and this is probably the most important advantage of the method.

Vivoli [5] and Vivoli and Filippi [6] were apparently the first to consider free flexural vibrations of plates by the constant element conventional BEM in its indirect form and provide numerical results. Niwa et al [7, 8] and Kitahara [9] presented a comprehensive treatment of free vibration analysis of plates by the indirect conventional BEM including detailed numerical results. They also presented the direct boundary integral formulation of the problem, involving lateral displacement, normal slope, bending moment and equivalent shear force which was applied to plates subjected to in-plane forces [9]. However, their analysis does not take into account the effect of corners and is restricted to straight or curved line elements with constant values of the functions of interest. Hutchinson and Wong [10] also presented a direct BEM involving lateral displacement, normal slope, Laplacian of the displacement and normal derivative of the Laplacian of the displacement by following Hansen [11] on static analysis of plates. They were able to obtain numerical results for plates involving simply supported and clamped edges by employing only the real part of the fundamental solution with obvious computational gains. However, this leads to spurious roots in addition to the correct ones in free vibration analysis and one has to investigate the mode shapes in order to identify and reject the spurious ones. Wong and Hutchinson [12] presented a complete formulation of the free plate vibration problem by the direct conventional BEM including the effect of corners and involving lateral displacement, normal slope, bending moment and equivalent shear force by following Stern [13] on static analysis of plates. However, no numerical results were reported in their work. This was accomplished later on by Providakis and Beskos [14-16] who employed quadratic isoparametric boundary elements in their formulation for increased accuracy.

Forced vibrations of plates were first considered by Bézine and Gamby [17] who employed a conventional direct BEM in the time domain in conjunction with constant boundary elements and a time marching scheme to obtain the transient response. Use was made of the time domain dynamic fundamental solution of the problem. The effect of the corners was considered in this work but no nodal points were placed at corners. Providakis and Beskos [14-16] presented a complete and general direct BEM in the frequency domain for obtaining the transient response of flexural plates by extending the static work of Stern [13] into the dynamic case. Their method works in the Laplace transformed with respect to time domain, employs quadratic isoparametric elements for increased accuracy and not only takes into account the effect of corners but also allows for nodal points to be placed at corners. The time domain response is finally obtained by a numerical inversion of the transformed solution. In this first category of BEM's employing the dynamic fundamental solution of the problem, one can also place the special indirect BEM of Heuer and Irschik [18] and Irschik et al [19] for free vibration analysis of plates. The method employs a finite domain Green's function and this results in a reduced boundary discretization.

Another direct BEM approach utilizes the static fundamental solution in the formulation of the problem and this creates domain integrals due to the presence of the inertia terms in addition to the boundary ones in the integral representation of the solution. Thus an interior or domain discretization is required in addition to the boundary one. For this reason this approach is called Domain/Boundary Element Method (D/BEM). In spite of this interior discretization, the simplicity of the real valued static fundamental solution as compared to the complicated complex valued dynamic one results in a more efficient scheme. The conventional direct D/BEM employs lateral displacement, normal slope, bending moment and equivalent shear in its formulation. This approach was first introduced by Bézine [20] in connection with free vibration analysis of plates with the aid of constant boundary and interior elements. O'Donoghue and Atluri [21, 22] and Providakis and Beskos [14, 23, 24], Beskos et al [25] and Beskos [26] extended D/BEM to forced vibrations of plates with the aid of a time and Laplace transformed domain formulation, respectively, while Tanaka et al [27, 28]to free vibrations of assembled plate structures exhibiting flexural as well as in-plane motion. Quadratic boundary and interior elements were used in [23-26]for increased accuracy, while linear boundary-constant interior and constant boundary and interior elements were employed in [21, 22] and [27, 28], respectively. In addition, reference [22] considered free vibrations and nonlinearities due to large deflections in the formulation. Free vibratios were also considered in references [14, 24, 26]. Free plate vibration analysis by a D/BEM similar to Bézine [20] using constant boundary and interior elements was recently presented by Costa [29]. A special version of D/BEM for free plate vibrations in which the static fundamental solution satisfies the boundary conditions of the problem and is numerically computed by the BEM was recently reported by Katsikadelis and Sapountzakis [30] and Katsikadelis et al [31]. Katsikadelkis and Sapountzakis [32] have also recently studied free and forced vibrations of plates with variable thickness by a D/BEM, which involves lateral displacement, Laplacian of the lateral displacement and various derivatives of this displacement in its formulation. The approach of Katsikadelis and Kandilas [33] employing the static BEM, simply to construct the flexibility matrix of the plate to be used in conjunction with its lumped mass matrix in a standard vibration analysis can also be considered as a degenerate D/BEM. Finally one can mention here the D/BEM of Shi and Bézine [34] and Shi [35] used for the dynamic analysis of anisotropic plates, which employs the static anisotropic fundamental solution of the problem in its formulation. Despite the required interior discretization, the D/BEM presents distinct advantages over the FEM, such as higher accuracy for the same number of degrees of freedom and more relaxed continuity requirements for the displacement function.

Free vibrations of plates have also been studied by various boundary methods, such as the collocation method of, e.g., Conway [36], Conway and Farnham [37], Mikami and Yoshimura [38] and Akkari and Hutchinson [39] and the edge function method of Nash et al [40] and O'Callaghan and Studdert [41].

This chapter deals with free and forced vibrations of homogeneous, isotropic and linear elastic Kirchhoff plates studied with the aid of the conventional direct BEM or the conventional direct D/BEM in the time or frequency domain. The conventional indirect BEM, special indirect BEM's and special direct D/BEM's are treated in the chapter on special methods for plate analysis, while boundary collocation is discussed in the last chapter of this book. More specifically, the present chapter consists of ten sections: The first section presents the governing equations of plates; the next two sections deal with free vibrations of plates studied with the aid of the conventional direct BEM and the direct D/BEM, respectively; sections four and five are concerned with forced vibrations of plates by using the direct BEM and D/BEM, respectively, in the time domain, while sections six and seven by using the direct BEM and D/BEM, respectively, in conjunction with Laplace transform; section eight deals with the effect of external viscous or internal viscoelastic damping as well as of in-plane forces on the response; finally section nine presents a number of representative numerical examples corresponding to previous sections, while section ten enumarates the conclusions of this chapter.

Governing Equations

Consider a homogeneous, isotropic, thin and linear elastic plate of surface S and perimeter Γ which is subjected to a lateral dynamic load as shown in Fig. 1. The governing equation of lateral (flexural) motion of this plate, on the basis of Kirchhoff's classical small deflection theory (Love [42]), has the form

$$\nabla^4 w + \frac{\rho h}{D}\ddot{w} = \frac{q}{D} \tag{1}$$

where $w = w(\underset{\sim}{x},t)$ is the lateral deflection, ρ is the mass density, h is the uniform thickness, $q = q(\underset{\sim}{x},t)$ is the lateral load per unit area and $D = Eh^3/12(1-v^2)$ is the flexural rigidity of the plate, with E and v being the modulus of elasticity and the Poisson's ratio, respectively. Also in the above, vector $\underset{\sim}{x}$ stands for a point with coordinates x and y, $\nabla^4(.) = \nabla^2(\nabla^2(.))$ with $\nabla^2(.) = \partial^2/\partial x^2(.) + \partial^2/\partial y^2(.)$ and overdots indicate differentiation with respect to time t.

At a regular (smooth) point on the boundary [13]

$$M_n(w) = \frac{D}{2}\{-(1+v)\nabla^2 w + (1-v)[(\frac{\partial^2 w}{\partial y^2} - \frac{\partial^2 w}{\partial x^2})\cos 2a - 2\frac{\partial^2 w}{\partial x \partial y}\sin 2a]\} \tag{2}$$

$$M_t(w) = -\frac{D(1-v)}{2}\{(\frac{\partial^2 w}{\partial y^2} - \frac{\partial^2 w}{\partial x^2})\sin 2a + 2\frac{\partial^2 w}{\partial x \partial y}\cos 2a\} \tag{3}$$

$$V_n(w) = -D\frac{d}{dn}(\nabla^2 w) + \frac{d}{ds}[M_t(w)] \tag{4}$$

where $M_n(w)$, $M_t(w)$ and $V_n(w)$ denote the bending moment, twisting moment and equivalent shear, respectively, a is the angle from the x-axis to the outward normal vector $\underset{\sim}{n}$ and d/dn and d/ds denote the normal and tangential derivative on the boundary as shown in Fig. 1. Thus the usual expressions for interior bending moments and shear forces referred to the Cartesian (x,y) system shown in Fig. 2 can be obtained as follows [13]:

$$M_{xx} = M_n(w)|_{a=o,\pi} = -D(\frac{\partial^2 w}{\partial x^2} + v\frac{\partial^2 w}{\partial y^2}) \tag{5}$$

$$M_{yy} = M_n(w)|_{a=\pm\pi/2} = -D(\frac{\partial^2 w}{\partial y^2} + v\frac{\partial^2 w}{\partial x^2}) \tag{6}$$

$$M_{xy} = M_t(w)|_{a=o,\pi} = -M_t(w)|_{a=\pm\pi/2} = -D(1-v)\frac{\partial^2 w}{\partial x \partial y} \tag{7}$$

$$Q_x = Q_n(w)|_{a=o} = -Q_n(w)|_{a=\pi} = -D\frac{\partial}{\partial x}(\nabla^2 w) \tag{8}$$

$$Q_y = Q_n(w)|_{a=\pi/2} = -Q_n(w)|_{a=-\pi/2} = -D\frac{\partial}{\partial y}(\nabla^2 w) \tag{9}$$

where

$$Q_n(w) = -D\frac{d}{dn}(\nabla^2 w) = V_n(w) - \frac{d}{ds}[M_t(w)] \tag{10}$$

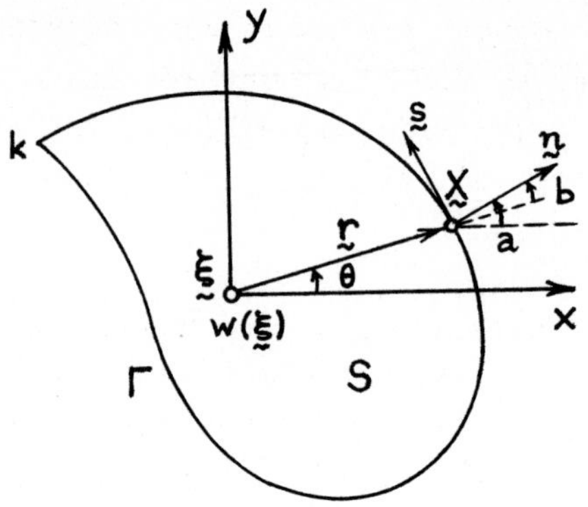

Fig. 1. General plate geometry and coordinate systems for an interior plate point ξ.

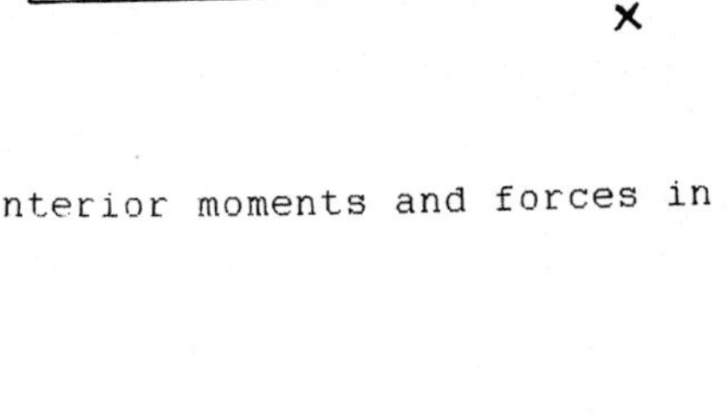

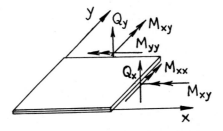

Fig. 2. Interior moments and forces in a plate.

In boundary element computations it is more convenient to work in terms of the polar system (r,Θ) rather than the Cartesian one (x,y) as shown in Fig. 1. Conversion from one system to the other can be easily done by employing standard relations.

Free Vibrations by Direct BEM

The developments of this section are based on the work of Providakis and Beskos [16]. Consider the plate of Fig. 1 under a lateral load q varying sinusoidally with time. In that case the deflection w varies also sinusoidally with time and one has

$$q(\underset{\sim}{x},t) = \tilde{q}(\underset{\sim}{x}) \sin\omega t$$
$$w(\underset{\sim}{x},t) = \tilde{w}(\underset{\sim}{x}) \sin\omega t \tag{11}$$

where $\tilde{q}(\underset{\sim}{x})$ and $\tilde{w}(\underset{\sim}{x})$ are the load and deflection amplitudes, respectively, and ω is the circular frequency of vibration. Substituting (11) into (1) yields

$$\nabla^4\tilde{w} - \beta^4\tilde{w} = \frac{\tilde{q}}{D} \tag{12}$$

where

$$\beta^4 = \rho h\omega^2/D \tag{13}$$

The static-like form of (12) suggests that an integral representation of the problem can be easily achieved by employing the Rayleigh-Green identity with K corners, which is valid for plate flexure under static loading. This identity is a reciprocal relationship between two plate elastostatic states represented by their lateral deflections u and υ and reads [13]

$$\int_S (\upsilon\nabla^4 u - u\nabla^4\upsilon)dS = \frac{1}{D}\int_\Gamma \left[V_n(\upsilon)u - M_n(\upsilon)\frac{du}{dn} + M_n(u)\frac{d\upsilon}{dn} - V_n(u)\upsilon\right]d\Gamma + $$
$$+ \frac{1}{D}\sum_{k=1}^{K}\left[[\![M_t(\upsilon)]\!]\, u - [\![M_t(u)]\!]\,\upsilon\right]_K \tag{14}$$

where $V_n(.)$, $M_n(.)$, $M_t(.)$, $d/dn(.)$ and n represent equivalent shear force, normal bending moment, twisting moment, normal slope and outward normal vector, respectively, and $[[.]]$ denotes the discontinuity jump in the direction of increasing arc length at a corner on the perimeter Γ, which has K corners in total.

The fundamental solution $U = U(\underset{\sim}{x},\underset{\sim}{\xi};\beta)$ of (3) is defined by

$$\nabla^4 U - \beta^4 U = -\delta(\underset{\sim}{x},\underset{\sim}{\xi}) \tag{15}$$

where $\delta(\underset{\sim}{x},\underset{\sim}{\xi})$ is the Dirac delta function, and represents the lateral deflection of an infinitely extended plate at point $\underset{\sim}{x}$ due to a unit concentrated lateral load at point $\underset{\sim}{\xi}$. The solution of (15) has the form [6, 7]

$$U(\underset{\sim}{x},\underset{\sim}{\xi},\beta) = -\frac{i}{8\beta^2}\left[H_0^{(1)}(\beta r) - H_0^{(1)}(i\beta r)\right] =$$

$$= -ic_1 J_0(\beta r) + c_1 Y_0(\beta r) + c_2 K_0(\beta r) \tag{16}$$

with

$$c_1 = 1/8\beta^2, \qquad c_2 = 1/4\pi\beta^2 \tag{17}$$

where $H_0^{(1)}(.)$ is the zero order Hankel function of the first kind, $J_0(.)$ and $Y_0(.)$ are the zero order Bessel functions of the first and second kind, respectively, $K_0(.)$ is the zero order modified Bessel function of the second kind, $i = \sqrt{-1}$, and $r = |\underset{\sim}{x}-\underset{\sim}{\xi}|$. Solution (16) satisfies Sommerfeld's radiation condition at infinity, i.e.

$$\lim_{r\to\infty}\left(\frac{\partial U}{\partial r} - i\beta U\right) = 0\,(r^{-3/2}) \tag{18}$$

and is unique [7]. The solution

$$U(\underset{\sim}{x},\underset{\sim}{\xi};\beta) = \frac{i}{8\beta^2}\,[H_o^{(2)}(\beta r) + H_o^{(1)}\,(i\beta r)] =$$

$$= ic_1\,J_o(\beta r) + c_1\,Y_o(\beta r) + c_2\,K_o(\beta r) \tag{19}$$

with $H_o^{(2)}(.)$ being the zero order Hankel function of the second kind, which was employed in [12, 16] is also a singular solution of (15) but does not satisfy condition (18). However, solution (19) can be used in place of (16) without any problem when solving interior problems, which is usually the case in most practical applications [43].

Identifying υ with U and u with $\tilde{w}$ in (14) and taking into account that

$$\int_S \tilde{w}(\underset{\sim}{x})\ \delta(\underset{\sim}{x},\underset{\sim}{\xi})\ ds = \tilde{w}(\underset{\sim}{\xi}) \tag{20}$$

one receives the integral representation

$$\tilde{w}(\underset{\sim}{\xi}) = \frac{1}{D}\int_\Gamma [V_n(U)\tilde{w}-M_n(U)\ \frac{d\tilde{w}}{dn} + M_n(\tilde{w})\ \frac{dU}{dn} -V_n(\tilde{w})U|\,d\Gamma(\underset{\sim}{X})$$

$$+ \frac{1}{D}\ \sum_{k=1}^{K}[\,[\![M_t(U)]\!]\ w-[\![M_t(w)]\!]\,U]_K - \frac{1}{D}\int_S \tilde{q}\ U\ dS\ (\underset{\sim}{x}) \tag{21}$$

for a point $\underset{\sim}{\xi}$ in the interior of the domain S with $\underset{\sim}{X}$ being a boundary point as shown in Fig. 1. Explicit expressions for dU/dn, $M_n(U)$, $M_t(U)$ and $V_n(U)$, when U is given by (19) can be found in [16]. When U is given by (16), these expressions are as follows:

$$\frac{dU}{dn} = ic_1\beta\ J_1(\beta r)\cos b - \beta[c_1\ Y_1(\beta r) + c_2\ K_1(\beta r)]\cos b \tag{22}$$

$$M_n(U) = -i\{c_1\ \frac{D}{2}\ [1+v+(1-v)\cos 2b]\beta^2 J_o(\beta r)-c_1 D\beta(1-v)\ \frac{J_1(\beta r)}{r}\ \cos 2b\}$$

$$+\frac{D}{2}\{\beta^2[1+v+(1-v)\cos 2b][c_1 Y_o(\beta r)-c_2 K_o(\beta r)]-2\beta(1-v)\frac{1}{r}$$

$$[c_1 Y_1(\beta r)+c_2 K_1(\beta r)]\cos 2b\} \tag{23}$$

$$M_t(U) = ic_1\frac{D(1-v)}{2}[\beta^2 J_o(\beta r)-2\beta\frac{J_1(\beta r)}{r}]\sin 2b -$$

$$-\frac{D(1-v)}{2}\{\beta^2[c_1 Y_o(\beta r)-c_2 K_o(\beta r)]-$$

$$-\frac{2\beta}{r}[c_1 Y_1(\beta r)+c_2 K_1(\beta r)]\}\sin 2b \tag{24}$$

$$V_n(U) = ic_1 D\{J_1(\beta r)[\beta^3\cos b+\frac{\beta^3(1-v)}{2}\sin 2b\sin b+\frac{2\beta(1-v)}{r}(\frac{\cos 3b}{r}-\frac{\cos 2b}{R})]+$$

$$+(1-v)\beta^2 J_o(\beta r)(\frac{\cos 2b}{R}-\frac{\cos 3b}{r})\}-D\beta^3[c_1 Y_1(\beta r)-c_2 K_1(\beta r)]\cos b$$

$$+D(1-v)\{\frac{\beta^2}{r}[c_1 Y_o(\beta r)-c_2 K_o(\beta r)]-\frac{2\beta}{r^2}[c_1 Y_1(\beta r)+c_2 K_1(\beta r)]\cos 3b\}$$

$$-D(1-v)\{\frac{\beta^2}{R}[c_1 Y_o(\beta r)-c_2 K_o(\beta r)]-\frac{2\beta}{rR}[c_1 Y_1(\beta r)+c_2 K_1(\beta r)]\cos 2b\}$$

$$-\frac{D(1-v)}{2}\beta^3[c_1 Y_1(\beta r)-c_2 K_1(\beta r)]\sin 2b\sin b \tag{25}$$

where $J_1(.)$ and $Y_1(.)$ are the first order Bessel functions of the first and second kind, respectively, $K_1(.)$ is the first order modified Bessel function of the second kind, the angle b is defined as shown in Fig. 1, and 1/R denotes the curvature at a regular boundary point.

Following a limiting process that brings point $\underset{\sim}{\xi}$ on the boundary in the position $\underset{\sim}{\Xi}$, one can use (21) to obtain the boundary integral equation

$$\frac{c}{2}\tilde{w}(\underset{\sim}{\Xi}) = \frac{1}{D}\int_\Gamma[V_n(U)\tilde{w}-M_n(U)\frac{d\tilde{w}}{dn}+M_n(\tilde{w})\frac{dU}{dn}-V_n(\tilde{w})U]\,d\Gamma(\underset{\sim}{X})$$

$$+\frac{1}{D}\sum_{k=1}^{\bar{K}}[[\![M_t(U)]\!]\tilde{w}-[\![M_t(\tilde{w})]\!]U]_k-\frac{1}{D}\int_S\tilde{q}U\,dS(\underset{\sim}{x})+\frac{1}{D}ic_1[\![M_t(\tilde{w})]\!]_{\underset{\sim}{\Xi}} \tag{26}$$

In the above, the jump term c is related to the internal angle $c\pi$ at the corner point $\underset{\sim}{\Xi}$, as shown in Fig. 3, and satisfies the inequality $0<c<2$. Thus, if the boundary Γ is smooth at $\underset{\sim}{\Xi}$, then one has $c = 1$. Also, the bar over K indicates that the summation includes corner points other than $\underset{\sim}{\Xi}$, and the symbol $⨍$ indicates a Cauchy principal value integral.

One more boundary integral equation is needed for a well posed plate bending problem. This can be an integral representation for the normal slope dw/dn at a boundary point $\underset{\sim}{\Xi}$. However, at a corner point Ξ the normal slope is discontinuous and thus two integral equations have to be written down. The starting point is the computation of the directional derivative of (26) in a fixed direction $\underset{\sim}{\zeta}$ at $\underset{\sim}{\Xi}$ as shown in Fig. 3. Thus, one can compute the function $U_\varphi = (-1/\beta)\,\partial U/\partial\zeta = (-1/\beta)(\partial U/\partial r)\cos\varphi$, which is also a fundamental solution of (15) and has the form

$$U_\varphi = -ic_1 J_1(\beta r)\cos\varphi + c_1 Y_1(\beta r)\cos\varphi + c_2 K_1(\beta r)\cos\varphi \tag{27}$$

where φ is the angle between r and ζ. Explicit expressions for dU_φ/dn, $M_n(U_\varphi)$, $M_t(U_\varphi)$ and $V_n(U_\varphi)$ are as follows:

$$\frac{dU_\varphi}{dn} = -ic_1\Big[\beta J_0(\beta r)\cos\varphi\cos b - \frac{J_1(\beta r)}{r}\cos(\varphi-b)\Big] + \beta\left[c_1 Y_0(\beta r) - c_2 K_0(\beta r)\right] \times$$
$$\cos\varphi\cos b - \frac{1}{r}\left[c_1 Y_1(\beta r) + c_2 K_1(\beta r)\right]\cos(\varphi-b) \tag{28}$$

$$M_n(U_\varphi) = -ic_1 D\Big\{ J_1(\beta r)\,\Big[\frac{\beta^2}{2}\cos\varphi(1+v+(1-v)\cos 2b) - \frac{2(1-v)}{r^2}\cos(\varphi-2b)\Big]$$
$$+ (1-v)\,\beta\,\frac{J_0(\beta r)}{r}\cos(\varphi-2b)\Big\} + \frac{D\beta^2}{2}\left[c_1 Y_1(\beta r) - c_2 K_1(\beta r)\right] \times$$
$$\times \left[1+v+(1-v)\cos 2b\right]\cos\varphi + D(1-v)\Big\{\frac{\beta}{r}\left[c_1 Y_0(\beta r) - c_2 K_0(\beta r)\right]$$
$$- \frac{2}{r^2}\left[c_1 Y_1(\beta r) + c_2 K_1(\beta r)\right]\Big\}\cos(\varphi-2b) \tag{29}$$

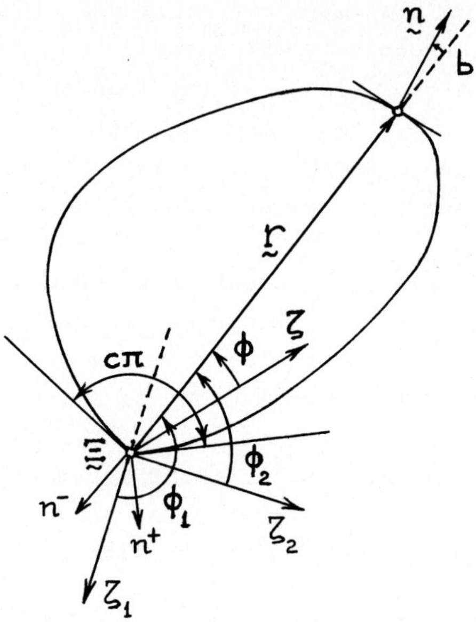

Fig. 3. Geometry for a plate corner point Ξ.

$$M_t(U_\varphi) = ic_1 D(1-\nu)\{J_1(\beta r)\,[\frac{\beta^2}{2}\cos\varphi\sin 2b + \frac{2}{r^2}\sin(\varphi-2b)] - \beta\,\frac{J_o(\beta r)}{r}\, x$$

$$x\,\sin(\varphi-2b)\} - D\,\frac{(1-\nu)}{2}\,\beta^2[c_1Y_1(\beta r)-c_2K_1(\beta r)]\cos\varphi\sin 2b +$$

$$+D(1-\nu)\{\frac{\beta}{r}\,[c_1Y_o(\beta r)-c_2K_o(\beta r)] - \frac{2}{r^2}\,[c_1Y_1(\beta r)+$$

$$+ c_2K_1(\beta r)]\sin(\varphi-2b)\} \qquad (30)$$

$$V_n(U_\varphi) = -ic_1D\{J_o(\beta r)[\beta^3(\cos\varphi\cos b + \frac{1-\nu}{2}\cos\varphi\sin 2b\sin nb) +$$

$$+ (1-\nu)(\cos(\varphi-3b) - \frac{2\beta}{rR}\cos(\varphi-2b))] + J_1(\beta r)[\frac{\beta^2}{r}(-\cos(\varphi-b) +$$

$$+ \frac{1-\nu}{2}(\cos(\varphi-3b) + \sin(\varphi-2b)\sin b + \cos 3b\,\cos\varphi)) -$$

$$- \frac{\beta^2}{R}(1-\nu)\cos\varphi\cos 2b - \frac{6(1-\nu)}{r^3}\cos(\varphi-3b) + \frac{4}{r^2R}(1-\nu)\cos(\varphi-2b)]\} +$$

$$+ D\beta^3[c_1Y_o(\beta r)+c_2K_o(\beta r)](\cos\varphi\cos b + \frac{1-\nu}{2}\cos\varphi\sin 2b\sin nb) +$$

$$+ \frac{D\beta^2}{r}[c_1Y_1(\beta r) - c_2K_1(\beta r)][-\cos(\varphi-b) + \frac{1-\nu}{2}(\cos(\varphi-3b)+\sin(\varphi-2b)\sin b +$$

$$+ \cos 3b\cos\varphi)] - \frac{D\beta^2}{R}[c_1Y_1(\beta r)-c_2K_1(\beta r)][(1-\nu)\cos\varphi\cos 2b] +$$

$$+ 3D(1-\nu)\{\frac{\beta}{r^2}(c_1Y_o(\beta r)-c_2K_o(\beta r)) - \frac{2}{r^3}[c_1Y_1(\beta r)+c_2K_1(\beta r)]\cos(\varphi-3b)\} -$$

$$- 2D(1-\nu)\{\frac{\beta}{rR}[c_1Y_0(\beta r)-c_2K_o(\beta r)] - \frac{2}{r^2R}[c_1Y_1(\beta r)+c_2K_1(\beta r)]\}\cos(\varphi-2b) \qquad (31)$$

Thus, for a corner point $\underset{\sim}{\Xi}$, one can write down the two independent boundary integral equations [13, 16]

$$- \frac{c\pm(\nu/2\pi)\sin c\pi}{4\beta(\sin,\cos)\frac{c\pi}{2}}\,[\frac{d\tilde{w}}{dn}(\underset{\sim}{\Xi}^+) \pm \frac{d\tilde{w}}{dn}(\underset{\sim}{\Xi}^-)] = \frac{1}{D}\int_\Gamma \{ V_n(U_{\varphi_{1,2}})[\tilde{w}(\underset{\sim}{X})-\tilde{w}(\underset{\sim}{\Xi})] -$$

$$- M_n(U_{\varphi_{1,2}})\frac{d\tilde{w}}{dn} + M_n(\tilde{w})\frac{dU_{\varphi_{1,2}}}{dn} - V_n(\tilde{w})U_{\varphi_{1,2}}\}\,d\Gamma(\underset{\sim}{X}) +$$

$$+ \frac{1}{D} \sum_{k=1}^{\bar{K}} \{ [\![M_t(U_{\varphi_{1,2}})]\!] [\tilde{w}(\underset{\sim}{X}) - \tilde{w}(\underset{\sim}{\Xi})] - [\![M_t(w)]\!] U_{\varphi_{1,2}} \}_k -$$

$$- \frac{1}{D} \int_S \tilde{q}\, U_{\varphi_{1,2}}\, dS(\underset{\sim}{x}) \qquad (32)$$

where φ_1 and φ_2 are the angles between the axes ζ_1 and ζ_2, respectively and the r direction, as shown in Fig. 3, with ζ_1 being the bisector of the interior angle $c\pi$ at $\underset{\sim}{\Xi}$ and ζ_2 the axis perpendicular to ζ_1 at $\underset{\sim}{\Xi}$. For a smooth point $\underset{\sim}{\Xi}$ one has $c = 1$ and only one normal vector $\underset{\sim}{n}$ and (32) simply become one equation with $(1/2\theta)\,(d\tilde{w}/dn)$ as its left hand side and with φ being the angle between $\underset{\sim}{n}$ and $\underset{\sim}{r}$ in its right hand side.

Thus, the general boundary integral formulation of harmonic dynamic analysis of plates consists of (26) and (32). In order to implement a numerical scheme to solve the system of these equations, the perimeter Γ of the plate is divided into a number of boundary elements, over which any function $\tilde{f}(\underset{\sim}{\Xi})$ of the problem can be expressed isoparametrically as

$$\tilde{f}(s) = \sum_{i=1}^{l} F^i(s)\, \tilde{f}_i \qquad (33)$$

where l denotes the element nodes, s is the intrinsic element coordinate varying between -1 and $+1$, $F^i(s)$ are interpolation or shape functions and $\tilde{f}_i$ are the nodal values of $\tilde{f}(\underset{\sim}{\Xi})$. Care is taken of placing nodes at each corner point. Quadratic isoparametric line elements are employed here for increased accuracy and in this case $l = 3$. When the spatial variation of the load q is complicated, the corresponding surface integrals have to be computed numerically. One way for accomplishing this is by using quadratic isoparametric quadrilaterals (interior 8-noded elements) with shape functions $N^i(p,\tau)$ and intrinsic coordinates p and τ, such that

$$\tilde{q}(p,\tau) = \sum_{i=1}^{m} N^{i}(p,\tau)\,\tilde{q}_{i} \qquad (34)$$

where m = 8 and $\tilde{q}_i$ are the nodal values of the load.

Thus discretization of (26) and (32) on the basis of (33) and (34) results in the following system of equations:

$$\frac{c}{2}\tilde{w}_j = \frac{1}{D}\sum_{m=1}^{M}\Big(\int_{\Gamma_m} F^{i}(s)V_n(U(s))\,|J(s)|\,d\Gamma\Big)\tilde{w}_i$$

$$-\sum_{m=1}^{M}\Big(\int_{\Gamma_m} F^{i}(s)M_n(U(s))\,|J(s)|\,d\Gamma\Big)\Big(\frac{d\tilde{w}}{dn}\Big)_i$$

$$+\sum_{m=1}^{M}\Big(\int_{\Gamma_m} F^{i}(s)\,\frac{dU(s)}{dn}\,|J(s)|\,d\Gamma\Big)(M_n(\tilde{w}))_i$$

$$-\sum_{m=1}^{M}\Big(\int_{\Gamma_m} F^{i}(s)U(s)\,|J(s)|\,d\Gamma\Big)(V_n(\tilde{w}))_i$$

$$+\frac{1}{D}\sum_{k=1}^{\bar{K}} [\![M_t(U)]\!]\tilde{w}_k - \frac{1}{D}\sum_{k=1}^{\bar{K}} U_k[\![M_t(\tilde{w})]\!]_k$$

$$+\frac{1}{D}\, i c_1 [\![M_t(\tilde{w})]\!]_j - \frac{1}{D}\sum_{l=1}^{L}\Big(\int_{S_1} N^{i}(p,\tau)\,|\overset{*}{J}(p,\tau)|\,dS\Big)\tilde{q}_i \qquad (35)$$

$$\frac{c\pm(\nu/2\pi)\sin c\pi}{4\beta(\sin,\cos)\frac{c\pi}{2}}\Big[\Big(\frac{d\tilde{w}^{+}}{dn}\Big)_j \pm \Big(\frac{d\tilde{w}^{-}}{dn}\Big)_j\Big] = \frac{1}{D}\Big\{\sum_{m=1}^{M}\Big(\int_{\Gamma_m} F^{i}(s)V_n(U_{\varphi_{1,2}}(s))\,\times$$

$$\times|J(S)|\,d\Gamma\Big)(\tilde{w}_i-\tilde{w}_j) - \sum_{m=1}^{M}\Big(\int_{\Gamma_m} F^{i}(s)M_n(U_{\varphi_{1,2}}(s))\,|J(s)|\,d\Gamma\Big)\times$$

$$\times\Big(\frac{d\tilde{w}}{dn}\Big)_i + \sum_{m=1}^{M}\Big(\int_{\Gamma_m} F^{i}(s)\,\frac{dU_{\varphi_{1,2}}(s)}{dn}\,|J(s)|\,d\Gamma\Big)(M_n(\tilde{w}))_i\; -$$

$$-\sum_{m=1}^{M}\Big(\int F^{i}(s)U_{\varphi_{1,2}}(s)\,|J(s)|\,d\Gamma\Big)(V_n(\tilde{w}))_i\Big\}$$

$$+\ \frac{1}{D}\sum_{k=1}^{\bar{K}}[\![M_t(U_{\varphi_{1,2}})]\!]_k(\tilde{w}_k-\tilde{w}_j)\ -\ \frac{1}{D}\sum_{k=1}^{K}[\![M_t(\tilde{w})]\!]_k U_{\varphi_{1,2}}\ -$$

$$-\ \frac{1}{D}\sum_{l=1}^{L}\left(\int_{S_l} N^i(p,\tau)U_{\varphi_{1,2}}(p,\tau)\,|\overset{*}{J}(p,\tau)|\,dS\right)\tilde{q}_i \tag{36}$$

In the above, M and L are the numbers and interior elements, respectively, and $|J(s)|$ and $|\overset{*}{J}(p,\tau)|$ are the Jacobians of integration for every boundary and interior element, respectively. Writing (35) and (36) for all boundary nodes and assembling them one can receive the matrix equation

$$[H]\{\tilde{u}\} = [G]\{\tilde{t}\} + \{\tilde{q}\} \tag{37}$$

where $\{\tilde{u}\}$ and $\{\tilde{t}\}$ are the vectors of the nodal boundary values of displacements (deflections, slopes) and stress resultants (moments, shears, corner forces), respectively, $\{\tilde{q}\}$ is the vector of nodal load values and [H] and [G] are the influence matrices with entries elemental boundary integrals involving the fundamental state of deformation. The various Bessel functions which appear in the fundamental solutions and their derivatives are computed by taking the first 10 terms of their series expansions as given in Abramowitz and Stegun [44]. Regular integrals for which $r \neq 0$ are evaluated numerically by a standard Gauss quadrature with 8 points. Problems arise, however, when these integrals are singular, i.e., when $r \to 0$. One has to deal then with O(lnr) for U, dU/dn, $M_n(U)$, U_φ and dU_φ/dn, O(1/r) for $V_n(U)$ and $M_n(U_\varphi)$ and $O(1/r^2)$ for $V_n(U_\varphi)$ singular functions. Function $V_n(U_\varphi)$, however, is multiplied in (13) by $\tilde{w}(\underset{\sim}{X}) - \tilde{w}(\underset{\sim}{\Xi})$ which is of O(r) (Stern [13]), and hence all the integrands here are of O(ln r) or O(1/r). If the origin (field) node coincides with one of the end nodes of the boundary element, integrals with O(ln r) integrands are computed numerically with the logarithmic integration rule of Stroud and Secrest [45] involving 8 points, while those with O(1/r) integrands are also computed numerically but using the standard Gauss quadrature with 20 points so as to have high accuracy and avoid a function evaluation at the singular point. If the origin node coincides with the middle node of the boundary element, this element is divided into two quadratic subelements and both of them are mapped into the original element so that the problem is essentially reduced to the previous one with the origin node coinciding with one of the end nodes.

There are four boundary variables at a regular (smooth) point, namely $\tilde{w}$, $d\tilde{w}/dn$, M_n and V_n, and only two of them are known. At a corner point, however, there are eight boundary variables, $\tilde{w}$, $(d\tilde{w}/dn)^-$, $(d\tilde{w}/dn)^+$, M_n^-, M_n^+, V_n^-, V_n^+ and M_t, and five of them are known. Prescribed boundary conditions for a regular nodal point can have one of the following forms:

$$
\begin{aligned}
&\tilde{w} = d\tilde{w}/dn = 0 && \text{for clamped boundary,} \\
&\tilde{w} = 0, \quad M_n = 0 && \text{for simply supported boundary,} \qquad (38) \\
&V_n = M_n = 0 && \text{for free boundary.}
\end{aligned}
$$

Prescribed boundary conditions for a corner point, on the other hand, can have one of the forms contained in Table 1 due to Stern [46], where $\tilde{w}_n = d\tilde{w}/dn$ and s.s. = simply supported. Application of the boundary conditions (38)

Corner support		
-side	+ side	Boundary conditions
clamped	clamped	$\tilde{w} = 0$, $\tilde{w}_n- = \tilde{w}_n^+ = 0$, $M_n^- = M_n^+ = 0$
s.s.	s.s.	$\tilde{w} = 0$, $M_n^- = M_n^+ = 0$, $\tilde{w}_n^- = \tilde{w}_n^+ = 0$
free	free	$M_n^- = M_n^+ = 0$, $V_n^- = V_n^+ = 0$, $[\![M_t]\!] = 0$
clamped	s.s.	$\tilde{w} = 0$, $\tilde{w}_n^- = 0$, $M_n^+ = 0$, $\tilde{w}_n^+ = 0$, $M_n^- = 0$
clamped	free	$\tilde{w} = 0$, $\tilde{w}_n^- = 0$, $M_n^+ = 0$, $V_n^+ = 0$, $\tilde{w}_n^+ = 0$
s.s.	free	$\tilde{w}=0$, $M_n^-=M_n^+ = 0$, $V_n^+=0$, $\tilde{w}_n^+ + \tilde{w}_n^-\cos\varphi = 0$

Table 1. Boundary conditions at a corner point of a plate

or those of Table 1 on (37) results in $2N_r$ unknown variables for every regular boundary node, with N_r being the number of regular boundary nodes, and in $3N_c$ unknown variables for every corner node with N_c being the number of corner boundary nodes. Thus, after separating known from the unknown nodal variables and reordering, (37) takes the form

$$[\tilde{A}(\theta)]\{\tilde{X}\} = \{\tilde{Q}\} \tag{39}$$

where the influence matrix $[\tilde{A}]$ is of the order of $(2N_r + 3N_c) \times (2N_r + 3N_c)$, $\{\tilde{X}\}$ and $\{\tilde{Q}\}$ are the vectors of the unknown and known variables respectively, and θ is the frequency parameter defined by (13).

For a plate experiencing free vibrations one has $\tilde{q} = 0$ and (39) becomes

$$[\tilde{A}(\theta)]\{\tilde{X}\} = \{0\} \tag{40}$$

Thus the condition for nontrivial solutions of (40) is the frequency equation

$$\det[\tilde{A}(\theta)] = |\tilde{A}(\theta)| = 0 \tag{41}$$

which provides all the infinitely many natural freqwuencies ω of the plate with the aid of (13). For every natural frequency one can then obtain the corresponding modal shape of the plate by solving (40) for $\{\tilde{X}\}$. It should be pointed out that the elements of matrix $[\tilde{A}]$ are complex numbers for real values of θ. Thus, using the determinant method based on (41), one computes the eigenvalues θ as the real values for which the complex function $|\tilde{A}(\theta)|$ attains minimum absolute values. For further details one can consult [7-9].

<u>Free Vibrations by Direct D/BEM</u>

The developments of this section are based on Providakis and Beskos [24]. Consider the governing equation of plate flexural motion, Eq. (1), and assume that q and w vary sinusoidally with time as described by Eq. (11). Substitution of (11) into (1) yields

$$\nabla^4 \tilde{w} = \frac{\tilde{q}^*}{D} \tag{42}$$

where

$$\tilde{q}^* = \tilde{q} + \rho h \omega^2 \tilde{w} \tag{43}$$

The static-like form of (42) suggests using the Rayleigh-Green identity (14) in order to achieve an integral formulation of the problem. The fundamental solution of the static problem, i.e.,

$$U(\underset{\sim}{x},\underset{\sim}{\xi}) = \frac{1}{8\pi D} r^2 \ln r \tag{44}$$

satisfying the equation

$$\nabla^4 U = \frac{\delta}{D} \tag{45}$$

is employed in this formulation. Function U physically represents the lateral deflection at $\underset{\sim}{x}$ of an infinitely extended plate due to a lateral concentrated unit load at $\underset{\sim}{\xi}$. Identifying υ with U and u with $\tilde{w}$, substituting (42) and (45) into (14) and taking into account (20), one receives the integral representation

$$\tilde{w}(\underset{\sim}{\xi}) = -\int_\Gamma \left| V_n(U)w - M_n(U)\frac{d\tilde{w}}{dn} + \frac{dU}{dn}M_n(\tilde{w}) - UV_n(\tilde{w})\right| d\Gamma(\underset{\sim}{X})$$
$$+ \int_S U\tilde{q}^* dS(\underset{\sim}{x}) + \sum_{k=1}^{K} \left\{ [\![M_t(w)]\!]U - [\![M_t(U)]\!]\tilde{w} \right\}_k \tag{46}$$

In the above U is defined by (44), while explicit expressions for dU/dn, $M_n(U)$, $M_t(U)$ and $V_n(U)$ are given as follows [13]:

$$\frac{dU}{dn} = \frac{1}{8\pi D}(1+2\ln r)\, r \cos b \tag{47}$$

$$M_n(U) = -\frac{1+v}{4\pi}(1+\ln r) - \frac{1-v}{8\pi}\cos 2b \tag{48}$$

$$M_t(U) = \frac{1-v}{8\pi}\sin 2b \tag{49}$$

$$V_n(U) = -\frac{\cos b}{4\pi r}\left[2+(1-v)\cos 2b\right] + \frac{1-v}{4\pi R}\cos 2b \tag{50}$$

One can now bring point $\underset{\sim}{\xi}$ to a position $\underset{\sim}{\Xi}$ on the boundary Γ through a limiting process and receive from (46) the boundary integral equation

$$\frac{1}{2}c\tilde{w}(\underset{\sim}{\Xi}) = -\int_{\Gamma}\left[V_n(U)\tilde{w} - M_n(U)\frac{d\tilde{w}}{dn} + \frac{dU}{dn}M_n(\tilde{w}) - UV_n(\tilde{w})\right]d\Gamma(\underset{\sim}{X})$$

$$+\int_S \tilde{q}U\,dS + \rho h\omega^2\int_S \tilde{w}dS + \sum_{k=1}^{K}\{U[\![M_t(\tilde{w})]\!] - \tilde{w}[\![M_t(U)]\!]\}_k \tag{51}$$

As in the previous section, for a well posed plate bending problem one more boundary integral equation is needed. This can be an integral representation for the normal slope $d\tilde{w}/dn$ at $\underset{\sim}{\Xi}$. However, if $\underset{\sim}{\Xi}$ is a corner point the normal slope has two values there and thus two boundary integral equations must be written down for such a point. A second fundamental solution of Eq. (45) is first introduced, which is actually two times the singular part of the directional derivative (slope) of U in a fixed direction ζ and has the form

$$U_\varphi = \frac{1}{2\pi D}r\ln r\cos\varphi \tag{52}$$

Explicit expressions for dU_φ/dn, $M_n(U_\varphi)$, $M_t(U_\varphi)$ and $V_n(U_\varphi)$ are as follows [13]:

$$\frac{dU_\varphi}{dn} = \frac{1}{2\pi D}\left[\cos\varphi\cos b + \ln r\cos(\varphi+b)\right] \tag{53}$$

$$M_n(U_\varphi) = -\frac{1+v}{2\pi r}\cos\varphi + \frac{1-v}{2\pi r}\sin\varphi\sin 2b \tag{54}$$

$$M_t(U_\varphi) = \frac{1-v}{2\pi r}\sin\varphi\cos 2b \tag{55}$$

$$V_n(U_\varphi) = \frac{1}{2\pi r^2}\{\cos(b-\varphi)[2+(1-v)\cos 2b]+$$

$$+2(1-v)\sin\varphi\cos b\sin 2b\} - \frac{1-v}{\pi R r}\sin\varphi\sin 2b \tag{56}$$

Thus for a corner point $\underset{\sim}{\Xi}$, one can write down the two independent boundary integral equations

$$-\frac{c\pm\frac{v}{\pi}\sin c\pi}{2(\sin,\cos)\frac{c\pi}{2}}\left[\frac{d\tilde{w}}{dn}(\underset{\sim}{\Xi}^{+}) \pm \frac{d\tilde{w}}{dn}(\underset{\sim}{\Xi}^{-})\right] = -\int_\Gamma\{V_n(U_{\varphi_{1,2}})[\tilde{w}(\underset{\sim}{X})-\tilde{w}(\underset{\sim}{\Xi})]$$

$$-M_n(U_{\varphi_{1,2}})\frac{d\tilde{w}}{dn} + \frac{dU_{\varphi_{1,2}}}{dn}M_n(\tilde{w}) - U_{\varphi_{1,2}}V_n(\tilde{w})\}d\Gamma(\underset{\sim}{X})$$

$$+\int_S \tilde{q}U_{\varphi_{1,2}}\,dS + \rho h\omega^2\int_S \tilde{w}U_{\varphi_{1,2}}\,dS + \sum_{k=1}^{\bar{K}}\{[\![M_t(\tilde{w})]\!]\,U_{\varphi_{1,2}}$$

$$-[\![M_t(U_{\varphi_{1,2}})]\!]\,[\tilde{w}(\underset{\sim}{X})-\tilde{w}(\underset{\sim}{\Xi})]\}_k \tag{57}$$

where the various symbols, such as c, φ_1 and φ_2 have been explained in the previous section. For a regular (smooth) point $\underset{\sim}{\Xi}$ one has $c = 1$ and the left hand side of (57) simply becomes $-d\tilde{w}/dn$, while in its right hand side $\varphi_{1,2}$ reduces to just φ.

The integral formulation of the problem consists of the two boundary integral equations (51) and (57) and the integral equation (46). Equation (46) is needed in the formulation because of the presence of unknown interior values of $\tilde{w}$ in Eqs. (51) and (57). For the numerical solution of the system of Eqs (51), (57) and (46), the boundary Γ and the interior domain S are both discretized into a number of boundary and interior elements, respectively. Discretization of the interior is here necessary owing to the presence of the surface integrals

$$\rho h\omega^2 \int_S \tilde{w}\, U\, dS, \qquad \rho h\omega^2 \int_S \tilde{w}\, U_{\varphi 1,2}\, dS \tag{58}$$

that accommodate the inertia effects. To be sure, there are also surface integrals accommodating the loading effects but their integrands consist of known quantities and their computation can be done either analytically or numerically in an independent manner. Boundary elements are chosen to be quadratic isoparametric for which (33) is valid, and interior elements quadratic isoparametric, for which (34) with $\tilde{q}$ and $\tilde{q}_i$ being replaced by $\tilde{w}$ and $\tilde{w}_i$, respectively, is valid, or constant. Thus, the discretized forms of Eqs (51), (57) and (46) read

$$\begin{aligned}
&\frac{c}{2}\tilde{w}_j + \sum_{m=1}^{M}\Big\{\Big(\oint_{\Gamma_m} F^i(s)V_n(U(s))\,|J(s)|\,d\Gamma_m\Big)\tilde{w}_i - \Big(\oint_{\Gamma_m} F^i(s)M_n(U(s))\,|J(s)|\,d\Gamma_m\Big)\times\\
&\times\Big(\frac{d\tilde{w}}{dn}\Big)_i + \Big(\oint_{\Gamma_m} F^i(s)\frac{dU(s)}{dn}\,|J(s)|\,d\Gamma_m\Big)(M_n(\tilde{w}))_i - \Big(\oint_{\Gamma_m} F^i(s)U(s)\,|J(s)|\,d\Gamma_m\Big)\times\\
&\times (V_n(\tilde{w}))_i\Big\} + \sum_{k=1}^{\bar{K}} [\![M_t(U)]\!]\tilde{w}_k - \sum_{k=1}^{\bar{K}} U[\![M_t(\tilde{w})]\!]_k\\
&- \rho h\omega^2 \sum_{l=1}^{L}\Big(\int_{S_l} N^i(p,\tau)U(p,\tau)\,|J^*(p,\tau)|\,dS_l\Big)\tilde{w}_i\\
&= \sum_{l=1}^{L}\Big(\int_{S_l} N^i(p,\tau)U(p,\tau)\,|J^*(p,\tau)|\,dS_l\Big)\tilde{q}_i
\end{aligned} \tag{59}$$

$$\frac{c\pm \frac{v}{\pi}\sin c\pi}{2(\sin,\cos)\frac{c\pi}{2}}\left[\left(\frac{d\tilde{w}}{dn}\right)^{+}_{j} \pm \left(\frac{d\tilde{w}}{dn}\right)^{-}_{j}\right] + \sum_{m=1}^{M}\left(\oint_{\Gamma_m} F^{i}(s)V_n(U_{\varphi_{1,2}}(s))|J(s)|\,d\Gamma_m\right)(\tilde{w}_i-\tilde{w}_j)$$

$$-\oint_{\Gamma_m} F^{i}(s)M_n(U_{\varphi_{1,2}}(s))|J(s)|\,d\Gamma_m)\left(\frac{d\tilde{w}}{dn}\right)_i$$

$$+\oint_{\Gamma_m} F^{i}(s)\frac{dU_{\varphi_{1,2}}(s)}{dn}|J(s)|\,d\Gamma_m)(M_n(\tilde{w}))_i$$

$$-\oint_{\Gamma_m} F^{i}(s)U_{\varphi_{1,2}}(s)|J(s)|\,d\Gamma_m)(V_n(\tilde{w}))_i$$

$$+\sum_{k=1}^{\bar{K}} [\![M_t(U_{\varphi_{1,2}})]\!](\tilde{w}_k-\tilde{w}_j) - \sum_{k=1}^{\bar{K}} U_{\varphi_{1,2}}[\![M_t(\tilde{w})]\!]_k$$

$$-\rho h\omega^2 \sum_{l=1}^{L}\left(\int_{S_l} N^{i}(p,\tau)U_{\varphi_{1,2}}(p,\tau)|J^*(p,\tau)|\,dS_l\right)$$

$$x\ (\tilde{w}_i-\tilde{w}_j) =$$

$$= \sum_{l=1}^{L}\left(\int_{S_l} N^{i}(p,\tau)U_{\varphi_{1,2}}(p,\tau)|J^*(p,\tau)|\,dS_l\right)\tilde{q}_i \tag{60}$$

$$\tilde{w}_j = -\sum_{m=1}^{M}\left(\oint_{\Gamma_m} F^{i}(s)V_n(U(s))|J(s)|\,d\Gamma_m\right)\tilde{w}_i$$

$$-\left(\oint_{\Gamma_m} F^{i}(s)M_n(U(s))|J(s)|\,d\Gamma_m\right)\left(\frac{d\tilde{w}}{dn}\right)_i$$

$$+\left(\oint_{\Gamma_m} F^{i}(s)\frac{dU(s)}{dn}|J(s)|\,d\Gamma_m\right)(M_n(\tilde{w}))_i$$

$$-\left(\oint_{\Gamma_m} F^{i}(s)U(s)|J(s)|\,d\Gamma_m\right)(V_n(\tilde{w}))_i + \sum_{k=1}^{\bar{K}} U[\![M_t(\tilde{w})]\!]_k -$$

$$- \sum_{k=1}^{K} [\![M_t(U)]\!] \tilde{w}_k + \rho h \omega^2 \sum_{l=1}^{L} \left(\int_{S_l} N^i(p,\tau) U(p,\tau) |J^*(p,\tau)| dS_l \right) \tilde{w}_i$$

$$+ \sum_{l=1}^{L} \left(\int_{S_l} N^i(p,\tau) U(p,\tau) |J^*(p,\tau)| dS_l \right) \tilde{q}_i \qquad (61)$$

All the integrations indicated in the above three equations are accomplished numerically. Line or surface integrals with regular integrands, i.e., integrands with $r \neq 0$ are computed with the aid of the standard Gauss quadrature formulas of Stroud and Secrest [45] with 6 and 4x4 points, respectively. However, as can be easily proved [13], U, dU/dn, $M_n(U)$, U_φ and dU_φ/dn become of O(lnr), $V_n(U)$ and $M_n(U_\varphi)$ become of O(1/r) and $V_n(U_\varphi)$ becomes of $O(1/r^2)$ when $r \rightarrow 0$ and the corresponding integrals become singular of O(lnr), or O(1/r) since $V_n(U_\varphi)$ is multiplied in (60) by $\tilde{w}(\underset{\sim}{X})-\tilde{w}(\underset{\sim}{\Xi})$ which is of O(r) [13]. These integrals are computed in the manner described in the previous section. Surface inertia and load integrals exhibit O(lnr) singularity when $r \rightarrow 0$ and their evaluation is done by dividing each 8-noded quadrilateral interior element into a number of triangular subelements with their apexes located at the origin point. The integral evaluation over each subelement is then accomplished by mapping each one of them onto a unit square and performing the resulting integrations by a 4x4 Gauss integration scheme.

Assuming that N_r, N_c and N_i represent the number of regular, corner and interior nodes, respectively, in a plate, one can assemble equations (59) and (60) in matrix form, use the boundary conditions and write

$$[\tilde{A}]\{\tilde{Y}\} - \omega^2 [\tilde{B}]\{\tilde{X}\} = \{\tilde{Q}\} \qquad (62)$$

where $[\tilde{A}]$ is a $(2N_r+3N_c)\times(2N_r+3N_c)$ matrix with entries values of boundary element integrals, $[\tilde{B}]$ is a $(2N_r+3N_c)\times N_i$ matrix with entries values of interior element inertia integrals, $\{\tilde{Y}\}$ is a $(2N_r+3N_c)$ vector with entries the unknown nodal boundary variables, $\{\tilde{X}\}$ is a N_i vector with entries the unknown interior nodal values of $\tilde{w}$ and $\{\tilde{Q}\}$ is a $(2N_r+3N_c)$ vector with entries nodal surface load integrals. Writing equation (61) in matrix form and employing the boundary conditions yield

$$\{\tilde{X}\} = -[\tilde{A}^*]\{\tilde{Y}\} + \omega^2[\tilde{B}^*]\{\tilde{X}\} + \{\tilde{Q}^*\} \tag{63}$$

where $[\tilde{A}^*]$ is a $N_i x(2N_r+3N_c)$ matrix with entries values of boundary element integrals, $[\tilde{B}^*]$ is a $N_i x N_i$ matrix with entries values on interior element inertia integrals and $\{\tilde{Q}^*\}$ is a N_i vector with entries nodal surface load integrals. Elimination of $\{\tilde{Y}\}$ between (62) and (63) yields

$$[[I]-\omega^2[[\tilde{B}^*]-[\tilde{A}^*][\tilde{A}]^{-1}[\tilde{B}]]]\{\tilde{X}\} = -[\tilde{A}^*][\tilde{A}]^{-1}\{\tilde{Q}\}+\{\tilde{Q}^*\} \tag{64}$$

where [I] is the identity matrix.

For the free vibration case the loading vector $\{\tilde{Q}\} = \{\tilde{Q}^*\} = 0$ and Eq. (64) reduces to the eigenvalue problem

$$[\tilde{C}]\{\tilde{X}\} = (1/\omega^2)\{\tilde{X}\} \tag{65}$$

where

$$[\tilde{C}] = [\tilde{B}^*]-[\tilde{A}^*][\tilde{A}]^{-1}[\tilde{B}] \tag{66}$$

Matrix $[\tilde{C}]$ is real and in general non-sparse, non-symmetric and non-positive definite. An efficient iterative algorithm for the solution of the above eigenvalue problem has been developed by Smith et al [47] and this algorithm was adopted in this work.

<u>Forced Vibrations by Direct BEM in Time Domain</u>

The developments of this section are based on the work of Bézine and Gamby [17], which is the only work available on the subject. Here one has to establish an integral representation of Eq. (1) in the time domain. This is accomplished as usual with the aid of a reciprocal identity between two plate flexural motion states and the fundamental solution of the problem. One can easily prove [17] that the following identity-reciprocal relationship holds true between two plate elastodynamic states represented by their lateral deflections u and υ:

$$\int_S (\upsilon*\nabla^4 u - u*\nabla^4 \upsilon)dS = \frac{1}{D}\int_\Gamma [V_n(\upsilon)*u - M_n(\upsilon)*\frac{\partial u}{\partial n} + M_n(u)*\frac{\partial \upsilon}{\partial n} -$$

$$- V_n(u)*\upsilon]d\Gamma + \frac{1}{D}\sum_{k=1}^{K}[[\![M_t(\upsilon)]\!]*u - [\![M_t(u)]\!]*\upsilon]_k \qquad (67)$$

In the above the star (*) symbol denotes convolution defined as

$$\upsilon*u = \int_0^t \upsilon(\underset{\sim}{x}, t-\tau)\, u(\underset{\sim}{x},\tau)\, d\tau \qquad (68)$$

while the remaining symbols have been defined in previous sections.

The fundamental solution $U = U(\underset{\sim}{x}, \underset{\sim}{\xi}, t)$ of (1) is defined by

$$\nabla^4 U + \frac{\rho h}{D}\ddot{U} = \delta(\underset{\sim}{x},\underset{\sim}{\xi})\,\delta(t) \qquad (69)$$

$$U(\underset{\sim}{x},\underset{\sim}{\xi},0) = \dot{U}(\underset{\sim}{x},\underset{\sim}{\xi},0) = 0 \qquad (70)$$

where H(t) is the Heaviside function. This function represents the lateral deflection of an infinitely extended plate at point $\underset{\sim}{x}$ due to a unit concentrated lateral impulsive load applied at point $\underset{\sim}{\xi}$. The solution of (69) and (70) has the form (Sneddon [48])

$$U(\underset{\sim}{x},\underset{\sim}{\xi},t) = \frac{\partial}{\partial t}\left[\frac{t}{4A} F\left(\frac{Ar^2}{4t}\right)\right] \qquad (71)$$

where

$$A^2 = \rho h/D, \qquad r = |\underset{\sim}{x}-\underset{\sim}{\xi}| \qquad (72)$$

$$\mathrm{Si}(\varphi) = \int_0^{\varphi} \frac{\sin\varphi}{\varphi} d\varphi, \quad \mathrm{Ci}(\varphi) = -\int_0^{\varphi} \frac{\cos\varphi}{\varphi} d\varphi \tag{73}$$

Identifying υ with U and u with w in (67) and taking into account that

$$\int_S w(\underset{\sim}{x},t) * \delta(\underset{\sim}{x},\xi)\ \delta(t) dS = w(\underset{\sim}{\xi},t) \tag{74}$$

one receives the integral representation

$$\begin{aligned} w(\underset{\sim}{\xi},t) = &-\frac{1}{D}\int_{\Gamma} \Big[V_n(U)*w - M_n(U)*\frac{\partial w}{\partial n} + M_n(w)*\frac{\partial U}{\partial n} - V_n(w)*U\Big] d\Gamma(\underset{\sim}{x}) \\ &+ \frac{1}{D}\int_S U*q\ dS(\underset{\sim}{x}) + \frac{1}{D}\overset{K}{\underset{k=1}{\mathrm{K}}}\{[\![M_t(w)]\!]*U - [\![M_t(U)]\!]*w\}_k + \\ &+ A^2\int_S [\dot{w}_0 U - w_0\dot{U}] dS(\underset{\sim}{x}) \end{aligned} \tag{75}$$

where

$$w_o = w(\underset{\sim}{x},o), \qquad \dot{w}_o = \dot{w}(\underset{\sim}{x},o) \tag{76}$$

One can now bring point $\underset{\sim}{\xi}$ to a position $\underset{\sim}{\Xi}$ on the boundary Γ through a limiting process and receive from (75) the boundary integral equation

$$\begin{aligned} \frac{1}{2} w(\underset{\sim}{\Xi},t) = &-\frac{1}{D}\int_{\Gamma} \Big[V_n(U)*w - M_n(U)*\frac{\partial w}{\partial n} + M_n(w)*\frac{\partial U}{\partial n} \\ &- V_n(w)*U\Big] d\Gamma(\underset{\sim}{x}) + \frac{1}{D}\int_S U*\ q\, d\, S(\underset{\sim}{x}) + \frac{1}{D}\sum_{k=1}^{K}\{[\![M_t(w)]\!]*U - \\ &- [\![M_t(U)]\!]*w\}_k + A^2\int_S [\dot{w}_0 U - w_0\dot{U}] dS(\underset{\sim}{x}) \end{aligned} \tag{77}$$

which is valid for a plate with K corners at a smooth point $\underset{\sim}{\Xi}$.

A second boundary integral equation for the normal slope can be easily obtained by taking the directional derivative $\partial w/\partial n_o$ of w of Eq. (77) along the direction of the outward normal vector $\underset{\sim}{n}_o$ at point $\underset{\sim}{\Xi}$. Thus one has

$$\frac{1}{2}\frac{\partial w}{\partial n_o}(\underset{\sim}{\Xi},t) = -\frac{1}{D}\int_\Gamma \Big[\frac{\partial V_n}{\partial n_o}(U)*w - \frac{\partial M_n}{\partial n_o}(U)*\frac{\partial w}{\partial n} + M_n(w)*\frac{\partial^2 U}{\partial n \partial n_o}$$

$$- V_n(w)*\frac{\partial U}{\partial n_o}\Big]\, d\Gamma(\underset{\sim}{X}) + \frac{1}{D}\int_S \frac{\partial U}{\partial n_o}*q dS(\underset{\sim}{x}) + \frac{1}{D}\sum_{k=1}^{K}\{[\![M_t(w)]\!]*\frac{\partial U}{\partial n_o} -$$

$$- [\![\frac{\partial M_t}{\partial n_o}(U)]\!]*w\}_k + A^2\int_S [\dot{w}_o\frac{\partial U}{\partial n_o} - w_o\frac{\partial \dot{U}}{\partial n_o}]\, dS(\underset{\sim}{x}) \qquad (78)$$

It is apparent that Eqs (77) and (78) can also be written for a corner point $\underset{\sim}{\Xi}$ by following the ideas presented in the two previous sections.

Equations (77) and (78) are solved numerically by discretizing both space and time. In particular, the perimeter of the plate is represented by line elements and its surface by interior elements, which are needed to accommodate the load and initial conditions integrals. The total time interval is divided into a number of time steps of length Δt. The simplest possible modelling is to use straight segments for the boundary and triangles or rectangles for the interior with constant values of the field variables. Both types of elements are then described by a single node (their centroid) where the generalized displacements (w, $\partial w/\partial n_o$) and the generalized tractions ($M_n(w)$, $V_n(w)$) collocate. These field variables remain constant for the duration of Δt. Nodal collocation results in the algebraic system

$$[A_1]*\{w\}+[A_2]*\{\partial w/\partial n_o\}+[B_1]*\{M_n(w)\}+[B_2]*\{V_n(w)\}+$$
$$+[B_3]*\{M_t(w)\} = [B_4]*\{q\} \qquad (79)$$

In the above, $[A_1]$, $[A_2]$, $[B_1]$, $[B_2]$ and $[B_4]$ contain the results of numerical integration of the kernels in (77) and

(78) over the boundary elements, while matrix $[B_3]$ contains the fundamental solution and its normal slope evaluated at all corners. Vectors $\{w\}$, $\{\partial w/\partial n_o\}$, $\{M_n(w)\}$, $\{V_n(w)\}$ and $\{M_t(w)\}$ contain nodal values of the boundary displacements, rotations, moments, shears and twisting moments, respectively, while vector $\{q\}$ contains values of the loading at interior nodes. The convolution integrals in (79) are computed analytically during every time step and after application of the boundary conditions and rearrangement resulting in only two types of vectors (known and unknown) one can construct a time marching scheme providing the unknown vector at time step $n\Delta t$ in terms of the known vector at time step $n\Delta t$ and the contributions of all time steps previous to $n\Delta t$, as in the case of elastodynamics [4].

It should be noticed that the above time domain methodology is recommended for the general case involving transient loading. However, if the load varies harmonically with time, then one has simply to solve Eq. (39) to obtain the amplitude of the response $\{\tilde{X}\}$ for a given value of the operational frequency ω (or θ) of the excitation and there is no need at all to work in the time domain.

Once all information on the boundary is known, one can proceed to compute $w(\underset{\sim}{\xi},t)$ at any interior point $\underset{\sim}{\xi}$ by using (75) in discretized form. Interior moments and forces can then be computed from (5)-(10) where the needed second and third order derivatives of w are obtained by repeated differentiation of (75). The differentiation is with respect to $\underset{\sim}{\xi}$ and thus only the singular kernels are affected inside the integrals of (75). In spite of the increased order of singularity due to kernel differentiation, there is no any computational problem since $r \neq 0$ inside the plate. Problems may arise, however, for points $\underset{\sim}{\xi}$ very near the boundary where $\underset{\sim}{r}$ attains very small values. In that case a very simple and practical way is to obtain results there by extrapolation.

Forced Vibrations by Direct D/BEM in Time Domain

O'Donoghue and Atluri [21,22] first employed the time domain D/BEM for computing flexural response of plates. An integral formulation of the problem described by Eq. (1) can be achieved by rewriting that equation in the form

$$\nabla^4 w = \frac{q^*}{D} \tag{80}$$

with

$$q^* = q - \rho h \ddot{w} \tag{81}$$

and following exactly the same procedure as in the case of free vibrations by the direct D/BEM. Indeed a comparison between Eqs (42) and (43) and Eqs (80) and (81) reveals that the integral formulation consisting of Eqs (51), (57) and (46) can also be used here, if one replaces $\tilde{q}(\underset{\sim}{x})$, $\tilde{w}(\underset{\sim}{x})$ and $\omega^2\tilde{w}(\underset{\sim}{x})$ by $q(\underset{\sim}{x},t)$, $w(\underset{\sim}{x},t)$ and $-\ddot{w}(\underset{\sim}{x},t)$, respectively. Thus the matrix formulation of the forced vibration problem in the time domain, under the aforementioned observation and in view of Eqs (62) and (63), takes the form

$$[A]\{Y\} + [B]\{\ddot{X}\} = \{Q\} \tag{82}$$

$$\{X\} = -[A^*]\{Y\} - [B^*]\{\ddot{X}\} + \{Q^*\} \tag{83}$$

Elimination of {Y} between (82) and (83) yields

$$[G]\{\ddot{Y}\} + \{X\} = \{P\} \tag{84}$$

where

$$\begin{aligned} [G] &= [B^*] - [A^*][A]^{-1}[B], \\ \{P\} &= \{Q^*\} - [A^*][A]^{-1}\{Q\} \end{aligned} \tag{85}$$

Equation (84) can be easily solved by any time integration algorithm, such as that due to Newmark or Houbolt. Once {X} is known, then {Y} can be obtained from (82) as

$$\{Y\} = [A]^{-1}\{Q\} - [A]^{-1}[B]\{\ddot{X}\} \tag{86}$$

Of course, if the load is harmonic with time, then it is much more convenient to obtain the response amplitude $\{\tilde{X}\}$ directly from (64) by a simple matrix inversion for every given value of the operational frequency ω. For computing interior moments and forces one can follow the procedure described at the end of the previous section.

<u>Forced Vibrations by Direct BEM-Laplace Transform</u>

The developments in this section are based on the work of Providakis and Beskos [16]. The equation of flexural motion (39) for a plate experiencing harmonic vibrations due to harmonically varying with time loads q can be easily solved for the response amplitude $\{\tilde{X}\}$ for a given value of the operational frequency ω (or δ). For general transient loading q use can be made of the Laplace transform with respect to time defined for a function $f(\underset{\sim}{x},t)$ as

$$\bar{f}(\underset{\sim}{x},\lambda) = \int_0^{\infty} f(\underset{\sim}{x},t)\, e^{-\lambda t}\, dt \tag{87}$$

where λ is the, in general complex, Laplace transform parameter (or complex frequency). Application of (87) on (1) yields

$$\nabla^4 \bar{w} + \mu^4 \bar{w} = \frac{\bar{q}}{D} + \frac{\rho h}{D}(\lambda w_0 + \dot{w}_0) = \frac{\bar{q}^*}{D} \tag{88}$$

where

$$\mu^4 = \rho h \lambda^2 / D \tag{89}$$

and w_o and $\dot{w}_o$ indicate initial deflection and velocity, respectively. A comparison between (3), (4) and (88), (89) easily reveals that the formulation of the harmonic vibration case be used in this case by simply replacing $-\delta^4$ by μ^4 (or equivalently ω by $i\lambda$), $\tilde{q}$ by $\bar{q}^*$ and tildes by overbars over the various quantities entering the equations. Thus, the general forced vibration problem of plates, in view of (39), can be expressed in the matrix form

$$[\bar{A}(\lambda)]\{\bar{X}\} = \{\bar{Q}\} \tag{90}$$

Solution of (90) for $\{\bar{X}\}$ provides the Laplace transformed boundary response of the plate. Its time domain response can be easily obtained by a numerical inversion of that transformed solution. This requires, of course, solution of (90) for a sequence of values of λ. Sometimes the transient load q is so complicated that its direct Laplace transform also has to be computed numerically. Both the direct and the inverse Laplace transforms can be very accurately computed numerically by the algorithm of Durbin [49] as explained in Narayanan and Beskos [50]. The disadvantage of this algorithm is that it works with complex values of λ and is not as efficient as other algorithms working with real data. Real data algorithms, however, are not accurate for dynamic problems [50]. Determination of interior deflections can be done with the aid of (21) in conjunction with the replacement of ω, $\tilde{q}$ and tildes by $i\lambda$, $\bar{q}^*$ and overbars, respectively, which in discretized form takes the form

$$\begin{aligned}
\bar{w}_j = \frac{1}{D}\Big\{ & \sum_{m=1}^{M} \Big(\int_{\Gamma_m} F^i(s) V_n(U(s))\, |J(s)|\, d\Gamma\Big)\bar{w}_i \\
& - \sum_{m=1}^{M} \Big(\int_{\Gamma_m} F^i(s) M_n(U(s))\, |J(s)|\, d\Gamma\Big)\Big(\frac{d\bar{w}}{dn}\Big)_i \\
& + \sum_{m=1}^{M} \Big(\int_{\Gamma_m} F^i(s)\, \frac{dU(s)}{dn}\, |J(s)|\, d\Gamma\Big)(M_n(\bar{w}))_i \\
& - \sum_{m=1}^{M} \Big(\int_{\Gamma_m} F^i(s) U(s)\, |J(s)|\, d\Gamma\Big)(V_n(\bar{w}))_i \Big\} \\
& + \frac{1}{D} \sum_{k=1}^{K} [\![M_t(U)]\!] \bar{w}_k - \frac{1}{D} \sum_{m=1}^{K} [\![M_t(\bar{w})]\!]_k\, U \\
& - \frac{1}{D} \sum_{l=1}^{L} \Big(\int_{S_l} N^i(p,\tau) U(p,\tau)\, |\overset{*}{J}(p,\tau)|\, dS\Big)\bar{q}^*_i
\end{aligned} \tag{91}$$

For the computation of interior moments and forces one can follow the procedure described in the previous two sections.

Forced Vibrations by Direct D/BEM - Laplace Transform

The content of this section is based on the work of Providakis and Beskos [24]. If the load q varies harmonically with time, one has to solve (64) or

$$[\tilde{D}]\{\tilde{X}\} = \{\tilde{P}\} \tag{92}$$

with

$$\begin{aligned} [\tilde{D}] &= [I]-\omega^2[[\tilde{B}^*]-[\tilde{A}^*][\tilde{A}]^{-1}[\tilde{B}]] \\ \{\tilde{P}\} &= -[\tilde{A}^*][\tilde{A}]^{-1}\{\tilde{Q}\}+\{\tilde{Q}^*\} \end{aligned} \tag{93}$$

for the solution amplitude $\{\tilde{X}\}$ as a function of the given operational frequency ω. If the load q has any arbitrary time variation, use is made of the Laplace transform with respect to time defined by (87). Application of (87) on (1) yields

$$\nabla^4\bar{w} = \bar{q}^{**}/D \tag{94}$$

where

$$\bar{q}^{**} = \bar{q} - \rho h\lambda^2\bar{w} + \rho h\lambda w_o + \rho h\dot{w}_o \tag{95}$$

Inspection of the pairs of Eqs (3), (4) and (94), (95) reveals that the general transient forced vibration problem can be expressed in the transformed domain by Eqs. (92) and (93) with $-\omega^2$, $\tilde{q}*$ and tildes being replaced by λ^2, $\bar{q}**$ and overbars, respectively. The transformed solution is obtained by solving (92) for $\{\bar{X}\}$ for a sequence of values of λ. A numerical inversion of this transformed solution, as described in the previous section, can finally provide the time domain response. Once $\{\bar{X}\}$ has been computed, $\{\bar{Y}\}$ can be obtained from the Laplace transformed version of (62) in the form

$$\{\bar{Y}\} = [\bar{A}]^{-1}\{\bar{Q}\}-\lambda^2[\bar{A}]^{-1}[\bar{B}]\{\bar{X}\} \qquad (96)$$

and {Y} by a numerical Laplace transform inversion. Once the interior displacement w of the plate is known, one can easily compute interior moments and forces by following the procedure described in the previous sections.

Effect of Damping and In-plane Forces on the Response

It is well known that damping, representing energy losses in a plate, reduces its dynamic response. Consider first the case of external viscous damping in a plate experiencing flexural motion. In this case Eq. (1) is replaced by

$$\nabla^4 w + \frac{\rho h}{D}\ddot{w} + \frac{c}{D}\dot{w} = \frac{q}{D} \qquad (97)$$

where c is the viscous damping coefficient. Application of Laplace transform with respect to time on (97) under zero initial conditions yields

$$\nabla^4 \bar{w} + \frac{(\rho h\lambda^2 + c\lambda)}{D}\bar{w} = \frac{\bar{q}}{D} \qquad (98)$$

indicating that, irrespectively of the kind of the fundamental solution used in the formulation (dynamic or static), the effect of the external viscous damping on the plate response can be very easily taken into account if $\rho h\lambda^2$ is replaced by $\rho h\lambda^2 + c\lambda$ in the previously discussed formulations associated with Laplace transform. These two cases have been discussed by Providakis and Beskos [16, 24], who have also presented numerical results.

When the forced vibration problem is formulated in the time domain with the aid of the dynamic fundamental solution of the problem, one is faced with the difficult problem of deriving that fundamental solution. To this author's best knowledge such a solution is not available in the literature. When the forced vibration problem is formulated in the time domain with the aid of the static fundamental solution, the presence of the additional term $-c\dot{w}$ in the right hand side of (81), finally creates the term $[C]\{\dot{X}\}$ in the left hand side of

(84), which can be easily solved by any time integration algorithm as before. One can consult here O'Donoghue and Atluri [21] for more details.

When, on the other hand, there exists internal linear viscoelastic damping in the plate, the correspondence principle, as described by Pan [51], states that the transformed viscoelastodynamic solution can be obtained from the corresponding transformed elastodynamic one if D is replaced by

$$\bar{D}(\lambda) = L\left[\left(\frac{2PQ'+P'Q}{PQ'+2QP'}\right)\frac{Q}{P}\right]\frac{h^3}{12} \tag{99}$$

In the above, L denotes the Laplace transform operator, P, Q, P' and Q' are linear differential operators of the form

$$P = \sum_{r=0}^{m} p_r \frac{\partial^r}{\partial t^r}, \qquad Q = \sum_{r=0}^{n} q_r \frac{\partial^r}{\partial t^r}$$
$$P' = \sum_{r=0}^{m'} p'_r \frac{\partial^r}{\partial t^r}, \qquad Q' = \sum_{r=0}^{n'} q'_r \frac{\partial^r}{\partial t^r} \tag{100}$$

which define the constitutive behaviour of a homogeneous, isotropic, linear viscoelastic material through the equations

$$P\, s_{ij} = Q e_{ij}$$
$$P'\sigma_{ii} = Q'\varepsilon_{ii} \tag{101}$$

with s_{ij} and e_{ij} being the stress and strain deviators, respectively, of the stress σ_{ij} and strain ε_{ij} tensors. For example, under the assumption of constant Poisson's ratio and the adoption of the standard viscoelastic solid model with elastic constants E_1 and E_2 and coefficient of viscosity c_1, Eq. (99) reduces to

$$\bar{D}(\lambda) = \frac{E_2 h^3}{12(1-v^2)}\left[\frac{1+\lambda_2\lambda}{1+\lambda_1\lambda}\right] \tag{102}$$

where

$$\lambda_1 = c_1/E_1, \quad \lambda_2 = \lambda_1\,[1+(E_1/E_2)] \tag{103}$$

The above hold true irrespectively of the static or dynamic character of the fundamental solution and have been developed by Providakis and Beskos [24].

Treatment of internal linear viscoelastic damping in the time domain presents difficulties and there is no as yet work available on the subject either in connection with the dynamic or the static fundamental solution.

The presence of constant in-plane forces in a plate experiencing flexural motion affects both its free vibrational characteristics (natural frequencies and modal shapes) and its response to external lateral load. If the in-plane forces are tensile, the plate becomes stiffer, while if they are compressive it becomes more flexible. This results in higher frequencies and reduced flexural response in the former case and in lower frequencies and increased response in the latter case. The governing equation of motion (1), in the presence of in-plane forces affecting the flexural motion, becomes

$$D\nabla^4 w+\rho h\ddot{w}+N_x\frac{\partial^2 w}{\partial x^2}+2\,N_{xy}\frac{\partial^2 w}{\partial x\partial y}+N_y\frac{\partial^2 w}{\partial y^2}=q \tag{104}$$

where N_x, N_{xy} and N_y are the known constant in-plane compressive forces. If the forces are tensile, one can simply put a minus sign in front of the N_x, N_{xy} and N_y. When the in-plane forces are uniform with intensity N, then (104) reduces to

$$D\nabla^4 w + \rho h\ddot{w} \mp N\nabla^2 w = q \tag{105}$$

where the upper (lower) sign in front of N must be taken for N tensile (compressive).

Niwa et al [8] and Kitahara [9] were the first to treat (105) with $q = 0$ in the context of the direct BEM employing the frequency domain dynamic fundamental solution, which was determined by the same authors to have the form

$$U = -\frac{1}{\alpha^2+\gamma^2}\frac{i}{4}\left[H_0^{(1)}(\alpha r) - H_0^{(1)}(i\gamma r)\right] \tag{106}$$

where

$$\alpha^2 = \frac{1}{2}\left[(\zeta^4 + 4\beta^4)^{1/2} \mp \zeta^2\right]$$
$$\gamma^2 = \frac{1}{2}\left[(\zeta^4 + 4\beta^4)^{1/2} \pm \zeta^2\right] \tag{107}$$
$$\zeta^2 = N/D$$

When there are no in-plane forces, $\zeta^2 = 0$ and $\alpha^2 = \gamma^2 = \beta^2$ and Eq. (1) is recovered. On the other hand, in the static case, $\beta^4 = 0$ and hence $\alpha^2 = 0$, $\gamma^2 = \zeta^2$ or $\alpha^2 = \zeta^2$, $\gamma^2 = 0$ and

$$U = \frac{1}{2\pi\zeta^2}\left[\ln r + K_0(\zeta r)\right] \tag{108}$$

$$U = -\frac{1}{4\pi\zeta^2}\left[i\pi H_0^{(1)}(\zeta r) + 2\ln r\right] \tag{109}$$

for tensile and compressive N, respectively. Eq. (109) is utilized in linear elastic stability analysis described in chapter six of this book.

When the direct BEM in conjunction with the static flexural fundamental solution is used, the presence of $N\nabla^2 w$ creates additional volume integrals of the form

$$\int_S U N \nabla^2 w \, dS, \qquad \int_S \frac{\partial U}{\partial n_0} N \nabla^2 w \, dS \tag{110}$$

which can be easily transformed into volume integrals containing only w. Thus, for example, using Green's second theorem one has

$$\int_S U N \nabla^2 w \, dS = \int_S N w \nabla^2 U \, dS + \int_\Gamma N(U \frac{\partial w}{\partial n} - w \frac{\partial U}{\partial n}) \, d\Gamma \qquad (111)$$

and a similar matrix formulation and solution procedure to the one for N = 0 can be followed in this case of N = 0. It should be noticed that expressions (110) and (111) hold true in the time or the Laplace transformed domain. More details about this subject can be found in O'Donoghue and Atluri [21] and Beskos et al [25] for the time and Laplace transformed domain cases, respectively.

Numerical Examples

This section presents a number of representative numerical examples from free and forced vibrations of plates in order to illustrate the various methods described in the previous sections and compare them against each other and against other analytical or numerical methods with respect to accuracy and efficiency.

Example 1 [24]

Consider a circular plate of radius R = 1.1, thickness h = 0.05, mass per unit area ρh = 0.01145 and elastic constants E = 1000 and ν = 0.3 experiencing free vibrations. Table 2 presents the first six natural frequencies ω_i (i = 1,2...6) for clamped boundary conditions all around the plate as computed by the quadratic boundary element direct D/BEM of Providakis and Beskos [24] and BEM of Providakis and Beskos [16], the constant boundary element indirect BEM of Niwa et al [7] and the general purpose FEM computer program SAP IV [52] that employs four-noded quadrilateral elements with three degrees of freedom per node in conjunction with a consistent mass model. The superscripts c and q used in connection with

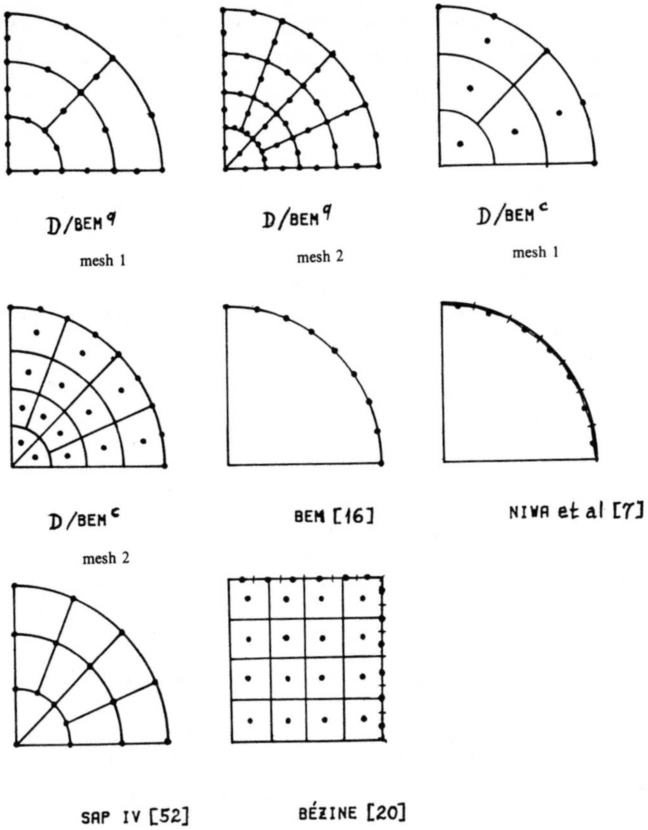

Fig. 4. Boundary and interior element discretizations of 1/4 of a plate.

D/BEM denote constant and quadratic interior elements, respectively, while the discretizations used in all the above methods for 1/4 of the plate are depicted in Fig. 4. The percentage error is defined as $(\omega_{ex}-\omega)/\omega_{ex}$ (%), where ω_{ex} represents "exact" or highly accurate values taken from Leissa [53]. Perusal of Table 2 in conjunction with knowledge of the basic characteristics of the various methods can lead to the following conclusions:

a) BEM with only quadratic boundary elements is the most accurate method with a rather small number of degrees of freedom (d.o.f.). However, it employs the complicated dynamic fundamental solution of the problem and requires extraction of frequencies by the inefficient method of determinant evaluation in conjunction with complex arithmetic. The constant element method of Niwa et al [7] has all the above disadvantages of BEM and in addition requires a larger number of d.o.f. for the same degree of accuracy.

b) D/BEM with both boundary and interior elements is not as accurate as BEM but it is more efficient because of the employment of the simple static fundamental solution of the problem and the extraction of frequencies by efficient iterative methods in conjunction with real arithmetic. D/BEM^q-mesh 1 and D/BEM^c-mesh 1 are less or equally accurate than the FEM but require a much lower number of d.o.f. D/BEM^q-mesh 2 and D/BEM^c-mesh 2 are more accurate that FEM with the latter requiring a much lower number of d.o.f. than the FEM. In addition, D/BEM approaches do not require the lateral deflection to be C^1 continuous as is the case with the FEM.

c) In conclusion, the methods that combine high accuracy with computational efficiency are the D/BEM^q-mesh 1 and the D/BEM^c-mesh 2, i.e., two D/BEM type of methods that employ boundary quadratic elements and interior quadratic elements with a rather coarse mesh or interior constant elements with a rather dense mesh.

Example 2 [24]

Method	ω_1	ω_2	ω_3	ω_4	ω_5	ω_6	No. d.o.f
Leissa [53]	8.443	17.570	28.826	32.869	42.182	50.265	
D/BEM^q-mesh 1	8.492	17.680	29.399	34.744	44.184	53.516	53
Error (%)	0.6	0.6	2.0	5.7	4.2	4.5	
D/BEM^q-mesh 2	8.455	17.586	28.924	33.040	42.484	50.524	153
Error (%)	0.1	0.1	0.3	0.5	0.7	0.5	
D/BEM^o-mesh 1	8.699	18.267	31.192	36.468	48.403	58.195	20
Error (%)	3.0	4.0	8.2	10.9	14.7	15.8	
D/BEM^o-mesh 2	8.521	17.718	29.540	33.203	44.130	53.552	56
Error (%)	0.9	0.8	2.5	1.0	4.6	6.5	
BEM [16]	8.462	17.563	28.864	32.904	42.129	50.278	64
Error (%)	0.22	0.04	0.13	0.11	0.12	0.02	
Niwa et al.[7]	8.462	17.486	28.767	32.799	42.840	51.575	112
Error (%)	0.22	0.04	0.20	0.21	1.55	2.61	
SAP IV [52]	8.552	19.020	32.362	33.200	45.655	50.841	99
Error (%)	1.3	8.3	12.27	1.0	8.2	1.1	

Table 2. Natural frequencies for a clamped circular plate

Method	ω_1	ω_2	ω_3	ω_4	ω_5	ω_6	No. d.o.f.
Leissa [53]	19.739	49.348	78.957	98.696	128.305	167.783	
D/BEM^q-mesh 1	19.925	49.988	81.622	101.399	130.566	175.780	53
Error (%)	0.9	1.3	3.4	2.7	1.8	4.8	
D/BEM^q-mesh 2	19.756	49.445	79.496	99.058	129.914	168.937	153
Error (%)	0.09	0.2	0.7	0.4	1.3	0.7	
D/BEM^o-mesh 1	20.265	50.130	81.193	111.705	153.233	170.691	20
Error (%)	2.7	1.6	2.8	11.6	19.4	1.7	
D/BEM^o-mesh 2	19.866	49.671	81.051	100.987	133.880	169.139	56
Error (%)	0.6	0.7	2.7	2.3	4.3	0.8	
BEM [16]	19.803	49.420	79.210	98.604	128.596	167.780	68
Error (%)	0.3	0.1	0.3	0.09	0.2	0.002	
Bézine [20]	19.866	50.145	80.971	101.864	133.681	----	64
Error (%)	0.6	1.6	2.6	3.2	4.2	----	
SAP IV [52]	19.764	51.801	84.780	97.987	133.880	173.710	99
Error (%)	0.1	5.0	7.4	0.7	4.3	3.5	

Table 3. Natural frequencies for a simply supported square plate

	D/BEM [20]			Ritz's method [54]	Experimental [55]	FEM [55]			
Comp. Time	50''	2'30				9'		2'50	40''
Mode	4x4	8x8	Error			5x5	Error	4x4	3x3
1	3.517	3.484	0,3%	3.494	3,43	3.470	0,7%	3.474	3.466
2	8.805	8.571	0,3%	8.547	7,91	8.509	0,4%	8.523	8.529
3	24.488	22.525	0,5%	21.44	21,19	21.459	0,1%	21.538	21.679
4	30.879	28.104	2,4%	27.46	27,73	27.063	1,5%	26.994	26.852
5	33.537	31.359	0,6%	31.17	28,35	30.948	0,7%	30.915	30.802

Table 4. Natural frequencies for a square cantilever plate

Consider a square plate of side α = 1, thickness h = 0.05, mass per unit area ρh = 0.01145 and elastic constants E = 1000 and v = 0.3 experiencing free vibrations. Table 3 provides the first six natural frequancies ω_i (i = 1,2...6) for simply supported boundary conditions, as obtained by D/BEM [24], BEM [16], Bézine [20] and SAP IV [25] by using the discretizations of Fig. 1. All these results are compared against those of Leissa [53]. Effect of corners in this simply supported plate is taken into account. Ispection of the results of Table 3 leads to exactly the same conclusions as in the previous example with respect to all the methods except those of Niwa et al [7], which is not included here and Bézine [20], which was not included in Table 2. Bézine's [20] method is a D/BEM type of method that employs constant boundary and constant interior elements. It is the third best D/BEM approach (after D/BEM^q-mesh 1 and D/BEM^c-mesh 2) both from the accuracy and efficiency viewpoints.

Example 3 [20]

Consider a square cantilever plate having three free edges and one edge clamped and a Poisson's ratio v = 0.3, experiencing free vibrations. Table 4 provides the first five natural frequency parameters β_i^2 (i = 1,2...,5) as computed by D/BEM of Bézine [20] with 48 constant boundary elements and 4x4 = 16 and 8x8 = 64 constant interior elements. The same Table provides also results from Young [54] as obtained by the Ritz method, as well as experimental and FEM results obtained by Bézine [55]. Percent error is calculated with respect to Young's [54] results. Computer times are also recorded in Table 4 in order to assess the efficiency of the methods. The first five modal shapes of the plate as computed by the D/BEM of Bézine [20] with an 8x8 interior discretization are shown pictorially in Fig. 5, where nodal curves are represented as broken lines. It is evident from Table 4 that the error in the frequency results of D/BEM is less than 3% and in very good agreement with the FEM results. It is also observed that the D/BEM is more efficient than the FEM and that for the same computation time gives a slightly better accuracy and allows a

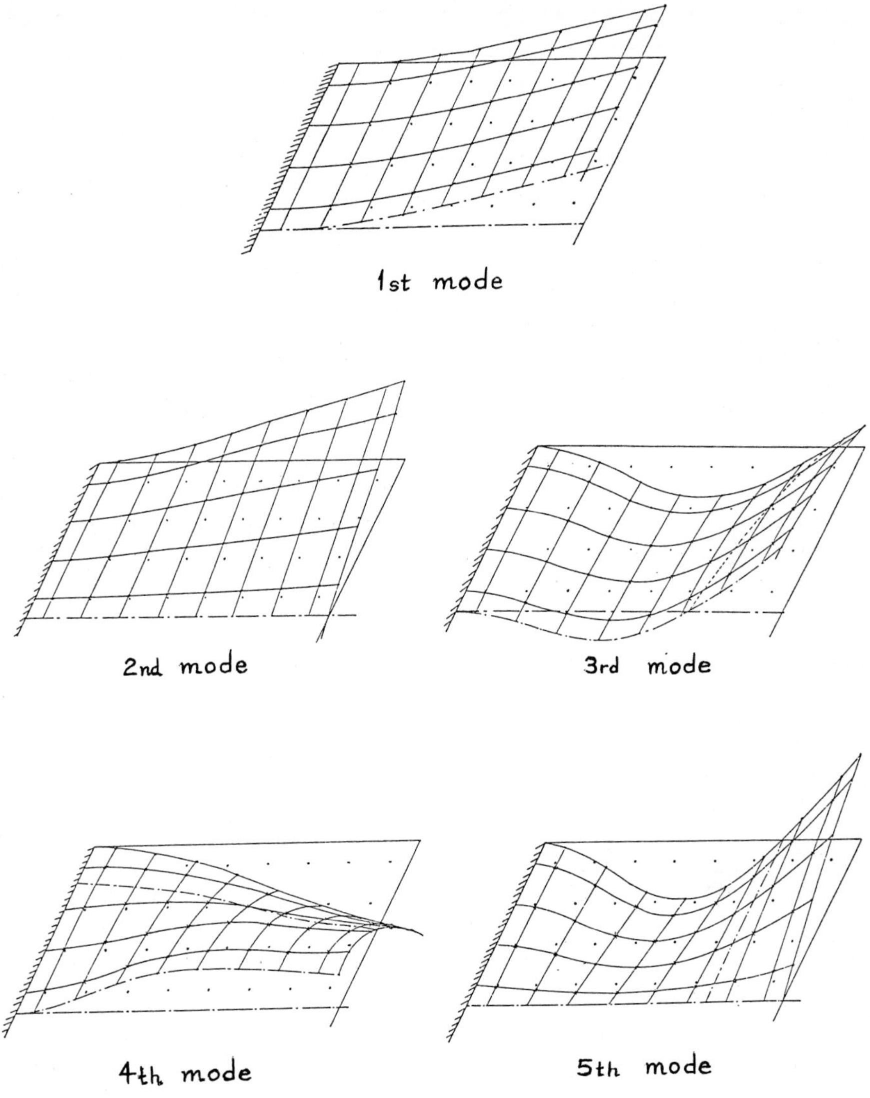

Fig. 5. First five modal shapes of vibration for a symmetric cantilever square plate.

finer discretization, thus permitting one to plot modal shapes with a greater precision. The modal shapes of Fig. 5 are in good agreement with those in Young [54].

Example 4 [28]

Consider the assembled plate structure of Fig. 6 composed of three equal rectangular plate components with an aspect ratio of the smaller to the larger edge of 0.5. The whole structure is assumed to be clamped only along the boundary ABCD, while the remaining boundary is free. A free vibration analysis of this structure has been done by Tanaka et al [28] by employing the D/BEM not only for the flexural motion but also for the in-plane (plane stress) motion and the results of this analysis are presented herein. Using consistant rectangular elements, the whole boundary and each joint edge are divided into 30 and 6 elements of equal size, respectively, as shown in Fig. 6. Fig. 7 (a-c) shows the first three modal shapes and corresponding natural frequencies (ω_1 = 0.409, ω_2 = 0.493, ω_3 = 1.139).

Example 5 [24]

Consider a circular plate of radius R = 1.1, thickness h = 0.05, mass per unit area ρh = 0.01145 and elastic constants E = 1000 and ν = 0.3. This plate is loaded by a concentrated vertical impulsive force P(t) at its center with magnitude P_o = 1 and duration t_o = 0.121. Figures 8 and 9 depict the history of the vertical central deflection, under clamped and simply supported, respectively, all around boundary conditions as obtained by D/BEM^q-mesh 1 and D/BEM^q-mesh 2, in conjunction with Laplace transform [24], direct BEM in conjunction with Laplace transform and 64 d.o.f. [16], direct BEM in time domain [17], SAP IV in conjunction with numerical integration and 99 d.o.f. [52] and the analytic expression of Sneddon [48]. In both plate cases the boundary is smooth and there is no effect of corners. An inspection of Figs 8 and 9 leads to the conclusion that all the methods provide results of very good accuracy, with BEM in conjunction with Laplace transform

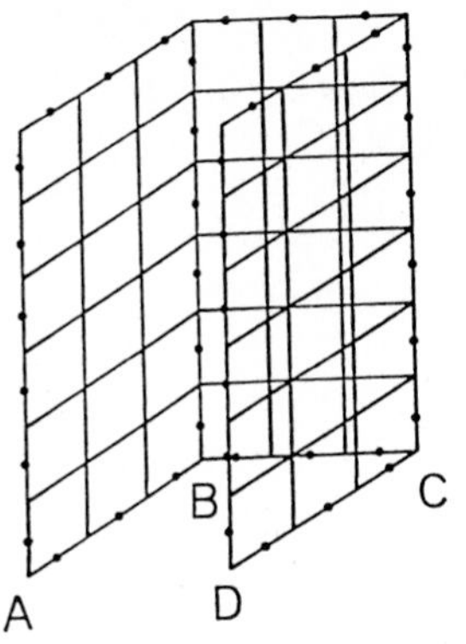

Fig. 6. Assembled plate structure and element subdivision.

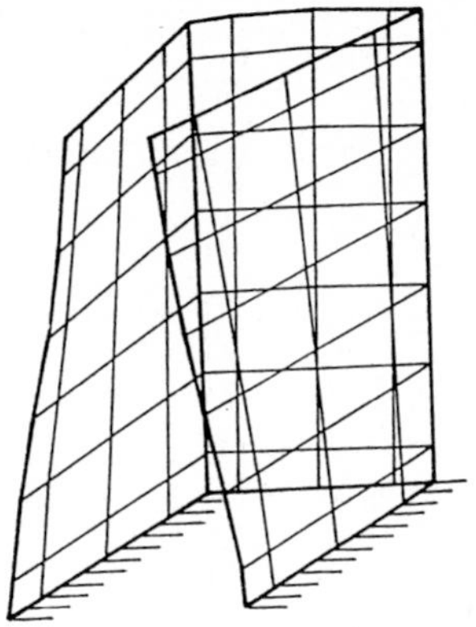

Fig. 7(a). First modal shape.

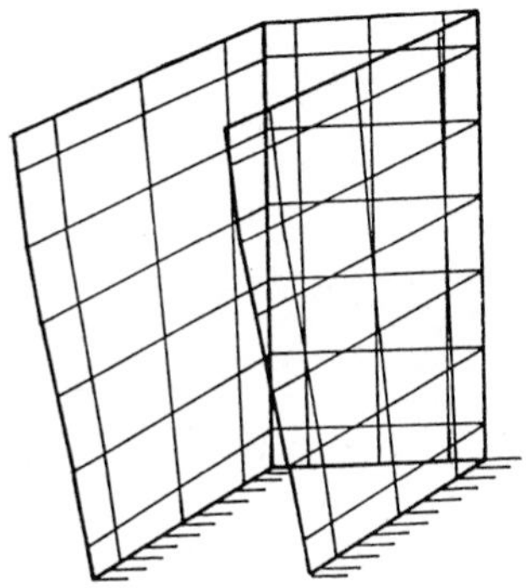

Fig. 7(b). Second modal shape.

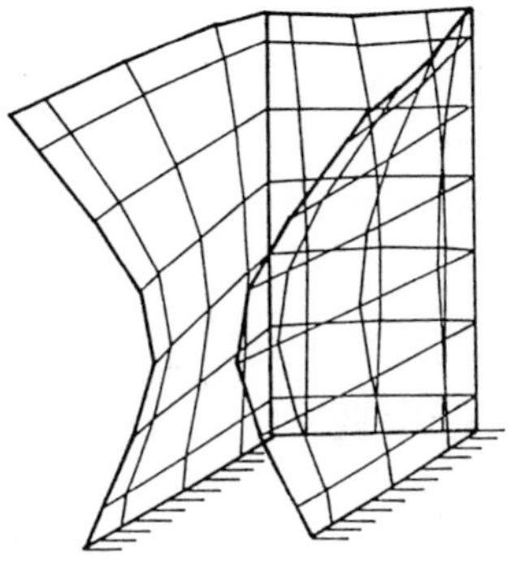

Fig. 7(c). Third modal shape.

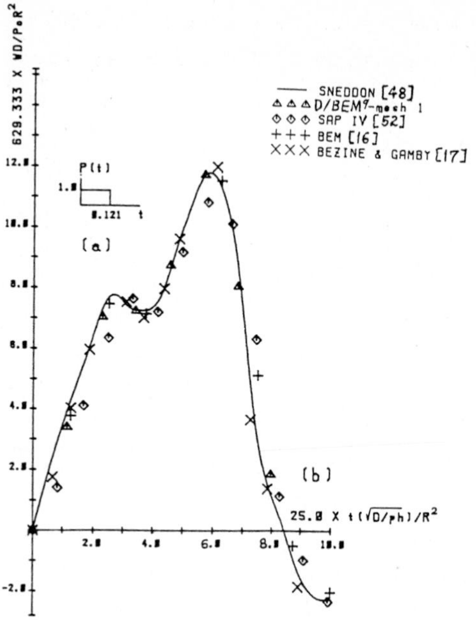

Fig. 8. History of central deflection of a clamped circular plate subjected to an impulsive force as its centre.

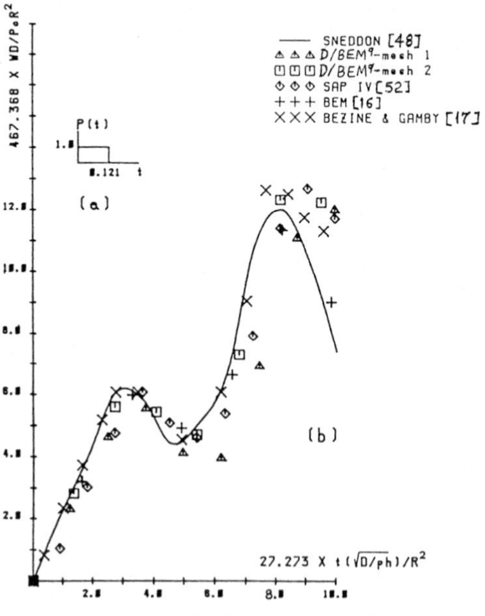

Fig. 9. History of central deflection of a simply supported circular plate subjected to an impulsive force at its centre.

[16] being the most accurate method. D/BEM^q-mesh1, however, requires the smallest number of d.o.f. and appears to be more economical.

Example 6 [24]

Consider a clamped circular plate of radius R = 1.1, thickness h = 0.05, mass per unit area ρh = 0.01145 and Poisson's ratio ν = 0.3, which is loaded by a concentrated vertical impulsive force P(t) at its center with magnitude P_o = 1 and duration t_o = 0.121. Figure 10 shows the history of the vertical central deflection for E = 1000 and various values of the external viscous damping coefficient c as obtained by D/BEM^q-mesh 1 in conjunction with Laplace transform [24]. Figure 11 depicts the history of the vertical central deflection for E_2 = E = 1000, E_1 = 10 and various values of the viscosity coefficient c_1 of the standard viscoelastic solid model of Eqs (102) and (103) as obtained by D/BEM^q-mesh 1 in conjunction with Laplace transform [24]. It is apparent from Figs 10 and 11 that, while the effect of external viscous damping is significant on the response, this is not the case for the internal viscoelastic damping which affects slightly the response only at later times, a fact also observed by Nagaya [56] in a similar problem.

Example 7 [25]

Consider the clamped circular plate of Example 6 loaded at its center with a lateral concentrated impulsive porce P(t) of magnitude P_o = 1 and duration t_o = 0.121 and at its perimeter, with an in-plane compressive force N. Figure 12 shows the history of the vertical central deflection for various values of N/N_{cr}, where N_{cr} = 0.1652917 is the elastic critical load of the plate, as obtained by the direct D/BEM^q-mesh 1 that includes the effect of N and employs Laplace transform. The P_{cr} is obtained by a linear stability analysis employing the fundamental solution (109) or directly from [8]. The curve for N/N_{cr} = 0 coincides with the one obtained by Providakis and Beskos [24] using the direct D/BEM^q-mesh 1 and the

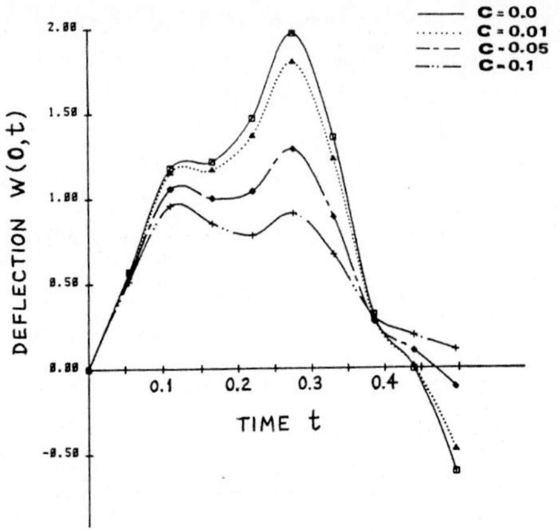

Fig. 10. History of central deflection of a clamped circular plate subjected to an impulsive force at its centre for various values of the external viscous damping coefficient c.

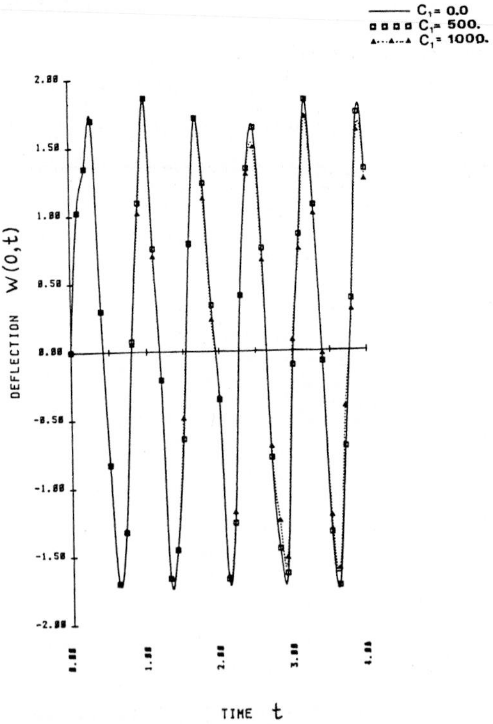

Fig. 11. History of central deflection of a clamped circular plate subjected to an impulsive force at its centre for various values of the internal viscosity coefficient c_1.

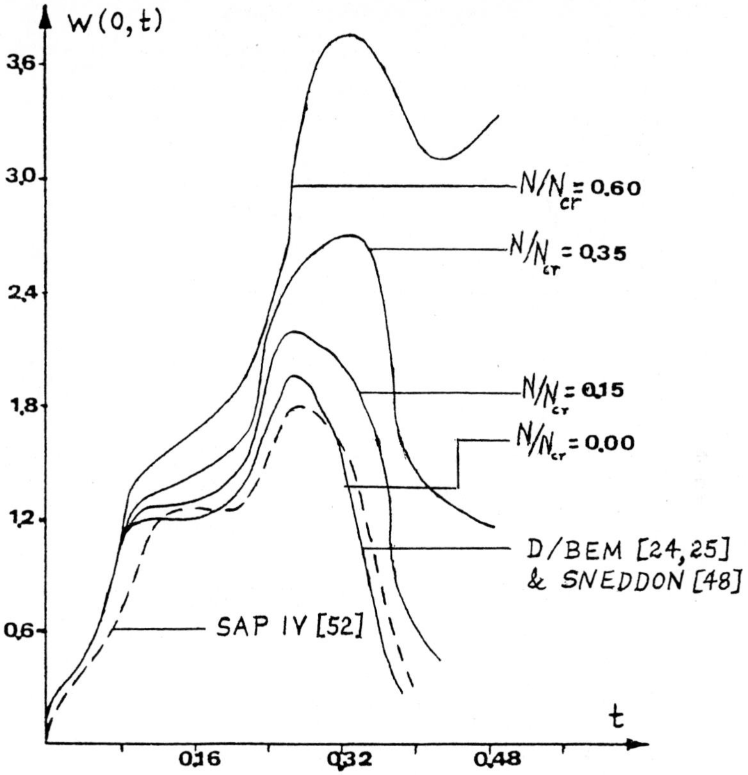

Fig. 12. History of central deflection of a circular clamped plate due to a vertical pulse at its center for different values of in-plane compressive forces P.

analytical one due to Sneddon [48]. Results obtained by the FEM program SAP IV [52] for $N/N_{cr} = 0$ using 10 elements per quadrant are also shown in Fig. 12 for comparison. The D/BEM discretization involved only 2 bounadry and 5 interior quadratic elements per quadrant. The response increase for increasing values of N is apparent.

Conclusions

On the basis of the preceding discussion the following conclusions can be drawn:

1. Two general and advanced direct boundary element methodologies for dynamic analysis of homogeneous, isotropic and linearly elastic thin flexural plates of arbitrary planform and boundary conditions have been presented. These are the BEM employing the dynamic fundamental solution and the D/BEM employing the static fundamental solution of the problem. Both free and forced vibrations can be treated by these two methods. Forced vibrations can be treated either in the time domain with the aid of a time marching scheme or in the complex frequency domain with the aid of the Laplace transform.
2. BEM essentially requires only a discretization of the perimeter of the plate, while in D/BEM both the perimeter and the interior domain have to be discretized. Quadratic isoparametric elements are used on the boundary and quadratic isoparametric or constant elements in the interior. In spite of the increased discretization in D/BEM, this method is more efficient than BEM due to the simplicity of the static fundamental solution. In general, eventhough BEM is more accurate than D/BEM, the latter combines very good accuracy with a lower computational cost and has to be preferred over the former method in both free and forced vibrations of plates and plate structures. D/BEM has also the advantage of being able to take into account other effects on the response, such as in-plane forces, variable thickness, anisotropy, etc, while BEM is limited by the availability or not of dynamic fundamental solutions which include these effects.

3. D/BEM appears to be similar to FEM in its final form but it is more accurate than FEM for the same degree of discretization and does not require C^1 continuous displacement functions as the FEM does.
4. The use of the Laplace transform in forced vibration analysis reduces the problem to a static-like form with obvious advantages in formulation and computer implementation over the time domain approach. In addition, it permits an easier treatment of initial conditions and external viscous or internal viscoelastic damping than do time domain formulations. However, time domain approaches can be easily extended to nonlinear problems, while Laplace transform techniques are restricted to linear problems. It also appears that time domain schemes are more efficient than Laplace transform schemes when they are used in conjunction with D/BEM, while the opposite is true with BEM.

Acknowledgements

The author is grateful to his former student Dr. C.P. Providakis for his valuable suggestions and assistance on many subjects of this chapter. He would like also to thank Professors S.N. Atluri, J.R. Hutchinson, J.T. Katsikadelis and E.N. Mastroyannis for helpful discussions and technical assistance. Finally many thanks are due to Mrs. H. Alexandridis-Balis for her excellent typing of this chapter.

References

1. Beskos, D.E.: Boundary element methods in dynamic analysis. Appl. Mech. Rev. 40 (1987) 1-23.

2. Beskos, D.E.: Dynamic analysis of beams, plates and shells, in: Boundary element methods in structural analysis. D.E. Beskos (ed.). New York: ASCE 1989. pp. 139-161.

3. Hutchinson, J.R.: Vibration of plates, in: Boundary elements X, Vol. 4: geomechanics, wave propagation and vibrations. C.A. Brebbia (ed.). Berlin: Springer-Verlag 1988. pp. 415-430.

4. Manolis, G.D.; Beskos, D.E.: Boundary element methods in elastodynamics. London: Unwin Hyman 1988.

5. Vivoli, J.: Vibrations de plaques et potentiels de couches. Acustica 26 (1972) 305-314.

6. Vivoli, J.; Filippi, P.: Eigenfrequencies of thin plates and layer potentials. J. Acoust. Soc. Am. 55 (1974) 562-567.

7. Niwa, Y.; Kobayashi, S.; Kitahara, M.: Eigenfrequency analysis of a plate by the integral equation method. Theor. Appl. Mech. 29 (1981) 287-307.

8. Niwa, Y.; Kobayashi, S.; Kitahara, M.: Determination of eigenvalues by boundary element methods, in: Developments in boundary element methods - 2. P.K. Banerjee and R.P. Shaw (eds.). London: Applied Science 1982. pp. 143-176.

9. Kitahara, M.: Boundary integral equation methods in eigenvalue problems of elastodynamics and thin plates. Amsterdam: Elsevier 1985.

10. Hutchinson, J.R.; Wong, G.K.K.: The boundary element method for plate vibrations, in: Proceedings of the ASCE 7th conference on electronic computation in St. Louis, Missouri. New York: ASCE 1979. pp. 297-311.

11. Hansen, E.B.: Numerical solution of integrodifferential and singular integral equations for plate bending problems. J. Elasticity 6 (1976) 39-56.

12. Wong, G.K.K.; Hutchinson, J.R.: An improved boundary element method for plate vibrations, in: Boundary element methods. C.A. Brebbia (ed.). Berlin: Springer-Verlag 1981. pp. 272-289.

13. Stern, M.: A general boundary integral formulation for the numerical solution of plate bending problems. Int. J. Solids Struct. 15 (1979) 769-782.

14. Providakis, C.P.; Beskos, D.E.: Two BEM approaches for plate dynamic analysis, in: Computational mechanics '88. S.N. Atluri and G. Yagawa (eds) Berlin: Springer-Verlag 1986. pp. 3.vi.1-3.vi.5.

15. Providakis, C.P.; Beskos, D.E.: Dynamic analysis of elastic plates, in: Boundary elements X, Vol. 4: geomechanics, wave propagation and vibrations. C.A. Brebbia (ed.). Berlin: Springer-Verlag 1988. pp. 403-413.

16. Providakis, C.P.; Beskos, D.E.: Free and forced vibrations of plates by boundary elements. Comp. Meth. Appl. Mech. Engng. 74 (1989) 231-250.

17. Bézine, G.; Gamby, D.: Étude des mouvements transitoires de flexion d'une plaque par la méthode des équations intégrales de frontière. J. Méc. Theor. Appl. 1 (1982) 451-466.

18. Heuer, R.; Irschik, H.: A boundary element method for eigenvalue problems of polygonal membranes and plates. Acta Mech. 66 (1987) 9-20.

19. Irschik, H.; Heuer, R.; Ziegler, F.: BEM using Green's functions of rectangular domains: static and dynamic problems of bending of plates, in: Boundary elements IX, Vol. 2: stress analysis applications. C.A. Bebbia, W.L. Wendland and G. Kuhn (eds). Berlin: Springer-Verlag 1987. pp. 35-45.

20. Bézine, G.: A mixed boundary integral-finite element approach to plate vibration problems. Mech. Res. Commun. 7 (1980) 141-150.

21. O'Donoghue, P.E.; Atluri, S.N.: Control of dynamic response of a continuum model of a large space structure. Comput. Struct. 23 (1986) 199-209.

22. O'Donoghue, P.E.; Atluri, S.N.: Field / boundary element approach to the large deflection of thin flat plates. Comput. Struct. 27 (1987) 427-435.

23. Providakis, C.P.; Beskos, D.E.: Forced vibrations of plates and shells by boundary-interior elements, in: Boundary elements IX, Vol. 2. stress-analysis applications. C.A. Brebbia, W.L. Wendland and G. Kuhn (eds.). Berlin: Springer-Verlag 1987. pp. 97-109.

24. Providakis, C.P.; Beskos, D.E.: Free and forced vibrations of plates by boundary and interior elements. Int. J. Num. Meth. Engng. 28 (1989) 1977-1994.

25. Beskos, D.E.; Providakis, C.P.; Stamos, C.A.: Dynamic response of plates by the domain / boundary element method, in Proceedings of 2nd national congress of mechanics, Athens, June 29-July 1, 1989.

26. Beskos, D.E.: Dynamic analysis of plates and shallow shells by the D/BEM, in: Advances in the theory of plates and shells. G.Z. Voyiadjis and D. Karamanlidis (eds). Amsterdam: Elsevier 1990. pp. 177-196.

27. Tanaka, M.; Yamagiwa, K.; Miyazaki, K.; Ueda, T.: Integral equation approach to free vibration problems of assembled plate structures, in: Theory and applications of boundary element methods. M. Tanaka and Q. Du (eds). Oxford: Pergamon Press 1987. pp. 375-384.

28. Tanaka, M.; Yamagiwa, K.; Miyazaki, K.; Ueda, T.: Free vibration analysis of elastic plate structures by boundary element method. Engng. Anal. 5 (1988) 182-188.

29. Costa, Jr., J.A.: Plate vibrations using B.E.M. App. Math. Modelling 12 (1988) 78-85.

30. Katsikadelis, J.T. ; Sapountzakis, E.J.: Numerical evaluation of the Green function for the biharmonic equation using BEM with application to static and dynamic analysis of plates, in: Boundary elements IX, Vol. 2: stress analysis applications. C.A. Brebbia, W.L. Wendland and G. Kuhn (eds). Berlin: Springer-Verlag 1987. pp. 51-67.

31. Katsikadelis, J.T.; Sapountzakis, E.J.; Zorba, E.G.: A BEM approach to static and dynamic analysis of plates with internal supports, in: Boundary elements X, Vol. 4: geomechanics, wave propagation and vibrations. C.A. Brebbia (ed.). Berlin: Springer-Verlag 1988. pp. 431-444.

32. Katsikadelis, J.T.; Sapountzakis, E.J.: A BEM solution to dynamic analysis of plates with variable thickness, in: Advances in boundary elements, Vol. 3: stress analysis. C.A. Brebbia and J.J. Connor (eds). Southampton: Comput. Mech. Publ. 1989. pp. 285-302.

33. Katsikadelis, J.T.; Kandilas, C.B.: A flexibility matrix solution to the vibration problem of plates based on the boundary element method, in: Proceedings of 2nd national congress of mechanics, Athens, June 29 - July 1, 1989.

34. Shi, G.; Bézine, G.: The direct boundary integral equation method for the free vibration analysis of orthotropic plates. Eur. J. Mech. A/Solids. 8 (1989) 277-291.

35. Shi, G.: Boundary element method in bending and eigenvalue problems of anisotropic plates, in: Boundary elements in mechanical and electrical engineering. C.A. Brebbia and A. Chaudouet-Miranda (eds). Southampton: Comput. Mech. Publ. 1990. pp. 123-138.

36. Conway, H.D.: The bending, buckling and flexural vibrations of simply supported polygonal plates by point - matching. J. Appl. Mech. 28 (1961) 288-291.

37. Conway, H.D.; Farnham, K.A.: The free flexural vibration of triangular, rhombic and parallelogram plates and some analogies. Int. J. Mech. Sci. 7 (1965) 811-816.

38. Mikami, T.; Yoshimura, J.: Application of the collocation method to vibration analysis of rectangular Mindlin plates. Comput. Struct. 18 (1984) 425-431.

39. Akkari, M.M.; Hutchinson, J.R.: An alternative BEM formulation applied to plate vibrations, in: Boundary elements VII, C.A. Brebbia and G. Maier (eds), Berlin: Springer-Verlag 1985. pp. 6.111-6.126.

40. Nash, W.A.; Tai, I.H.; O'Callaghan, M.J.A.; Quinlan, P.M.: Statics and dynamics of elastic bodies - a new approach, in: Proceedings of international symposium on innovative numerical analysis in applied engineering science, Versailles, France, T.A. Cruse et al (eds.) Senlis: CETIM 1977. pp. 8.3-8.8.

41. O'Callaghan, M.J.A.; Studdert, R.P.: The edge-function method for the free vibrations of thin orthotropic plates, in: Boundary elements VII, C.A. Brebbia and G. Maier (eds.). Berlin: Springer-Verlag 1985. pp. 6.37-6.52.

42. Love, A.E.H.: A treatise on the mathematical theory of elasticity. Cambridge: Cambridge University Press 1927.

43. Hutchinson, J.R.: Private communication, December 30, 1988.

44. Abramowitz, M.; Stegun, I.R.: Handbook of mathematical functions. New York: Dover 1965.

45. Stroud, A.H.; Secrest, D.: Gaussian quadrature formulas. Englewood Cliffs, N.J.: Prentice Hall 1966.

46. Stern, M.: Static analysis of beams, plates and shells, in: Boundary element methods in structural analysis, D.E. Beskos (ed.). New York: ASCE 1989. pp. 41-64.

47. Smith, B.T.; Boyle, J.M.; Dongarra, J.J.; Garbow, B.S.; Ikebe, Y.; Klema, V.C.; Moler, C.B.: Matrix eigensystem routines - EISPACK guide. Berlin: Springer-Verlag 1976.

48. Sneddon, I.N.: The symmetrical vibrations of a thin elastic plate. Proc. Cambridge Phil. Soc. 41 (1945) 27-43.

49. Durbin, F.: Numerical inversion of Laplace transforms: an efficient improvement to Dubner's and Abate's method. Comput. J. 17 (1974) 371-376.

50. Narayanan, G.V.; Beskos, D.E.: Numerical operational methods for time dependent linear problems. Int. J. Num. Meth. Engng. 18 (1982) 1829-1854.

51. Pan, H.H.: Vibrations of viscoelastic plates. J. Mecan. 5 (1966) 355-374.

52. Bathe, K.J.; Wilson, E.L.; Paterson, F.E.: SAP IV, a structural analysis program for static and dynamic response of linear systems. report No. EERC 73-11. Berkeley: University of California 1973.

53. Leissa, A.W.: Vibration of plates. NASA SP-160. Washington D.C.: NASA 1969.

54. Young, D.: Vibration of rectangular plates by the Ritz method. J. Appl. Mech., ASME. 17 (1950) 448-453.

55. Bézine, G.: Étude des vibrations libres des plaques élastiques minces éventuellement multiplement connexes ou "sandwich" à l' aide des méthodes duales d' éléments finis. Thèse de Docteur-Ingenieur. Poitiers: Université de Poitiers 1975.

56. Nagaya, K.: Dynamics of viscoelastic plate with curved boundaries of arbitrary shape. J. Appl. Mech. ASME. 45 (1978) 629-635.

Static and Dynamic Analysis of Shells

D.E. BESKOS

Department of Civil Engineering
University of Patras, GR-261 10 Patras, Greece

Summary

Homogeneous, isotropic and linear elastic Vlasov-Reissner thin shallow shells under static and dynamic conditions are numerically analysed with the aid of the boundary element method and its variations. Static analysis of shallow shells can first be accomplished by the conventional direct or indirect boundary element method, which employs the fundamental solution of the problem and is based on the displacement or the flexural displacement - membrane stress function formulation of shallow shells. This method which requires only a boundary discretization, is not efficient for the general case due to the complexity of the fundamental solution and only for the special cases of spherical and circular cylindrical shells, for which simpler fundamental solutions exist, may be advantageous. A better approach is the direct domain/boundary element method, which employs the plate fundamental solutions in flexure and stretching in its formulation. This creates boundary as well as domain integrals due to the flexure-stretching coupling terms and thus requires a boundary as well as an interior discretization. However, the simplicity of the fundamental solution results in a more efficient and general scheme. Free and forced vibrations of shallow shells are also treated by the direct domain/boundary element method, which employs the static fundamental solutions of a plate in flexure and stretching. This creates domain integrals due to the flexure-stretching coupling terms as well as due to the inertia terms. Transient forced vibrations are analysed with the aid of a time marching scheme in the time domain or Laplace transform with respect to time, in which case a numerical inversion of the transformed solution is required to obtain the time domain response. The effect of external viscous or internal viscoelastic damping on the response is also studied. Various numerical examples are presented for illustrating the aforementioned boundary element approaches and some comparisons against analytical methods and the finite element method are made to point out their advantages.

Introduction

Static and dynamic analysis of linear elastic thin shells characterized by complex geometry, loading and boundary conditions requires the use of numerical methods, such as the Finite Difference Method (FDM) and especially the Finite Element Method (FEM). Both of these methods, in spite of some shortcomings, have been successfully used for the solution of a variety of static and dynamic shell problems.

During the last few years the Boundary Element Method (BEM) has also been successfully used for statically and dynamically analysing linear elastic shallow shells. This is evident in the recent review articles of Beskos [1-3] and Stern [4] and the book of Manolis and Beskos [5]. There are basically two BEM approaches for the static analysis of shallow shells. The first approach is the conventional BEM in its direct or indirect form which employs the fundamental solution of the problem and is based on the displacement or the flexural displacement - membrane stress function formulation of shallow shells. This approach requires only a boundary discretization. However, it is not computationally efficient for the general case due to the high complexity of the fundamental solution (Simmonds and Bradley [6], Matsui and Matsuoka [7]) and only for special cases involving spherical and circular cylindrical shallow shells, for which simpler fundamental solutions exist, may be advantageous. The second approach is the direct domain/boundary element method (D/BEM), which employs the plate fundamental solutions in flexure and stretching in its formulation. This creates boundary as well as domain integrals due to the flexure-stretching coupling terms and thus requires a boundary as well as an interior discretization. However, the simplicity of the fundamental solution results in a more general and efficient scheme than in the first approach.

Newton and Tottenham [8] were apparently the first to employ the BEM in a special form for the static analysis of shallow shells. An exposition of their work can also be found in the review article of To nbnham [9]. The starting point is the decomposition of the fourth order system of the governing equations involving the flexural displacement w and the stress function φ of the membrane forces (w-φ formulation) into a system of second order equations. This system is reduced with the aid of complex variables into a system of real singular integral equations which are solved by the BEM. This approach has been successfully used for analysing spherical shallow shells. However, it is rather involved and lacks the usual BEM structure. Starting again from the w-φ formulation and transforming the system of these equations into boundary integral equations by weighted residuals or other means Tosaka and Miyake [10], Gospodinov [11] and Lu et al [12] were able to develop direct BEM's associated with the exact fundamental solutions of the problem. The first two works also provide numerical results to demonstrate the advantages of the method.

Forbes and Robinson [13] were the first to develop the direct D/BEM for the static analysis of shallow shells and demonstrate its merits by means of numerical examples. An exposition of their pioneering work can also be found in the review article of Stern [4]. Zhang and Atluri [14,15] have also successfully employed the D/BEM for the static and dynamic analysis of shallow shells. Their integral formulation was accomplished with the aid of the weighted residuals method in contrast to Forbes and Robinson [13] who utilized a reciprocal relation between two elastostatic shallow shell states. In addition Zhang and Atluri [15] extended their formulation to large deflection analysis. Starting with the w-φ formulation and rewriting the governing equations as two equations for plate bending with displacements w and φ, Wang et al [16] and Ye [17] were able to statically analyse shallow shells by employing simultaneously two D/BEM's, one for w and the other for φ, and present numerical results. This method was also extended to large deflection analysis.

Antes [18] was apparently the first to present a direct boundary integral formulation BEM for the static analysis of general shells based on reciprocity. Explicit expressions for the fundamental solution of the special case of circular cylindrical shells were also given. However, no numerical examples were reported. Tepavitcharov [19] and Hadjikov et al [20] using also reciprocity relations were able to formulate direct BEM's for bending of shallow spherical and circular cylindrical shells, respectively. In both works explicit expressions for the corresponding fundamental solutions were provided but no numerical results were presented. Peng and He [21], Lei and Huang [22] and Miyake et al [23] have also constructed direct BEM's for static analysis of shallow shells employing the fundamental solution of the problem and obtained numerical results. Lei and Huang [22] even considered the effect of shear deformation in their formulation. Spherical shells under axisymmetric static loading have also been analysed by the direct BEM employing the fundamental solution of the problem by Fu and Harb [24] and Harb and Fu [25]. In all the above works [15-22] the starting point is the governing equations in terms of displacements, which are subsequently transformed to direct boundary integral equations through reciprocity relations or the method of weighted residuals. These equations utilize the fundamental solution of the problem and thus the discretization is essentially restricted to the boundary. In this same category one can also include the work of Tepavitcharov and Gospodinov [26] on shallow membrane shells of positive Gaussian curvature. The indirect BEM in conjunction with the fundamental solution of a complete spherical shell has been utilized by Simos and Sadegh [27] for the static analysis of general spherical shells.

Recently a general and completely different approach for the static analysis of general elastic and inelastic shells has been presented by Mukherjee and Poddar [28] and Poddar and Mukherjee [29]. According to this approach the elastic three - dimensional integral equations in Cartesian coordinates are transformed into integral equations in terms of shell curvilinear coordinates. The resulting equations are solved numerically in the usual BEM fashion to yield displacements and tractions on the upper and lower surfaces S^+ and S^- of the shell, respectively, as well as on the surface S_e of its edges. Suitable kinematic assumptions concerning the variation of displacement with the shell thickness are made, strains and stresses are determined inside the shell and stress resultants are computed by integration of the stresses over the shell thickness. Numerical results concerning axisymmetric shells as well as more information on this general and accurate approach can be found in the chapter on inelastic analysis of plates and shells.

Eventhough the literature on the static analysis of shallow shells by the BEM and the D/BEM is rather rich, this is not the case with the dynamic analysis of these structures. Free and forced vibrations of shallow shells have been recently studied by the D/BEM which employs the static fundamental solutions of a plate in flexure and stretching. This creates domain integrals due to the flexure-stretching coupling terms as well as due to the inertia terms. This is apparently the only viable solution to the problem since there is no any shallow shell fundamental solution for the dynamic case in the literature, while the shallow shell static fundamental solution is very complicated and domain integrals are necessarily present in the formulation due to the existence of inertia terms. Zhang and Atluri [14,15] were apparently the first to employ the D/BEM to the dynamic analysis of shalow shells exhibiting small [14] and large [15] deformations. Their formulation is based on the weighted residuals approach. Providakis and Beskos [30-32,3] developed also a D/BEM for linear elastic shallow shells on the basis of reciprocity relations by essentially extending the method of Forbes and Robinson [13] from the static to the dynamic case. Transient forced vibrations have been treated by a time marching scheme [14,15] or by Laplace transform with respect to time in conjunction with a numerical inversion of the transformed solution to obtain the time domain response [30-32]. The effect of external viscous or internal viscoelastic damping on the response has also been studied in [32].

Finally, one should mention here that some static and dynamic shallow shell problems have been solved by boundary collocation (e.g., Conway and Leissa [33]) and the edge function method (e.g., Nash et al [34]), i.e., methods similar to the conventional BEM in the sense that the discretization is restricted to the boundary of the domain of interest. More on these methods and their application to shallow shell problems can be found in the chapter on the analysis of plates and shells by boundary collocation and the book of Manolis and Beskos [5].

This chapter deals with the static and dynamic analysis of homogeneous, isotropic and linear elastic Vlasov-Reissner shallow shells studied with the aid of the conventional direct BEM or the conventional direct D/BEM in the time or frequency domain. More specifically, the present chapter consists of nine sections: the first section presents the governing equations of shallow shells; sections two and three deal with static analysis by the direct BEM based on the displacement and the w-φ formulation, respectively; the fourth section discusses static analysis by the direct D/BEM, while the fifth one free vibrations by the direct D/BEM; sections six and seven describe forced vibrations by the direct D/BEM - Laplace transform and the time domain direct D/BEM, respectively; finally, section eigth presents a number of representative numerical examples and section nine closes the subject with conclusions concerning the importance of BEM type of approaches for static and dynamic shallow shell analysis, especially against other numerical methods.

Governing Equations of Shallow Shells

A shell is said to be shallow when the deviation of its middle surface from a plane is small compared with its projected dimensions on this plane, as shown in Fig. 1. Thus the curvilinear coordinate lines of the middle surface of the shallow shell may be selected as the Cartesian coordinates x and y defining its projection plane. The geometry of a shallow shell with boundary (perimeter) Γ and projected domain (surface) S on the (x, y) plane can be described by the equation

$$z = z_o + (1/2)(k_1x^2 + k_2y^2) = z_o + (1/2)\,k\,(x^2 + \lambda y^2) \qquad (1)$$

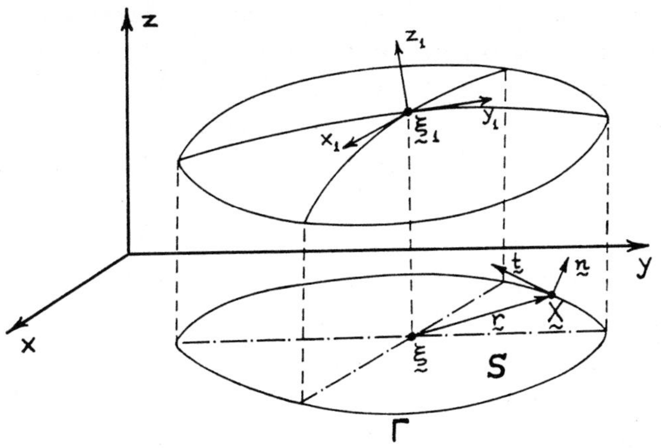

Fig. 1. Geometry of shallow shell

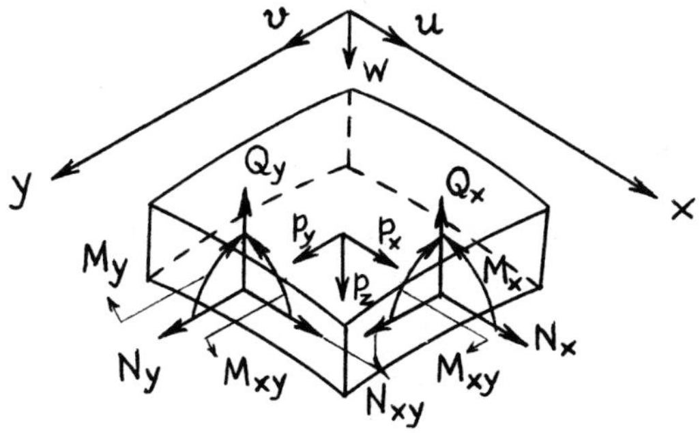

Fig. 2. Stress resultants, loads and displacements on shell element

where z_0 is a constant, k_1 and k_2 are the principal curvatures of the middle surface along the coordinate lines x and y, respectively, and

$$k = k_1, \qquad \lambda = k_2/k_1 \tag{2}$$

Depending on whether λ is positive, zero or negative, Eq. (1) represents an elliptic paraboloid, parabolic cylinder or hyperbolic paraboloid. For a flat plate one has $k = 0$ and $\lambda = 0$.

According to the Vlasov-Reissner [35, 36] theory of shallow shells as described, for example, in Forbes and Robinson [13], the basic equations consist of the equations of motion (without body forces)

$$\frac{\partial N_x}{\partial x} + \frac{\partial N_{xy}}{\partial y} - \rho h \ddot{u} + p_x = 0 \tag{3}$$

$$\frac{\partial N_{xy}}{\partial x} + \frac{\partial N_y}{\partial y} - \rho h \ddot{u} + p_y = 0 \tag{4}$$

$$-k_1 N_x - k_2 N_y + \frac{\partial Q_x}{\partial x} + \frac{\partial Q_y}{\partial y} - \rho h \ddot{w} + p_z = 0 \tag{5}$$

$$\frac{\partial M_x}{\partial x} + \frac{\partial M_{xy}}{\partial y} - Q_x = 0, \quad \frac{\partial M_{xy}}{\partial x} + \frac{\partial M_y}{\partial y} - Q_y = 0 \tag{6}$$

and the force-displacement relations

$$N_x = C\left[\frac{\partial u}{\partial x} + \nu \frac{\partial u}{\partial y} + k\,(1+\nu\lambda)w\right] \tag{7}$$

$$N_y = C\left[\frac{\partial \upsilon}{\partial y} + \nu \frac{\partial u}{\partial x} + k\,(\nu+\lambda)w\right] \tag{8}$$

$$N_{xy} = \frac{1-\nu}{2}\, C\, \left(\frac{\partial u}{\partial y} + \frac{\partial \upsilon}{\partial x}\right) \tag{9}$$

$$Q_x = -D\, \frac{\partial}{\partial x}\, (\nabla^2 w), \qquad Q_y = -D\, \frac{\partial}{\partial y}\, (\nabla^2 w) \tag{10}$$

$$M_x = -D\left(\frac{\partial^2 w}{\partial x^2} + \nu\, \frac{\partial^2 w}{\partial y^2}\right), \qquad M_y = -D\left(\frac{\partial^2 w}{\partial y^2} + \nu\, \frac{\partial^2 w}{\partial x^2}\right) \tag{11}$$

$$M_{xy} = -(1-\nu)D\, \frac{\partial^2 w}{\partial x \partial y} \tag{12}$$

In the above, N_x, N_y and N_{xy} are the membrane stress resultants, M_x, M_y and M_{xy} are the bending moment stress resultants, Q_x and Q_y are the shear stress resultants and p_x, p_y and p_z are the externally applied dynamic surface loads along the x, y and z direction, respectively, as shown in Fig. 2. Furthermore, u, υ and w are the displacement components along the x, y and z direction, respectively (Fig. 2), ρ is the mass density and h the thickness of the shell, subscripts denote coordinate directions, overdots indicate differentiation with respect to time t, $\nabla^2(.) = \partial^2/\partial x^2(.) + \partial^2/\partial y^2(.)$ and C and D are the extensional and bending rigidities, respectively, of the shell, which are given in terms of the modulus of elasticity E and the Poisson's ratio ν by

$$C = Eh/(1-\nu^2), \qquad D = Eh^3/12(1-\nu^2) \tag{13}$$

It should be added that all the above functions representing displacements or stress resultants are of the general form $f = f(\underset{\sim}{x},t) = f(x,y,t)$, where $\underset{\sim}{x}$ denotes a point with coordinates x, y and $z = z(x,y)$ on the middle shell surface.

Using the above two sets of basic equations one can derive the governing equations of the problem either in terms of displacements or in terms of the lateral (flexural) displacement w and the membrane stress function φ to be defined in the following. The displacement formulation is obtained if one substitutes the force - displacement relations (7)-(9) and (11), (12) into the equations of motion (3), (4) and the one produced by eliminating Q_x and Q_y between (5) and (6). The result reads

$$C\nabla^2 u+C\,\frac{(1+\nu)}{2}\,\frac{\partial}{\partial y}\left(\frac{\partial \upsilon}{\partial x}-\frac{\partial u}{\partial y}\right)+C(1+\nu\lambda)k\,\frac{\partial w}{\partial x}-\rho h\ddot{u}+p_x = 0 \tag{14}$$

$$C\nabla^2 \upsilon+C\,\frac{(1+\nu)}{2}\,\frac{\partial}{\partial x}\left(\frac{\partial u}{\partial y}-\frac{\partial \upsilon}{\partial x}\right)+C(\nu+\lambda)k\,\frac{\partial w}{\partial y}-\rho h\ddot{\upsilon}+p_y = 0 \tag{15}$$

$$C(1+\nu\lambda)k\,\frac{\partial u}{\partial x}+C(\nu+\lambda)k\,\frac{\partial \upsilon}{\partial y}+C(1+2\nu\lambda+\lambda^2)k^2 w + D\nabla^4 w+\rho h\ddot{w}-p_z = 0 \tag{16}$$

where $\nabla^4(.) = \nabla^2(\nabla^2(.))$.

A membrane stress function $\varphi = \varphi(\underset{\sim}{x},t)$ is now introduced, such that

$$N_x = \frac{\partial^2\varphi}{\partial y^2} - B_x, \qquad N_y = \frac{\partial^2\varphi}{\partial x^2} - B_y$$
$$N_{xy} = -\frac{\partial^2\varphi}{\partial x\partial y} \tag{17}$$

where

$$B_x = \int (p_x-\rho h\ddot{u})dx, \qquad B_y = \int (p_y-\rho h\ddot{\upsilon})dy \tag{18}$$

Substitution of expressions (17) into (3) and (4) indicates that these equations of motion are identically satisfied. Substitution of (17) into the equation of motion that results from elimination of Q_x and Q_y between (5) and (6) and the subsequent use of (11) and (12) finally yields

$$D\nabla^4 w + \nabla^2_k\varphi = p_z - \rho h\ddot{w} + k(B_x + \lambda\, B_y) \tag{19}$$

where $\nabla^2_k(.) = k[\partial^2/\partial y^2(.) + \lambda\, \partial^2/\partial x^2(.)]$. For the derivation of the second governing equation of the w-φ formulation one starts from the compatibility equation between displacement w and membrane strains and uses the membrane strain-membrane stress resultants relation as well as Eqs (17). The result is (e.g. Møllmann [37])

$$\nabla^4\varphi - Eh\nabla^2_k w = (1-v)(B_{x,yy} + B_{y,xx}) - v\,\nabla^2\,(B_x+B_y) \tag{20}$$

where commas indicate spatial differentiation.

<u>Static Analysis by Direct BEM based on Displacement Formulation</u>

The developments of this section are primarily based on the work of Miyake et al [23]. Consider the displacement equations of equilibrium, i.e., Eqs (14)-(16) with zero acceleration terms, and rewrite them in matrix form as

$$R_{ij}\,u_j + p_i = 0 \tag{21}$$

where i, j = 1, 2, 3, $u_1 = u$, $u_2 = v$, $u_3 = w$, $p_1 = p_x$, $p_2 = p_y$, $p_3 = -p_z$, summation convention holds true and the components of the symmetric linear differential operator R_{ij} are defined as follows:

$$R_{11} = C[D_1^2 + \frac{1-v}{2}D_2^2], \qquad R_{22} = C[D_2^2 + \frac{1-v}{2}D_1^2]$$

$$R_{12} = R_{21} = C\,\frac{1+v}{2}D_1D_2, \qquad R_{13} = R_{31} = C\,(1+v\lambda)\,k\,D_1 \tag{22}$$

$$R_{23} = R_{32} = C\,(\lambda+v)\,k\,D_2, \qquad R_{33} = D\nabla^4 + C(1+2v\lambda+\lambda^2)\,k^2$$

with $D_1 = \partial/\partial x$ and $D_2 = \partial/\partial y$

The starting point for an integral formulation of the problem is the weighted residual statement

$$\int_S (R_{ij}\,u_j + p_i)\,U_{ik}\,dS(\underset{\sim}{x}) = 0 \tag{23}$$

where U_{ik} is the fundamental solution tensor of the problem defined by the equation

$$R_{ij}\, U_{jk} = \delta_{ik}\, \delta\, (\underset{\sim}{x}, \underset{\sim}{\xi}) \tag{24}$$

with δ_{ik} being Kronecker's delta and δ Dirac's delta function of two interior points $\underset{\sim}{x}$ and $\underset{\sim}{\xi}$. Integration by parts of Eq. (23) and employement of Eq. (24) results in the boundary integral equations [22]

$$\begin{aligned} u_k(\underset{\sim}{\Xi}) = & \int_S (-p_\beta U_{\beta k} - p_3 U_{3k}) dS(\underset{\sim}{x}) \\ & + \int_\Gamma \{[u_n N_{nk}(U) + u_t N_{tk}(U)] - (N_n U_{nk} + N_t U_{tk})\}\, d\Gamma(\underset{\sim}{X}) \\ & + \int_\Gamma \{[M_n \frac{\partial U_{3k}}{\partial n} - \frac{\partial w}{\partial n} - M_{nk}(U)] - [V_n U_{3k} - w V_{nk}(U)]\}\, d\Gamma(\underset{\sim}{X}) \\ & + \sum_{k=1}^{K} ([\![w M_{tk}(U)]\!] - [\![M_t U_{3k}]\!])_k \end{aligned} \tag{25}$$

where $\underset{\sim}{\Xi}$ and $\underset{\sim}{X}$ are boundary points, $\beta = 1,2$, $k = 1,2,3$, $[\![\ ]\!]$ denotes the discontinuity jump at a corner on Γ, which has K corners in total, u_n and u_t are the normal and tangential components, respectively, of the membrane displacements at the boundary, N_n and N_t are the normal and tangential components, respectively, of the membrane stress resultants (forces) at the boundary, M_n and M_t are the normal and tangential, respectively, moment stress resultants at the boundary and V_n is the equivalent shear force at the boundary. These displacements, forces and moments are connected with the corresponding ones of Eqs (7)-(12) by the relations

$$\begin{aligned} u_n &= u_\beta\, n_\beta & u_t &= \varepsilon_{\beta\gamma}\, n_\gamma\, u_\beta \\ N_n &= N_{\alpha\beta}\, n_\alpha\, n_\beta & N_t &= \varepsilon_{\beta\gamma}\, N_{\alpha\beta}\, n_\alpha\, n_\gamma \\ M_n &= M_{\alpha\beta}\, n_\alpha\, n_\beta & M_t &= \varepsilon_{\beta\gamma}\, M_{\alpha\beta}\, n_\alpha\, n_\gamma \\ V_n &= Q_\alpha\, n_\alpha + \partial M_t / \partial s & & \end{aligned} \tag{26}$$

where α, β, γ = 1, 2, $\varepsilon_{\beta\gamma}$ are permutation tensors, n_α are the components of the outward normal vector to the boundary curve Γ and $\partial/\partial s$ denotes tangential derivative on the boundary. Fundamental solution quantities U_{nk}, U_{tk}, $N_{nk}(U)$, $N_{tk}(U)$, $V_{nk}(U)$, $M_{nk}(U)$ and $M_{tk}(U)$ can be obtained in terms of U_{jk} ($j,k = 1,2,3$) and its derivatives by combining relations (26) and (7)-(12).

Since one can prescribe four boundary conditions at every point along Γ, the three boundary integral equations (25) are not enough and one should supplement them with one more equation. This additional boundary integral equation can be obtained for a smooth boundary point $\underset{\sim}{\Xi}$ by differentiating Eq. (25) for k = 3 along the normal direction $\underset{\sim}{n}_o$ at point $\underset{\sim}{\Xi}$ and reads [22]

$$\begin{aligned}\frac{1}{2}\frac{\partial w}{\partial n_o}(\underset{\sim}{\Xi}) = &\int_S \left(-p_\beta \frac{\partial U_{\beta k}}{\partial n_o} - p_3 \frac{\partial U_{3k}}{\partial n_o}\right) dS(\underset{\sim}{x}) \\ &+\int_\Gamma \left\{\left[u_n \frac{\partial N_{nk}(U)}{\partial n_o} - u_t \frac{\partial N_{tk}(U)}{\partial n_o}\right] - \left(N_n \frac{\partial U_{nk}}{\partial n_o} + N_t \frac{\partial U_{tk}}{\partial n_o}\right)\right\} d\Gamma(\underset{\sim}{x}) \\ &+\int_\Gamma \left\{\left[M_n \frac{\partial^2 U_{3k}}{\partial n \partial n_o} - \frac{\partial w}{\partial n}\frac{\partial M_{nk}(U)}{\partial n_o}\right] - \left[V_n \frac{\partial U_{3k}}{\partial n_o} - w \frac{\partial V_{nk}(U)}{\partial n_o}\right]\right\} d\Gamma(\underset{\sim}{x}) \\ &+\sum_{k=1}^{K} \left(\left[\!\left[w \frac{\partial M_{tk}(U)}{\partial n_o}\right]\!\right] - \left[\!\left[M_t \frac{\partial U_{3k}}{\partial n_o}\right]\!\right]\right)_k \end{aligned} \tag{27}$$

If $\underset{\sim}{\Xi}$ is a corner point, Eq. (27) has to be modified as explained in the section on free vibrations. Thus the integral formulation of the problem consisting of Eqs (25) and (27) involves only boundary integrals, apart, of course, from the domain integrals containing the loading, which are characterized by known integrands. This essentially implies only a boundary discretization for the numerical solution of these equations.

For the numerical solution of Eqs (25) and (27) according to Miyake et al [23] the boundary Γ is divided into constant boundary elements and the surface S into constant interior elements. Calculation of regular boundary integrals is accomplished numerically by standard Gaussian quadrature, while of singular ones analytically [23]. Calculation of domain (interior) integrals is done numerically by Gaussian quadrature. Thus writing the system of Eqs (25) and (27) in discretized form for all nodal points at the boundary and assembling the resulting equations one can obtain the matrix equation

$$\left[\underset{\sim}{G}_1\ \underset{\sim}{G}_2\ \underset{\sim}{G}_3\ \underset{\sim}{G}_4\right]\left\{\begin{matrix}\underset{\sim}{u}_n\\ \underset{\sim}{u}_t\\ \underset{\sim}{w}\\ \frac{\partial \underset{\sim}{w}}{\partial n}\end{matrix}\right\} + \left[\underset{\sim}{M}_1\ \underset{\sim}{M}_2\right]\left\{\begin{matrix}\underset{\sim}{N}_n\\ \underset{\sim}{N}_t\end{matrix}\right\} + \left[\underset{\sim}{K}_1\ \ \underset{\sim}{K}_2\right]\left\{\begin{matrix}\underset{\sim}{M}_n\\ \underset{\sim}{V}_n\end{matrix}\right\} = \left\{\begin{matrix}\underset{\sim}{P}_1\\ \underset{\sim}{P}_2\\ \underset{\sim}{P}_3\\ \underset{\sim}{P}_4\end{matrix}\right\} \tag{28}$$

where $\underset{\sim}{G}_i$ (i = 1,2,3,4), $\underset{\sim}{M}_i$ (i = 1,2) and $\underset{\sim}{K}_i$ (i = 1,2) are the coefficient matrices obtained from the boundary integral terms, $\underset{\sim}{P}_i$ (i = 1,2,3,4) are the components of the loading obtained from the domain integral terms and the tildes at the bottom of $\underset{\sim}{u}_n$, $\underset{\sim}{w}$, $\underset{\sim}{N}_n$, etc., indicate vectors. After using the boundary conditions of the problem one can rearrange Eq. (28) and re-write it in the form

$$[A]\ \{x\} = \{b\} \tag{29}$$

with {x} and {b} being the vectors of unknown and known quantities, respectively, which can be solved for the unknown vector {x}. Some boundary conditions usually encountered in practice are as follows:

rigidly clamped edge: $w = \partial w/\partial n = u_n = u_t = 0$
loosely clamped edge: $w = \partial w/\partial n = N_n = N_t = 0$
in-plane movable simply supported edge: $w = M_n = N_n = N_t = 0$
in-plane immovable hinged edge: $w = u_n = u_t = M_n = 0$
free edge: $N_n = N_t = M_n = V_n = 0$ (30)

According to Matsui and Matsuoka [7] the fundamental solution U_{ij} involving the displacement components u, υ and w can be written in the form

$$\begin{Bmatrix} u \\ \upsilon \\ w \end{Bmatrix} = \begin{bmatrix} L_{11} & L_{12} & L_{13} \\ L_{21} & L_{22} & L_{23} \\ L_{31} & L_{32} & L_{33} \end{bmatrix} \begin{Bmatrix} \varphi_1 \\ \varphi_2 \\ \varphi_3 \end{Bmatrix} \qquad (31)$$

where L_{ij} $(i,j = 1,2,3)$ are the linear differential operators

$$L_{11} = \frac{h^2}{12}\left(D_1^2 + \frac{2}{1-v} D_2^2\right)\nabla^4 + (1+2v\lambda+\lambda^2)k^2D_1^2 + 2\,(1+v)k^2D_2^2$$

$$L_{12} = L_{21} = -\left(\frac{1+v}{1-v}\right)\frac{h^2}{12} D_1D_2\nabla^4 - (1-\lambda^2)k^2D_1D_2$$

$$L_{22} = \frac{h^2}{12}\left(\frac{2}{1-v} D_1^2+D_2^2\right)\nabla^4 + 2(1+v)\lambda^2k^2D_1^2 + (1+2v\lambda+\lambda^2)k^2D_2^2$$

$$L_{13} = L_{31} = (1+v\lambda)kD_1^3 + (2+v-\lambda v)kD_1D_2^2 \qquad (32)$$

$$L_{23} = L_{32} = (\lambda+v)kD_2^3 + [(2+v)\,\lambda-1]kD_1^2D_2$$

$$L_{33} = \nabla^4$$

and the displacement potentials $\varphi_i = \varphi_i(x,y)$ $(i = 1,2,3)$ are defined for every state of concentrated loading {X, Y, Z} in an infinitely extended shallow shell as follows:

$$\{X,Y,Z\} = \{p_x\ \delta(x,y),0,0\} \rightarrow \{\varphi_1\ \varphi_2\ \varphi_3\} = \{-\ p_x\Phi\ /D,0\ ,0\}$$

$$\{X,Y,Z\} = \{0,\ p_y\ \delta(x,y),0\} \rightarrow \{\varphi_1\ \varphi_2\ \varphi_3\} = \{0,-p_y\Phi/D,0\} \qquad (33)$$

$$\{X,Y,Z\} = \{0,0,\ p_z\delta(x,y)\} \rightarrow \{\varphi_1\ \varphi_2\ \varphi_3\} = \{0,0,p_z\Phi/D\}$$

In the above equation the function $\Phi = \Phi(x,y)$ has the series representation

$$\Phi = \frac{1}{2\pi b^6} \sum_{n=-\infty}^{\infty} (-1)^n \cos 2n\theta \left\{ \sum_{\substack{m=[|n|/2] \\ m \geq 1}} \frac{(-1)^{m-1}}{(2m+1-n)!(2m+1+n)!} \left(\frac{br}{2}\right)^{4m+2} \right.$$

$$\times \left[\Pi_{2m-2,|n|} \left(\log \frac{br}{2} + g - \sum_{s=1}^{2m+1-n} \frac{1}{2s} - \sum_{s=1}^{2m+1+n} \frac{1}{2s} \right) + \sum_{l=-2m+2}^{2m-2} \Pi_{2m-2,|l|} F_{|n-l|} \right]$$

$$\left. + \frac{\pi}{4} \sum_{\substack{m=[(|n|+1)/2] \\ m \geq 2}}^{\infty} \frac{(-1)^{m-1}}{(2m-n)!(2m+n)!} \left(\frac{br}{2}\right)^{4m} \sum_{l=-2m+3}^{2m-3} \Pi_{2m-3,|l|} G_{|n-l|} \right\} + \Phi_p \qquad (34)$$

$$\Phi_p = \frac{1}{24b^6} \left(\frac{br}{2}\right)^4 \frac{1}{\sqrt{\tau}} \left[\frac{3}{4} + \left(\frac{1-\sqrt{\tau}}{1+\sqrt{\tau}}\right) \cos 2\theta + \frac{1}{4} \left(\frac{1-\sqrt{\tau}}{1+\sqrt{\tau}}\right)^2 \cos 4\theta \right] \qquad (35)$$

if $0 < \tau \leq 1$

$$\Phi_p = -\frac{1}{24b^6} \left(\frac{br}{2}\right)^4 \left(\frac{1}{1-\tau}\right) \left\{ \left(1 - \frac{4}{\pi} \arctan\sqrt{|\tau|}\right) \left[\cos 2\theta + \left(\frac{1+\tau}{1-\tau}\right) \cos 4\theta \right] - \frac{2}{\pi} \sin(\arctan\sqrt{|\tau|}) \cos 4\theta \right\} \qquad (36)$$

if $-1 \leq \tau < 0$,

and

$$a^2 = \frac{k\lambda}{h} \sqrt{12(1-v^2)}, \qquad b^2 = \frac{k}{h} \sqrt{12(1-v^2)},$$

$$g = \text{Euler's constant}, \quad \tau = a/b \qquad (37)$$

$$\theta = \arctan(y/x), \qquad r = \sqrt{x^2 + y^2}$$

$[N]$ is the nearest integer equal to or less than N,

$$\Pi_{i,|l|} = \sum_{f=0}^{(i-l)/2} \binom{i}{|l|+2f} \binom{|l|+2f}{f} \left(\frac{1+\tau}{2}\right)^{i-|l|-f} \left(\frac{1-\tau}{4}\right)^{|l|+2f}, \qquad (i \geq |l|)$$

$$\Pi_{i,|l|} = 0, \qquad (i < |l|) \qquad (38)$$

$$F_0 = \log\left(\frac{1+\sqrt{\tau}}{2}\right), \quad F_l = \frac{(-1)^{l-1}}{2l} \qquad (l > 0,\ 0 < \tau \leq 1)$$

$$F_0 = \log\left(\frac{\sqrt{1-\tau}}{2}\right), \quad F_l = \frac{(-1)^{l-1}}{2l}\cos 2l\theta^* \ (l > 0,\ -1 \leq \tau < 0) \tag{39}$$

$$G_0 = 1 - \frac{4\theta^*}{\pi}, \quad G_l = \frac{2}{\pi}\frac{(-1)^{l-1}}{l}\sin 2l\theta^*, \quad (l > 0)$$

$$\theta^* = \begin{cases} 0 \text{ for } 0 < \tau \leq 1 \\ \arctan\sqrt{|\tau|} \quad \text{for } -1 \leq \tau < 0 \end{cases} \tag{40}$$

$$\binom{i}{j} = \frac{i!}{(i-j)!\,j!}, \quad \text{binomial coefficients;}$$

$$\binom{i}{0} = \binom{0}{0} = 1, \quad 0! = 1 \tag{41}$$

Explicit expressions for the derivatives of Φ needed for the computation of $\partial U/\partial n$, $N_n(U)$, $M_n(U)$, etc., as well as of $\partial^2 U/\partial n \partial n_o$, $\partial M_n(U)/\partial n_o$, etc., can be found in Matsui and Matsuoka [7]. Analogous expressions for U_{ij} can also be found in Peng and He [21]. It is obvious that the static fundamental solution of general shallow shells is highly complicated. For the special case of spherical shallow shells for which $\lambda = 1$, $k = 1/R$, where R the radius of the shell, the above expressions become simpler and have the explicit form [23]

$$AU_{ij} = \frac{CD\sqrt{i}(1+\nu)}{16}\left[\sqrt{i}\, r_{,i}\, r_{,j}\, X_o + \frac{1}{\eta r}(\delta_{ij} - 2\, r_{,i}\, r_{,j})\bar{X}_1\right]$$

$$- \frac{CD}{2\pi}(\log r + 1)\,\delta_{ij}$$

$$AU_{i3} = \frac{CD}{16R}\left(i\sqrt{i}\,\eta X_1 + \frac{4}{\pi r}\right) r_{,i} \qquad (42)$$

$$AU_{3j} = -AU_{j3}, \quad AU_{33} = -\frac{(1-\nu)C^2}{16\eta^2}\bar{X}_o$$

where

$$\eta^4 = 12(1-\nu^2)/h^2R^2, \qquad A = -(1-\nu)C^2D/2$$

$$X_o = H_o^{(2)}(\sqrt{i}\,\eta r) + \frac{2i}{\pi}K_o(\sqrt{i}\,\eta r)$$

$$\bar{X}_o = H_o^{(2)}(\sqrt{i}\,\eta r) - \frac{2i}{\pi}K_o(\sqrt{i}\,\eta r) \qquad (43)$$

$$X_1 = H_1^{(2)}(\sqrt{i}\,\eta r) + \frac{2i}{\pi}K_1(\sqrt{i}\,\eta r)$$

$$\bar{X}_1 = H_1^{(2)}(\sqrt{i}\,\eta r) - \frac{2i}{\pi}K_1(\sqrt{i}\,\eta r)$$

with K_o and K_1 being the modified Bessel functions of the second kind and of zero and first orders, respectively and $H_o^{(2)}$ and $H_1^{(2)}$ the Hankel functions of the second kind and zero and first orders, respectively. Of course, all these special functions should be expanded in series form by following, e.g., Abramowitz and Stegun [38], for computational purposes and the resulting U_{ij} will have a series form as the one for the general case of shallow-shells.

Static Analysis by Direct BEM Based on w-φ Formulation

The approach of Tosaka and Miyake [10] will be employed in this section for the special case of a shallow spherical shell subjected only to lateral loads. The w-φ formulation of Eqs (19) and (20) with zero external membrane loads and inertia terms takes the form

$$D\nabla^4 w + \nabla^2_k \varphi = p_z$$
$$\nabla^4 \varphi - Eh\, \nabla^2_k w = 0 \tag{44}$$

The above two equations can be reduced to the single complex - valued equation

$$\nabla^4 \psi - ik\, Eh\, \nabla^2_k \psi = p_z/D \tag{45}$$

for the complex function

$$\psi = w + i\, \kappa\, \varphi \tag{46}$$

where

$$\kappa = 1/\sqrt{EhD} \tag{47}$$

The integral formulation of the problem starts with the weighted residual statement

$$\int_S [\, \nabla^4 \psi - i\kappa Eh\, \nabla^2_k \psi - (p_z/D)]\, U dS = 0 \tag{48}$$

where U is the weighting function. Integrating the above expression by parts four times under Green's theorem, one finally obtains for the special case of a spherical shell (λ = 1, $k = 1/R$, $\nabla^2_k(.) = (1/R)\, \nabla^2(.)$) [10]

$$c\tilde{\psi}(\underset{\sim}{\xi}) = \int_S p_z \varepsilon^4 U dS(\underset{\sim}{x}) + i\varepsilon^2 \int_\Gamma \left(\frac{\partial \tilde{\psi}}{\partial n} U - \tilde{\psi} \frac{\partial U}{\partial n}\right) d\Gamma(\underset{\sim}{X})$$
$$+ \int_\Gamma \left[\tilde{\psi} \frac{\partial(\nabla^2 U)}{\partial\, n} - \frac{\partial(\nabla^2 \tilde{\psi})}{\partial\, n} U + \nabla^2 \tilde{\psi} \frac{\partial U}{\partial n} - \frac{\partial \tilde{\psi}}{\partial n} \nabla^2 U\right] d\Gamma(\underset{\sim}{X}) \tag{49}$$

where $c = 1$ for $\underset{\sim}{\xi} \in S$ and $c = 1/2$ for $\underset{\sim}{\xi} \rightarrow \underset{\sim}{\Xi} \in \Gamma$

$$\tilde{\varphi} = \tilde{w} + i\tilde{\varphi}, \qquad \tilde{\psi} = (Eh/R^2)\psi$$

$$\tilde{\varphi} = (\sqrt{Eh}/R^2\sqrt{D})\varphi, \qquad \tilde{w} = (Eh/R^2)w \tag{50}$$

$$\varepsilon^2 = \kappa Eh/R = (\sqrt{Eh/D})/R \tag{51}$$

Eq. (45) takes the form

$$\nabla^4\tilde{\psi} - i\,\varepsilon^2\,\nabla^2\,\tilde{\psi} = p_z\,\varepsilon^4 \tag{52}$$

the fundamental solution U satisfies the equation

$$\nabla^4 U - i\,\varepsilon^2\,\nabla^2 U = \delta\,(\underset{\sim}{x},\underset{\sim}{\xi}) \tag{53}$$

and $\underset{\sim}{n}$ denotes the outward normal vector at the boundary point $\underset{\sim}{X}$. The solution of (53) is [10]

$$U = U_1 + iU_2 = -(1/2\pi\varepsilon^2)\mathrm{kei}(\varepsilon r) + \\ + i(1/2\pi\varepsilon^2)[\ln(\varepsilon r) + \mathrm{ker}(\varepsilon r)] \tag{54}$$

where $r = |\underset{\sim}{x}-\underset{\sim}{\xi}|$ and kei are Kelvin functions, which can be expanded in series for computational purposes by following, e.g., Abramowitz and Stegun [38].

A differentiation of Eq. (49) along the normal direction $\underset{\sim}{n}_o$ at the smooth point $\underset{\sim}{\Xi}$ at the boundary, yields the equation

$$\frac{1}{2}\frac{\partial\tilde{\psi}}{\partial n_o}(\underset{\sim}{\Xi}) = \int_S p_z\varepsilon^4\frac{\partial U}{\partial n_o}\,dS(\underset{\sim}{x}) + i\varepsilon^2\int_\Gamma\left(\frac{\partial\tilde{\psi}}{\partial n}\frac{\partial U}{\partial n_o} - \tilde{\psi}\frac{\partial^2 U}{\partial n\partial n_o}\right)d\Gamma(\underset{\sim}{X})$$

$$+\int_\Gamma\left[\tilde{\psi}\frac{\partial^2(\nabla^2 U)}{\partial n\partial n_o} - \frac{\partial(\nabla^2\tilde{\psi})}{\partial n}\frac{\partial U}{\partial n_o} + \nabla^2\tilde{\psi}\frac{\partial^2 U}{\partial n\partial n_o} - \frac{\partial\tilde{\psi}}{\partial n}\frac{\partial(\nabla^2 U)}{\partial n_o}\right]d\Gamma(\underset{\sim}{X}) \tag{55}$$

Separating the two boundary integral equations (49) and (55) into their real and imaginary parts one obtains a coupled system of four boundary integral equations involving $\tilde{w}$, $\tilde{\varphi}$, $\partial\tilde{w}/\partial n$, $\partial\tilde{\varphi}/\partial n$, $\nabla^2\tilde{w}$, $\nabla^2\tilde{\varphi}$, $\partial(\nabla^2\tilde{w})/\partial n$ and $\partial(\nabla^2\tilde{\varphi})/\partial n$. For the numerical solution of this system according to Tosaka and

Miyake [10], the boundary and the domain are discretized into constant boundary and interior, respectively, elements and the integral equations written for all the boundary nodes in their discretized form are assembled to form a coupled system of four matrix equations for the vectors $\{\tilde{w}\}$, $\{\tilde{\varphi}\}$, $\{\partial\tilde{w}/\partial n\}$, $\{\partial\tilde{\varphi}/\partial n\}$, $\{\nabla^2\tilde{w}\}$, $\{\nabla^2\tilde{\varphi}\}$, $\{\partial(\nabla^2\tilde{w})/\partial n\}$ and $\{\partial(\nabla^2\tilde{\varphi})/\partial n\}$. Use of the boundary conditions finally yields a coupled system of four matrix equations to be solved for four unknown vectors. For example, for the case of simply supported edges, $\tilde{w} = \tilde{\varphi} = \nabla^2\tilde{w} = \nabla^2\tilde{\varphi} = 0$ and the four unknown vectors are $\{\partial\tilde{w}/\partial n\}$, $\{\partial\tilde{\varphi}/\partial n\}$, $\{\partial(\nabla^2\tilde{w}/\partial n\}$ and $\{\partial(\nabla^2\tilde{\varphi})/\partial n\}$. Regular boundary and domain integrals are computed numerically by standard Gaussian quadrature, while singular boundary integrals analytically [10].

Static Analysis by Direct D/BEM

Static analysis of shallow shells, by the direct D/BEM, first presented by Forbes and Robinson [31], can also be considered as a special case of the corresponding dynamic analysis, which is described in the next three sections. More specifically the case of static analysis is briefly discussed at the end of the next section, which deals with free vibrations by the direct D/BEM.

Free Vibrations by Direct D/BEM

The developments of this section are based on the work of Providakis and Beskos [32]. Consider the shallow shell of Fig. 1 under loads p_x, p_y and p_z sinusoidally varying with time, in which case the deflections u, υ and w of the shell also vary sinusoidally and one has

$$
\begin{aligned}
p_i(\underset{\sim}{x},t) &= \tilde{p}_i(\underset{\sim}{x}) \sin\omega t \\
u_i(\underset{\sim}{x},t) &= \tilde{u}_i(\underset{\sim}{x}) \sin\omega t
\end{aligned}
\qquad (56)
$$

where i = x, y, z, u_x = u, u_y = υ and u_z = w, tildes denote amplitudes and ω is the circular frequency of vibration. Substitution of (56) into Eqs (14)-(16) results in

$$C\nabla^2\tilde{u} + C\frac{(1+\nu)}{2}\frac{\partial}{\partial y}\left(\frac{\partial\tilde{\upsilon}}{\partial x} - \frac{\partial\tilde{u}}{\partial y}\right) + \tilde{p}_x^* = 0 \qquad (57)$$

$$C\nabla^2\tilde{u} + C\,\frac{(1+\nu)}{2}\,\frac{\partial}{\partial x}\left(\frac{\partial\tilde{u}}{\partial y} - \frac{\partial\tilde{u}}{\partial x}\right) + \tilde{p}_y^* = 0 \tag{58}$$

$$D\nabla^4\tilde{w} - \tilde{p}_z^* = 0 \tag{59}$$

where

$$\tilde{p}_x^* = C(1+\nu\lambda)k\,\frac{\partial\tilde{w}}{\partial x} + \rho h\omega^2\tilde{u} + \tilde{p}_x$$

$$\tilde{p}_y^* = C(\nu+\lambda)k\,\frac{\partial\tilde{w}}{\partial y} + \rho h\omega^2\,\tilde{u} + \tilde{p}_y$$

$$\tilde{p}_z^* = -C(1+\nu\lambda)k\,\frac{\partial\tilde{u}}{\partial x} - C(\nu+\lambda)k\,\frac{\partial\tilde{u}}{\partial y} -$$

$$- C(1+2\nu\lambda+\lambda^2)k^2\tilde{w} + \rho h\omega^2\tilde{w} + \tilde{p}_z \tag{60}$$

Equations (57)-(58) and (59) have the form of in-plane and lateral, respectively, static deformations of a plate for which integral formulation procedures are well known. Thus an integral representation of Eqs (57)-(58) can be achieved by employing the reciprocal theorem for two dimensional elastostatics, which reads

$$\int_S \tilde{u}_j\, b_{ij}\, dS + \int_\Gamma \tilde{u}_j\, T_{ij}\, d\Gamma = \int_S \tilde{p}_j^*\, U_{ij} dS + \int_\Gamma \tilde{t}_j\, U_{ij} d\Gamma \tag{61}$$

where $i,j = 1,2$ and summation is assumed over repeated indices. In the above, the actual system consists of the displacements $\tilde{u}_j$ ($\tilde{u}_1 = \tilde{u}$, $\tilde{u}_2 = \tilde{u}$), the corresponding tractions $\tilde{t}_j$ and the forces $\tilde{p}_j^*$, while the elastostatic fundamental solution system (Kelvin's solution in two-dimensions) of the displacements U_{ij}, the corresponding tractions T_{ij} and the forces $b_{ij} = [4\pi Eh / (1+\nu)(3-\nu)]\,\delta_{ij}\,\delta(\underset{\sim}{x},\underset{\sim}{\xi})$ with δ_{ij} and δ being Kronecker's and Dirac's delta functions, respectively, and points $\underset{\sim}{x}$ and $\underset{\sim}{\xi}$ lying onto the (x,y) plane. Taking into account the definition of the delta function, Eqs $(60)_{1,2}$ and employing the divergence theorem on integrals over S with integrands containing $\partial\tilde{w}/\partial x$ and $\partial\tilde{w}/\partial y$, one can obtain from (61) the integral formulation

$$\gamma\tilde{u}_i(\underset{\sim}{\xi}) + \int_\Gamma \tilde{u}_j\, T_{ij} d\Gamma(\underset{\sim}{x}) - \int_\Gamma \tilde{t}_j^*\, U_{ij} d\Gamma(\underset{\sim}{x}) = \int_S \tilde{p}_j\, U_{ij} dS(\underset{\sim}{x}) +$$

$$+ \rho h\omega^2 \int_S \tilde{u}_j U_{ij} dS(\underset{\sim}{x}) - \int_S Q_i \tilde{w}\, d\, S(\underset{\sim}{x}) \qquad (62)$$

for Eqs (57) and (58) expressing in-plane shallow shell deformation. In Eq. (62), $i,j = 1,2$, $\underset{\sim}{\xi}, \underset{\sim}{x} \varepsilon S$, $\underset{\sim}{X} \varepsilon \Gamma$ and

$$\gamma = -4\pi Eh \;/\; (1+v)(3-v) \qquad (63)$$

$$\tilde{t}_1{}^* = \tilde{t}_1 + C(1+v\lambda)\; k\tilde{w}n_x$$

$$(64)$$

$$\tilde{t}_2{}^* = \tilde{t}_2 + C(v+\lambda)\; k\tilde{w}n_y$$

$$Q_1 = C(1+v\lambda)k(\partial U_{11}/\partial x) + C(v+\lambda)k(\partial U_{12}/\partial y)$$

$$(65)$$

$$Q_2 = C(1+v\lambda)k(\partial U_{21}/\partial x) + C(v+\lambda)k(\partial U_{22}/\partial y)$$

with $\underset{\sim}{n}$ being the unit outward normal vector on the boundary projected on the (x,y) plane, as shown in Fig. 1, and $n_x = \cos(x,\underset{\sim}{n})$, $n_y = \cos(y,\underset{\sim}{n}) = \sin(x,\underset{\sim}{n})$. Explicit expressions for U_{ij}, T_{ij}, Q_1 and Q_2 are given as follows:

$$U_{ij} = \delta_{ij} \ln r - \left(\frac{1+v}{3-v}\right) r,_i\, r,_j$$

$$(66)$$

$$T_{ij} = \frac{C(1-v)^2}{(3-v)r}\left[\frac{\partial r}{\partial n}\left(\delta_{ij} + \frac{2(1+v)}{1-v}\, r,_i\, r,_j\right) + r,_j\, n_i - r,_i\, n_j\right]$$

$$Q_1 = C\,\frac{(1-v)}{(3-v)}\, K\, \frac{r,_1}{r}\left[3 + v - (1-v)\lambda - 2(1+v)(1-\lambda)r,_2^2\right]$$

$$(67)$$

$$Q_2 = C\,\frac{(1-v)}{(3-v)}\, K\, \frac{r,_2}{r}\left[(3+v)\lambda - (1-v) + 2(1+v)(1-\lambda)r,_1^2\right]$$

In the above, $i,j = 1,2$ with 1 and 2 identified with x and y, respectively, $r = |\underset{\sim}{x} - \underset{\sim}{\xi}|$ and commas denote spatial defferentiation. When point $\underset{\sim}{\xi}$ is brought to the boundary point $\underset{\sim}{\Xi}$ through a limiting process, Eq. (62) retains its form with γ being replaced by

$$\Lambda_{ij} = aC \begin{bmatrix} (1+\frac{b}{2})c\pi + \frac{b}{4}[\sin 2(c\pi+\psi)-\sin 2\psi], & -\frac{b}{8}[\sin^2(c\pi+\psi)-\sin^2\psi] \\ -\frac{b}{8}[\sin^2(c\pi+\psi)-\sin^2\psi], & (1+\frac{b}{2})c\pi - \frac{b}{4}[\sin 2(c\pi+\psi)-\sin 2\psi] \end{bmatrix} \tag{68}$$

if $\underset{\sim}{\Xi}$ is at a corner of internal angle $c\pi$, or by

$$\Lambda_{ij} = -[2\pi Eh/(1+\nu)(3-\nu)]\,\delta_{ij} \tag{69}$$

if $\underset{\sim}{\Xi}$ is a smooth point. In Eq. (68) ψ is the angle between the x axis and the tangent vector $\underset{\sim}{t}$ to the boundary, as shown in Fig. 1, while the constants a and b have the values

$$a = -(1-\nu)^2/(3-\nu), \qquad b = 2(1+\nu)/(1-\nu) \tag{70}$$

It should also be noticed that the first integral over Γ in (62) with $\underset{\sim}{\xi}$ replaced by $\underset{\sim}{\Xi}$ is a Cauchy principal value one.

An integral formulation of Eq. (59) can now be achieved by employing the reciprocal theorem for static plate bending, which reads

$$\int_S \tilde{w} f dS + \int_\Gamma [\tilde{w}V_n(W) + \tilde{\theta}_n M_n(W)]\,d\Gamma + \sum_{l=1}^{L} \tilde{w}\,[\![M_t(W)]\!] = \\ = \int_S W\tilde{p}_3^* \,dS + \int_\Gamma [WV_n(\tilde{w}) + \theta_n(W)M_n(\tilde{w})]\,d\Gamma + \sum_{l=1}^{L} W\,[\![M_t(\tilde{w})]\!] \tag{71}$$

where the actual system consists of the lateral deflection $\tilde{w}$, the normal slope $\tilde{\Theta}_n = -\partial\tilde{w}/\partial n$, the Kirchhoff shear force $V_n(\tilde{w})$, the normal bending moment $M_n(\tilde{w})$, the twisting moment $M_t(\tilde{w})$ and the force $\tilde{p}_3{}^*$, while the static plate bending fundamental solution system of the corresponding quantities W, $\Theta_n(W) = -\partial W/\partial n$, $V_n(W)$, $M_n(W)$, $M_t(W)$ and $f = 8\pi D\delta(\underset{\sim}{x},\underset{\sim}{\xi})$ with points $\underset{\sim}{x}$ and $\underset{\sim}{\xi}$ lying in the (x,y) plane and the symbol $[\![\,.\,]\!]$ denoting discontiniuity jump at every corner point l. Taking into account the definition of the delta function, the expression $(60)_3$ of the force $\tilde{p}_3{}^*$ and em ploying the divergence theorem on integrals over S with integrands containing $\partial\tilde{u}/\partial x$ and $\partial\tilde{u}/\partial y$, one can obtain from (71) the integral representation

$$\gamma_w \tilde{w}(\underset{\sim}{\xi}) + \int_\Gamma W_i \tilde{u}_i d\Gamma(X) + \int_\Gamma [\tilde{w}V_n(W) + \tilde{\theta}_n M_n(W) - WV_n(\tilde{w}) - \theta_n(W)M_n(\tilde{w})] d\Gamma(\underset{\sim}{X}) +$$
$$+ \sum_{l=1}^{L} \tilde{w}[\![M_t(W)]\!] - W[\![M_t(\tilde{w})]\!] = \int_S W\tilde{p}_3 dS(\underset{\sim}{x}) + \rho h\omega^2 \int_S W\tilde{w} dS(\underset{\sim}{x}) + \tag{72}$$
$$+ \int_S C(1+\nu\lambda)k\tilde{u}\frac{\partial W}{\partial x} dS(\underset{\sim}{x}) + \int_S C(\nu+\lambda)k\tilde{u}\frac{\partial W}{\partial y} dS(\underset{\sim}{x}) - \int_S (1+2\nu\lambda+\lambda^2)k^2 W\tilde{w} dS(\underset{\sim}{x})$$

for the lateral shallow shell deformation. In Eq. (72), $\underset{\sim}{\xi}$, $\underset{\sim}{x} \in S$, $\underset{\sim}{X} \in \Gamma$, $\gamma_w = 8\pi D$ and

$$W_1 = W\,C\,(1+\nu\lambda)k\,n_x$$
$$W_2 = W\,C\,(\nu+\lambda)k\,n_y \tag{73}$$

Explicit expressions for W, $\partial W/\partial n$, $V_n(W)$, $M_n(W)$ and $M_t(W)$ can be found in the chapter on dynamic analysis of plates, while for $\partial W/\partial x$ and $\partial W/\partial y$ are given as follows:

$$\partial W/\partial x = r\,r_{,x}\,(1+2\ln r)$$
$$\partial W/\partial y = r\,r_{,y}\,(1+2\ln r) \tag{74}$$

When point $\underset{\sim}{\xi}$ is brought to the boundary point $\underset{\sim}{\Xi}$ through a limiting process, Eq. (72) retains its form with γ_w being replaced by $\gamma_w^* = 4\pi kD$ and with l denoting corner points other than $\underset{\sim}{\Xi}$ in case there is a corner there. Furthermore, the second integral over Γ in (72) is a Cauchy principal value one.

It is well known in plate bending theory that in addition to the integral representation of the lateral deflection, an integral representation of the slope of the lateral deflection is needed for a complete integral formulation of Eq. (59). In case there are corners at the boundary, this second integral equation is obtained as described in the chapter on the dynamic analysis of plates. Thus, the integral representation for the normal slopes $\tilde{\Theta}_n(\underset{\sim}{\Xi}^{\pm})$ at a corner point $\underset{\sim}{\Xi}$ is obtained in the form

$$2D\,\frac{c\pi\pm\nu\sin c\pi}{\sin,\cos(c\pi/2)}\left[\tilde{\theta}_n(\underset{\sim}{\Xi}^+)\pm\tilde{\theta}_n(\underset{\sim}{\Xi}^-)\right]+\int_\Gamma W_i^{\varphi_1,\varphi_2}\tilde{u}_i\,d\Gamma(\underset{\sim}{X})+\int_\Gamma\left[V_n(W^{\varphi_1,\varphi_2})(w(\underset{\sim}{X})-w(\underset{\sim}{\Xi}))\right.$$

$$\left.+\,\tilde{\theta}_n M_n(W^{\varphi_1,\varphi_2})-W^{\varphi_1,\varphi_2}V_n(\tilde{w})-\theta_n(W^{\varphi_1,\varphi_2})M_n(\tilde{w})\right]d\Gamma(\underset{\sim}{X})\;+$$

$$+\sum_{l=1}^{L}\left\{(\tilde{w}(\underset{\sim}{X})-\tilde{w}(\underset{\sim}{\Xi}))[\![M_t(W^{\varphi_1,\varphi_2})]\!]-W^{\varphi_1,\varphi_2}[\![M_t(\tilde{w})]\!]\right\}=\int_S W^{\varphi_1,\varphi_2}\tilde{p}_3\,dS(\underset{\sim}{x})\;+$$

$$+\,\rho h\omega^2\int_S W^{\varphi_1,\varphi_2}\tilde{w}\,dS(\underset{\sim}{x})+\int_S C(1+\nu\lambda)k\tilde{u}\,\frac{\partial W^{\varphi_1,\varphi_2}}{\partial x}\,dS(\underset{\sim}{x})+\int_S C(\nu+\lambda)k\tilde{u}\,\frac{\partial W^{\varphi_1,\varphi_2}}{\partial y}\,dS(\underset{\sim}{x})$$

$$-\int_S C(1+2\nu\lambda+\lambda^2)k^2\,W^{\varphi_1,\varphi_2}\tilde{w}\,d\,S(\underset{\sim}{x}) \tag{75}$$

where φ_1 and φ_2 are the angles between the axes d_1 and d_2, respectively and the vector $\underset{\sim}{r}$ connecting $\underset{\sim}{\Xi}$ and $\underset{\sim}{X}$, with d_1 being the bisector of the interior angle $c\pi$ at $\underset{\sim}{\Xi}$ and d_2 the axis perpendicular to d_1 at $\underset{\sim}{\Xi}$, l denotes corner points other than $\underset{\sim}{\Xi}$, and where W^φ is two times the singular part of the directional derivative (slope) of W along a direction d at $\underset{\sim}{\Xi}$ that forms an angle φ with $\underset{\sim}{r}$. In addition, the second integral over Γ in (75) is a Cauchy principal value one. Explicit expressions for W^φ, $\Theta_n(W^\varphi) = -\partial W^\varphi/\partial n$, $V_n(W^\varphi)$, $M_n(W^\varphi)$ and $M_t(W^\varphi)$ can be found in the chapter on the dynamic analysis of plates, while for $\partial W^\varphi/\partial x$ and $\partial W^\varphi/\partial y$ are given as follows:

$$\begin{aligned}\partial W^\varphi/\partial x &= -[l_o(1+2\ln r) + 2r_{,x}\,r_{,d}]\\ \partial W^\varphi/\partial y &= -[m_o(1+2\ln r) + 2r_{,y}\,r_{,d}]\\ l_o = \cos(x,d), &\qquad m_o = \cos(y,d) = \sin(x,d)\end{aligned} \tag{76}$$

Thus for a corner point $\underset{\sim}{\Xi}$, the integral formulation of shallow shell dynamics consists of Eqs. (62) for both $\underset{\sim}{\xi}\in S$ and $\underset{\sim}{\Xi}\in\Gamma$ with Λ_{ij} given by (68), Eq. (72) for both $\underset{\sim}{\xi}\in S$ and $\underset{\sim}{\Xi}\in\Gamma$ and Eqs. (75). For a regular (smooth) point $\underset{\sim}{\Xi}$, the formulation consists of Eqs (62) for both $\underset{\sim}{\xi}\in S$ and $\underset{\sim}{\xi}\in\Gamma$ with Λ_{ij} given by (69), Eq. (72) for both $\underset{\sim}{\xi}\in S$ and $\underset{\sim}{\Xi}\in\Gamma$ and Eq. (75) for c = 1 and $\varphi = \varphi_1$. The present formulation is characterized by the employment of the static fundamental solutions of a plate under in-plane and lateral deformation. This creates not only boundary integrals but domain integrals as well that take care of the inertia loadings and the coupling of in-plane and lateral shallow shell deformations. To be sure load domain integrals also appear in the formulation. Their computation, however, presents no problem since their integrands are known functions. The presence of boundary as well as domain integrals in this frequency formulation of shallow shell dynamics requires discretization of the boundary as well as the interior domain for the numerical solution of the governing integral equations. Even though the continuity requirements for $\tilde{u}_i$ and $\tilde{w}$ are here more relaxed than in the FEM, i.e., $\tilde{u}_i$ and $\tilde{w}$ need only be piecewise constant functions and not C^0 (for $\tilde{u}_i$) and C^1 (for $\tilde{w}$) as in the FEM, higher order elements are chosen here for increased accuracy. Thus the boundary of the shell is discretized into a number of three-node quadratic isoparametric line elements, while its domain into a number of eight-node quadrilateral quadraticue isoparametric interior elements. The aforementioned integral equations are then written in their discretized form. As an example, the explicit discretized form of Eq. (72) for $\underset{\sim}{\xi} \varepsilon S$ is given below:

$$V_w w_m + \sum_{b=1}^{B} \left(\int_{\Gamma_b} F^q(\zeta) W_1(\zeta) |J_1(\zeta)| d\Gamma_b \right) \tilde{u}_q + \sum_{b=1}^{B} \left(\int_{\Gamma_b} F^q(\zeta) W_2(\zeta) |J_1(\zeta)| d\Gamma_b \right) \tilde{u}_q +$$

$$+ \sum_{b=1}^{B} \left(\int_{\Gamma_b} F^q(\zeta) V_n(W(\zeta)) |J_1(\zeta)| d\Gamma_b \right) \tilde{w}_q + \sum_{b=1}^{B} \left(\int_{\Gamma_b} F^q(\zeta) M_n(W(\zeta)) |J_1(\zeta)| d\Gamma_b \right) (\tilde{\theta}_n)_q$$

$$- \sum_{b=1}^{B} \left(\int_{\Gamma_b} F^q(\zeta) W(\zeta) |J_1(\zeta)| d\Gamma_b \right) (V_n(\tilde{w}))_q - \sum_{b=1}^{B} \left(\int_{\Gamma_b} F^q(\zeta) \theta_n(W(\zeta)) |J_1(\zeta)| d\Gamma_b \right) (M_n(\tilde{w}))_q$$

$$+ \sum_{l=1}^{L} \left\{ \tilde{w}_l [\![M_t(W)]\!] - W [\![M_t(\tilde{w})]\!]_l \right\} = \sum_{i=1}^{I} \left(\int_{S_i} N^g(p,\tau) W(p,\tau) |J_2(p,\tau)| dS_i \right) (\tilde{p}_3)_g$$

$$+ \rho h \omega^2 \sum_{i=1}^{I} \left(\int_{S_i} N^g(p,\tau) W(p,\tau) |J_2(p,\tau)| dS_i \right) \tilde{w}_g + C(1+\nu\lambda)k \sum_{i=1}^{I} \left(\int_{S_i} N^g(p,\tau) . \right.$$

$$\cdot \frac{\partial W}{\partial x}(p,\tau)|J_2(p,\tau)|dS_i)\tilde{u}_g + C(\nu+\lambda)k \sum_{i=1}^{I}\left(\int_{S_i} N^g(p,\tau)\frac{\partial W}{\partial y}(p,\tau)|J_2(p,\tau)|dS_i\right)\tilde{\upsilon}_g -$$

$$- C(1+2\nu\lambda+\lambda^2)k^2 \sum_{i=1}^{I}\left(\int_{S_i} N^g(p,\tau)W(p,\tau)|J_2(p,\tau)|dS_i\right)\tilde{w}_g \tag{77}$$

In the above, B and I represent the total number of boundary and interior elements, respectively, $F^q(\zeta)$ and $N^g(p,\tau)$ with $q = 1,2,3$ and $g = 1,2,\ldots 8$ are the interpolation functions for boundary and interior elements respectively, with corresponding intrinsic (local) coordinates ζ and (p,τ) and $|J_1(\zeta)|$ and $|J_2(p,\tau)|$ are the Jacobians of the coordinate transformations between local and global coordinates for boundary and interior elements, respectively. All the integrations indicated in the discretized forms of the governing integral equations are accomplished numerically. When $r \neq 0$ line and surface integrals are regular and are computed with the aid of standard Gauss quadrature formulae involving 6 and 4×4 points, respectively. When $r \to 0$ the various fundamental solution expressions involving U_{ij}, W, W^{φ} and their derivatives exhibit singularities of $O(\ln r)$ and $O(1/r)$ and the corresponding singular line and surface integrals are computed as described in the chapter on dynamic analysis of plates. Every regular (smooth) boundary node is associated with eight boundary quantities, namely, $\tilde{u}$, $\tilde{\upsilon}$, $\tilde{t}_1^*$, $\tilde{t}_2^*$ $\tilde{w}$, $\tilde{\Theta}_n$, $M_n(\tilde{w})$ and $V_n(\tilde{w})$, from which only four are known in a well posed boundary value problem. When the boundary node is at a corner, there are fourteen boundary qwuantities, namely, $\tilde{u}$, $\tilde{\upsilon}$, $\tilde{t}_1^{*-}$, $\tilde{t}_2^{*+}$, $\tilde{t}_2^{*-}$, $\tilde{t}_2^{*+}$, $\tilde{w}$, $\tilde{\Theta}_n^-$, $\tilde{\Theta}_n^+$, $M_n(\tilde{w})^-$, $M_n(\tilde{w})^+$, $V_n(\tilde{w})^-$, $V_n(\tilde{w})^+$ and $[[M_t(\tilde{w})]]$, from which only seven are known. However, there are two additional equations available due to Chaudonneret [39] relating $\tilde{t}_i^{\pm}$ $(i = 1,2)$ as a result of the symmetry of the stress tensor and the invariance of the trace of the strain tensor. Because of the complexity of these two equations the approximate relations of Howell and Doyle [40] $\tilde{t}_i^- = \tilde{t}_i^+$ can also be used.

Assuming now that N_r, N_c and N_i represent the number of regular, corner and interior nodes, respectively, one can assemble the discretized governing integral equations in matrix form and, after using the bounadry conditions, write the equations

$$[\tilde{A}]\{\tilde{y}\} - \omega^2[\tilde{B}]\{\tilde{x}\} + [\tilde{C}]\{\tilde{x}\} = \{\tilde{Q}\} \tag{78}$$

$$[\Lambda^*]\{\tilde{x}\} + [\tilde{A}^*]\{\tilde{y}\} - \omega^2[\tilde{B}^*]\{\tilde{x}\} + [\tilde{C}^*]\{\tilde{x}\} = \{\tilde{Q}^*\} \tag{79}$$

for $\underset{\sim}{\Xi}\varepsilon\Gamma$ and $\underset{\sim}{\xi}\varepsilon S$, respectively, where $[\tilde{A}]$ is a $(4N_r+5N_c)$ x $(4N_r+5N_c)$ coefficient matrix with entries values of boundary element integrals, $[\tilde{B}]$ and $[\tilde{C}]$ are $(4N_r+5N_c)$ x $(3N_i)$ coefficient matrices with entries values of integrals of inertia and curvature terms, respectively, in interior elements, $\{\tilde{y}\}$ is a $(4N_r+5N_c)$ vector with entries the unknown nodal boundary values, $\{\tilde{x}\}$ is a $(3N_i)$ vector with entries the unknown interior nodal values of $\tilde{u}$, $\tilde{\upsilon}$ and $\tilde{w}$, $\{\tilde{Q}\}$ is a $(4N_r+5N_c)$ vector with entries nodal surface load integrals, $[\Lambda^*]$ is the $(3N_i)$ x $(3N_i)$ diagonal jump term matrix, $[\tilde{A}^*]$ is a $(3N_i)$ x $(4N_r+5N_c)$ coefficient matrix with entries values of boundary element integrals, $[\tilde{B}^*]$ and $[\tilde{C}^*]$ are $(3N_i)$ x $(3N_i)$ coefficient matrices with entries values of integrals of inertia and curvature terms, respectively, in interior elements and $\{\tilde{Q}^*\}$ is a $(3N_i)$ vector with entries nodal surface load integrals. Elimination of $\{\tilde{y}\}$ between (78) and (79) yields the equation

$$[\tilde{D}]\{\tilde{x}\} = \{\tilde{P}\} \tag{80}$$

where

$$[\tilde{D}] = [[\Lambda^*]-\omega^2([\tilde{B}^*]-[\tilde{A}^*][\tilde{A}]^{-1}[\tilde{B}])-([\tilde{C}^*]-[\tilde{A}^*][\tilde{A}]^{-1}[\tilde{C}])] \tag{81}$$

$$\{\tilde{P}\} = \{\tilde{Q}^*\}-[\tilde{A}^*][\tilde{A}]^{-1}\{\tilde{Q}\} \tag{82}$$

For the free vibration case the loading vectors $\{\tilde{Q}\} = \{\tilde{Q}^*\} = 0$ and Eqs. (80)-(82) reduce to the generalized eigenvalue problem

$$[\tilde{R}]\{\tilde{x}\} = \omega^2[\tilde{E}]\{\tilde{x}\} \tag{83}$$

where

$$[\tilde{R}] = [\Lambda^*]-[\tilde{C}^*] + [\tilde{A}^*][\tilde{A}]^{-1}[\tilde{C}]$$

$$[\tilde{E}] = [\tilde{B}^*]-[\tilde{A}^*][\tilde{A}]^{-1}[\tilde{B}] \tag{84}$$

Matrices $[\tilde{R}]$ and $[\tilde{E}]$ above are real and in general non-sparse, non-symmetric and non-positive definite. An efficient iterative algorithm for the solution of the above eigenvalue problem has been developed by Smith at al [41] and this algorithm was adopted in [32].

It is interesting to observe that the methodology of this section can also be used for static analysis of shallow shells after some modifications. Indeed, if one assumes that all quantities are independent of time and $\omega = 0$, Eq. (80) can be written as

$$[D]\{x\} = \{P\} \tag{85}$$

where

$$[D] = [[\Lambda^*]-[C^*]-[A^*][A]^{-1}[C]] \tag{86}$$

$$\{P\} = \{Q^*\}-[A^*][A]^{-1}\{Q\} \tag{87}$$

Once $\{x\}$ is solved from (85), $\{y\}$ can be obtained from modified (78) in the form

$$\{y\} = [A]^{-1}\{Q\} - [A]^{-1}[C]\{x\} \tag{88}$$

Interior forces and moments can then be obtained as explained in the next section.

Forced Vibrations by Direct D/BEM - Laplace Transform

This section is based on the work of Providakis and Beskos [32]. In the forced vibration case the loading $p_i(\underset{\sim}{x},t)$ (i= 1,2,3) can be either harmonically varying with time or can have any arbitrary time variation. In the former case the operational frequency is known and one simply has to solve (80) for $\{\tilde{x}\}$ and subsequently obtain $\{\tilde{y}\}$ from (78). In the latter case, use is made of the Laplace transform with respect to time, defined for a function $f(\underset{\sim}{x},t)$ as

$$L[f(\underset{\sim}{x},t)] = \bar{f}(\underset{\sim}{x},s) = \int_0^\infty f(\underset{\sim}{x},t)\, e^{-st}\, dt \tag{89}$$

where s is the, in general complex, Laplace transform parameter. Application of (89) on Eqs (14)-(16) under zero initial conditions yields Eqs (57)-(60) with the tildes being replaced by overbars and ω^2 by $-s^2$. This indicates that the general forced vibration problem in the Laplace transformed domain has the form of Eqs (80)-(82) with the tildes and ω^2 being replaced by overbars and $-s^2$, respectively. The transformed solution is obtained by solving (80) for $\{\bar{x}\}$ for a sequence of complex values of s and then solving the transformed version of (78) for $\{\bar{y}\}$ for the same sequence of values of s. The solution of systems of linear equations involving non-sparse and non-symmetric coefficient matrices, such as (80), can be efficiently accomplished by an out-of-core complex equation solver [32]. A numerical inversion of this transformed solution can finally provide the time domain response. The numerical Laplace transform inversion is done with the aid of the algorithm of Durbin [42], which has been found by Narayanan and Beskos [43] to be the most accurate one for dynamic problems in a comparison study involving eight promising inversion algorithms. When the applied loads have a complicated time variation their direct Laplace transform has to be computed numerically. In this case the algorithm of Durbin [42] suitably modified as explained in [43] can also be used. Finally, when there are nonzero initial conditions, their effect can be easily absorbed into the transformed loads $\bar{p}_i$ $(i = 1,2,3)$.

Once boundary quantities and interior displacements are known, one can easily compute interior forces and moments. This can be accomplished by employing Eqs (7)-(12) where the needed first, second and third order derivatives of displacements can be obtained by repeated differentiation of Eqs (62) and (72). The differentiation is with respect to $\underset{\sim}{\xi}$ and thus only the singular kernels are affected inside the integrals of (62) and (72). In spite of the increased order of singularity due to kernel differentiation, there is no any computational problem since $r \neq 0$ inside the shell. Problems may arise, however, for points $\underset{\sim}{\xi}$ very near the boundary where $\underset{\sim}{r}$ attains very small values. In that case a very simple and practical way is to obtain results there by extrapolation. A very easy and practical but approximate way of obtaining interior forces and moments is also to use Eqs (7)-(12) in a finite difference form that involves values of displacements at interior points.

The formulation of the forced shallow shell vibration problem in the Laplace transformed domain has the advantage of treating the effect of external viscous or internal viscoelastic damping on the response very easily. Thus, when there exists external viscous damping on the shell affecting its flexural motion the term cw appears in the left hand side of Eq. (16), where c is the viscous damping coefficient. Application of Laplace transform (89) on this augmented Eq. (16) under zero initial conditions reveals that the effect of external viscous damping on the shell response can be very easily taken into account if ρhs^2 is replaced by ρhs^2+cs in the previous forced vibration formulation. When, on the other hand, there exists internal linear viscoelastic damping in the plate, the correspondence principle, as described in Pan [44] for flexural motion of flat plates, is extended here to shallow shell dynamics. Thus one can easily prove that the transformed viscoelastodynamic solution can be obtained from the corresponding transformed elastodynamic one if the rigidities C and D of Eqs. (13) are replaced by

$$\begin{aligned} \bar{C}(s) &= L\left[\left(\frac{2PQ'+P'Q}{PQ'+2QP'}\right)\frac{Q}{P}\right]h \\ \bar{D}(s) &= L\left[\left(\frac{2PQ'+P'Q}{PQ'+2QP'}\right)\frac{Q}{P}\right]\frac{h^3}{12} \end{aligned} \qquad (90)$$

where P, Q, P' and Q' are linear differential operators of the form

$$P = \sum_{r=o}^{m} p_r \frac{\partial^r}{\partial t^r}, \qquad Q = \sum_{r=o}^{n} q_r \frac{\partial^r}{\partial t^r}$$

$$P' = \sum_{r=o}^{m'} p'_r \frac{\partial^r}{\partial t^r}, \qquad Q' = \sum_{r=o}^{n'} q'_r \frac{\partial^r}{\partial t^r} \tag{91}$$

which define the constitutive behavior of a homogeneous isotropic, linear viscoelastic material through the equations

$$P\, s_{ij} = Q\, e_{ij}$$

$$P'\sigma_{ii} = Q'\varepsilon_{ii} \tag{92}$$

with s_{ij} and e_{ij} being the stress and strain deviators, respectively, of the stress σ_{ij} and strain ε_{ij} tensors. Under the assumption of constant Poisson's ratio and the adoption of Kelvin's viscoelastic solid model with

$$P = 1, \qquad Q = 2G\left(1 + \frac{\eta}{G}\frac{\partial}{\partial t}\right) \tag{93}$$

where $G = E/2(1+v)$ is the shear modulus and η the viscosity coefficient, Eqs. (90) reduce to

$$\bar{C}(s) = \left[\frac{E}{1+v} + 2\eta s\right]\frac{h}{(1-v)}$$

$$\bar{D}(s) = \left[\frac{E}{1+v} + 2\eta s\right]\frac{h^3}{12(1-v)} \tag{94}$$

Forced Vibrations by Time Domain D/BEM

Forced vibrations of shallow shells by the time domain direct D/BEM were first studied by Zhang and Atluri [14]. Instead of following their approach in this section, forced vibrations in the time domain are studied herein by appropriately modifying the approach of Providakis and Beskos [32] as described in the section of free vibrations. Indeed, if one considers Eqs (62), (72) and (75) and replaces amplitudes of the various quantities like $\tilde{u}_j(\underset{\sim}{x})$, $\tilde{w}(\underset{\sim}{x})$, $\partial\tilde{w}(\underset{\sim}{x})/\partial n$, etc., by their time dependent expressions $u_j(\underset{\sim}{x},t)$, $w(\underset{\sim}{x},t)$ $\partial w(\underset{\sim}{x},t)/\partial n$, etc., respectively, as well as the quantities $-\omega^2\tilde{u}_j$ and $-\omega^2\tilde{w}_j$ in the inertia terms by $\ddot{u}_j$ and $\ddot{w}$, respectively, then the resulting equations constitute the integral formulation of the problem in the time domain. The result of these changes is that the matrix equations (78) and (79) take now the form

$$[A]\{y\} + [B]\{\ddot{x}\} + [C]\{x\} = \{Q\} \tag{95}$$

$$[\Lambda^*]\{x\} + [A^*]\{y\} + [B^*]\{\ddot{x}\} + [C^*]\{x\} = \{Q^*\} \tag{96}$$

Elimination of {y} between the above two equations yields

$$[M]\{\ddot{x}\} + [K]\{x\} = \{P\} \tag{97}$$

where

$$\begin{aligned} [M] &= [B^*] - [A^*][A]^{-1}[B] \\ [K] &= [\Lambda^*] + [C^*] - [A^*][A]^{-1}[C] \\ \{P\} &= \{Q^*\} - [A^*][A]^{-1}\{Q\} \end{aligned} \tag{98}$$

Equation (97) can be easily solved by standard step-by-step time integration algorithms, such as those of Newmark or Houbolt. Once {x} and $\{\ddot{x}\}$ are known, then {y} can be obtained from (95) as

$$\{y\} = [A]^{-1}\{Q\} - [A]^{-1}[B]\{\ddot{x}\} - [A]^{-1}[C]\{x\} \tag{99}$$

Of course, if the load is harmonic with time, then it is much more convenient to obtain the amplitude response $\{\tilde{x}\}$ directly from (80) by a simple matrix inversion for the given value of the operational frequency ω. For computing interior moments and forces according to the time domain D/BÈM, one can follow the procedure described in the previous section.

Numerical Examples

This section presents some representative numerical examples from static and dynamic analysis of shallow shells in order to illustrate the various methods described in the previous sections and compare them against other analytical or numerical methods with respect to accuracy and efficiency.

Example 1 [23]

Consider a simply supported (edges movable in-plane) shallow spherical shell with square projection on the (x,y) plane of side a = 18.0 m and with h = 0.15 m, $E = 2.1 \times 10^6$ t/m², ν = 0.0 and R = 10.00 m., as shown in Fig. 3(a), which is subjected to a uniform pressure p_z = 0.1 t/m². Fig. 3(b) depicts the variation of the lateral deflection w along an axis of symmetry of the shell as obtained by the direct BEM of Miyake at al [23] based on the displacement formulation. Results are shown for two different kinds of discretization: case A involves 24 constant boundary elements and 72 triangular constant interior elements, while case B 32 and 128 constant boundary and interior elements, respectively. It should be noticed that use of interior discretization is done only for the computation of the load integral and does not affect the number of the unknowns of the problem. It is observed that the numerical results are in good agreement with the Fourier series analytic solution [45] except for points near the boundary.

Example 2 [10]

Consider the shallow spherical shell of the previous example with the same geometry, boundary conditions and loading apart from the fact that here R = 50 m. Figs. 4(a) and 4(b) depict the variation of the lateral deflection w and the stress function φ along an axis of symmetry of the shell as obtained by the direct BEM of Tosaka and Miyake [10] based on the w-φ formulation. Results are shown for three different kinds of discretization: case m = 12 involves 12 constant boundary elements and 9 constant interior square elements, case m = 16 involves 16 and 16 constant boundary and interior elements, respectively and case m = 36 involves 36 and 81 constant boundary and interior elements, respectively. It is evident in both figures that there is a very good to excellent agreement of all numerical results with the Fourier series analytic solution [45]. A comparison of the results of the method of this example against those of the method of the previous

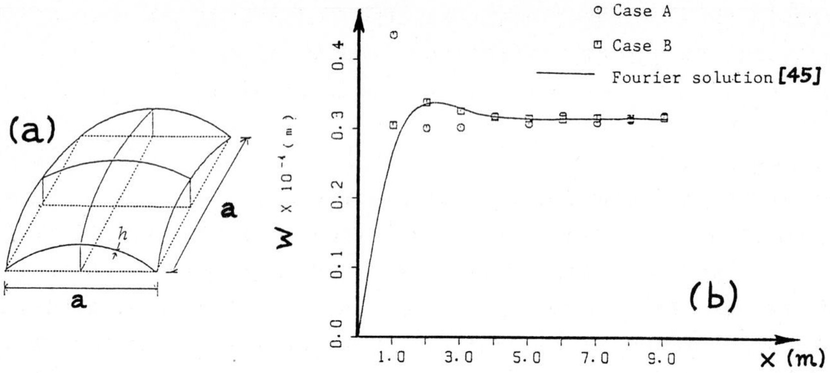

Fig. 3. Simply supported shallow spherical shell with square projection subjected to a uniform vertical pressure: (a) shell geometry; (b) lateral deflection w along a symmetry axis

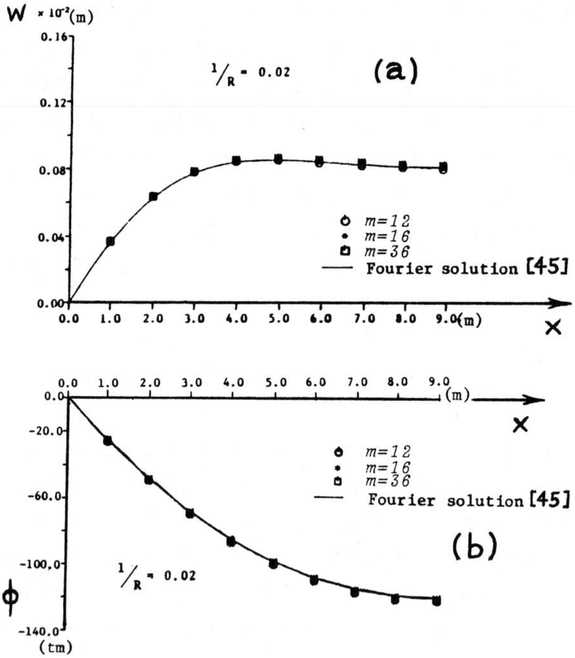

Fig. 4. Simply supported shallow spherical shell with square projection subjected to a uniform vertical pressure: (a) lateral deflection w along a symmetry axis; (b) membrane stress function φ along a symmetry axis

example shows a superiority of the present method with respect to both accuracy and efficiency, which can be attributed mainly to the much smaller curvature in this example.

Example 3 [13]

Consider a shallow shell of circular planform of radius $r_o = 1$, fixed at its edge and uniformly loaded laterally with $E = 1000$, $v = 0.25$, $h = 0.05$, $z_o = kr_o^2/2$ and with i) $k = 0.1$, $\lambda = 1$ (spherical shell), ii) $k = 0.1$, $\lambda = 0$ (cylindrical shell) and iii) $k = 0.1$, $\lambda = -1$ (hyperbolic paraboloidal (hypar) shell). All these kinds of shallow shells were analysed by the D/BEM of Forbes and Robinson [13] using 16 boundary and 16 interior (square) constant elements. Table 1 shows the deflection and stress resultants at the center and boundary of the spherical shell as computed by the D/BEM and the exact solution of Wan [46]. The agreement of the two solutions is very good (max relative error 4%). Table 2 provides maximum displacements and stress resultants for the three kinds of shallow shells mentioned above as ob tained by the D/BEM of Forbes and Robinson [13]. Figure 5 depicts the variation of the lateral deflection w of the three kinds of shells along one radius of the planform of the shells, which for the cylindrical shell case coincides with the direction of the zero curvature, as obtained again by the D/BEM [13].

Example 4 [32]

Consider a clamped, shallow shell with circular projection on the (x,y) plane of radius $r_o = 1.0$, thickness $h = 0.05$, modulus of elasticity $E = 1000.0$, Poisson's ration $v = 0.25$ and density per unit volume $\rho = 0.222$, experiencing free vibrations. Table 3 provides values of the lowest natural frequency for various values of the radius of curvature $R = 1/k$ and for $\lambda = 1.0$, i.e., for a shallow spherical cap, as obtained in Providakis and Beskos [32] by the D/BEM in conjunction with mesh-2 (171 degrees of freedom) of Fig. 6, as well as by the analytic formula of Reissner [46] and the finite element computer program SAP IV [48] with mesh-3 (198 degrees of freedom) of Fig. 6. These results clearly show that the D/BEM is not only more efficient but also more accurate than SAP IV,

Quantity	Point (0,0)		Point (r_o,0)	
	D/BEM	Exact	D/BEM	Exact
w	0.732	0.752	0.0	0.0
N_x	3.62	3.57	1.70	1.72
Q_x	0.0	0.0	-0.338	-0.329
M_x	0.0413	0.0397	-0.0748	-0.0740
M_y	0.0413	0.0397	-0.0187	-0.0185

Table 1. Deflection and stress resultants at center and boundary of a uniformly loaded clamped, shallow spherical cap

Shell Shape	Maximum Values				
	u,v	w	N_x,N_y	Q_x,Q_y	M_x,M_y
Cylindrical	-0.0144	1.027	3.95	-0.428	-0.0988
Spherical	-0.0111	0.732	3.62	-0.338	-0.0748
Hypar	±0.0112	0.902	±2.76	-0.406	-0.0885

Table 2. Maximum displacements and stress resultants for uniformly loaded shallow shells of circular planform and fixed edge

Radius of curvature	Analytic Reissner [47]	D/BEM mesh-2	error %	SAP IV [48] mesh-3	error %
R = 10	13.714	13.780	0.48	13.750	0.26
R = 20	11.196	11.223	0.24	11.303	0.96
R = 30	10.660	10.667	0.07	10.788	1.20
R = 40	10.467	10.465	0.02	10.595	1.22

Table 3. First natural frequency of clamped shallow spherical shell with circular planform for various values of curvature

Frequency No	Analytic Kalnins [49]	D/BEM mesh-1	D/BEM mesh-2	SAP IV [48] mesh-3
1	31.648	32.129	32.050	31.920
2	60.940	57.111	57.206	65.415
3	99.975	106.118	102.928	110.560
4	112.627	129.519	116.021	113.569
5	144.873	152.537	148.476	155.816
6	172.072	191.481	172.200	172.230

Table 4. First six natural frequencies of clamped shallow spherical shell with circular planform

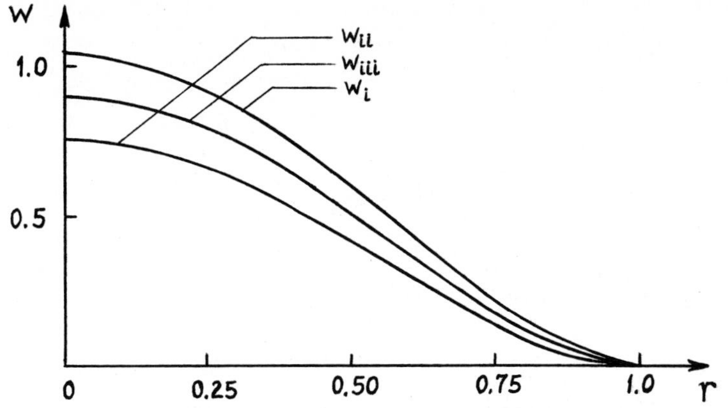

Fig. 5. Lateral deflection w along a radius of shallow shell fixed at its edge and uniformly loaded: (i) spherical; (ii) cylindrical; (iii) hypar

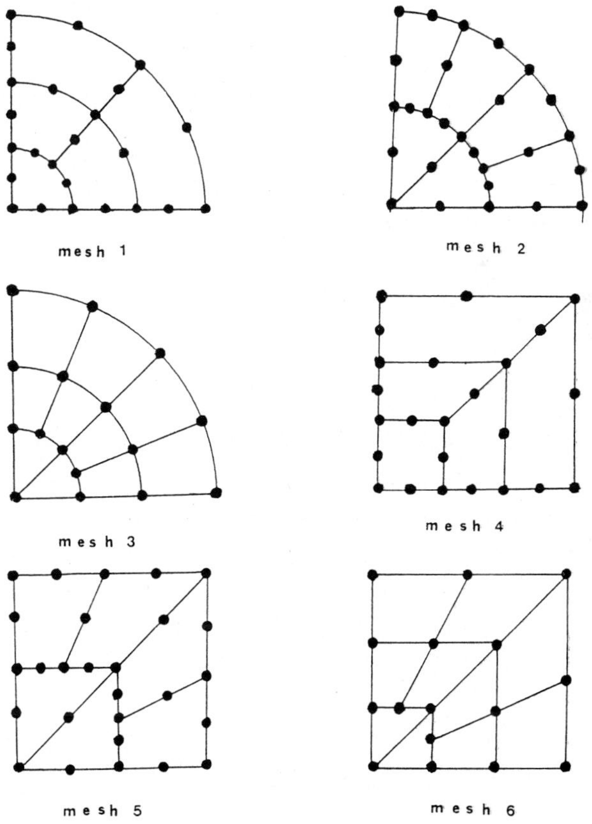

Fig. 6. Various meshes for circular and square shallow spherical shells

especially for small shell curvatures. Consider now a clamped shallow spherical cap with $\rho h = 0.01145$, $v = 0.30$, $k = 0.1$, $\lambda = 1.0$ and remaining properties as before, experiencing free vibrations. Table 4 shows the first six natural frequencies of this shell as computed in [32] by the D/BEM (mesh-1 and mesh-2) the SAP IV [48] (mesh-3) and the analytic approach of Kalnins [49]. The results show that D/BEM (especially with mesh-2) is, in general, more accurate and efficient than SAP IV especially for higher frequencies.

Example 5 [32]
Consider a clamped shallow shell with square projection on the (x,y) plane of side $a = 1.0$, and with $h = 0.05$, $E = 1000.0$, $v = 0.3$, $\rho h = 0.01145$, $k = 0.1$ and $\lambda = 1.0$ (spherical), which is subjected to a vertical concentrated impulsive force of magnitude $p_o = 1$ and duration $t_o = 0.1$ applied at its apex. Figure 7 shows the history of the vertical central deflection of the shell, as obtained in Providakis and Beskos [32] by D/BEM - Laplace transform with mesh-4 and mesh-5 (Fig. 6) as well as by SAP IV [48] with mesh-6 (Fig. 6). A comparison of the results of Fig. 7 reveals that one can achieve with the D/BEM about the same accuracy as with the FEM of SAP IV [48] while employing a smaller number of degrees of freedom.

Example 6 [32]
Consider the shallow spherical shell of Table 4 with $k = 0.05$, which is subjected to the same load as in the previous example. However, non-zero damping is assumed in this example. Figure 8 portrays the history of the vertical central deflection of the shell for various values of the external viscous damping coefffcient c, as obtained in [32] by the D/BEM - mesh 2 in conjunction with Laplace transform. The response reduction for increasing damping is apparent.

Example 7 [14]
Consider a shallow spherical shell with a circular projection of radius $r_o = 5.0$ with $E = 1000.0$, $v = 0.25$, $h = 10$ and $R = 100.0$. The shell is loosely clamped at its edge (Eq. $(30)_2$) and is subjected to a vertical, concentrated, transient load at

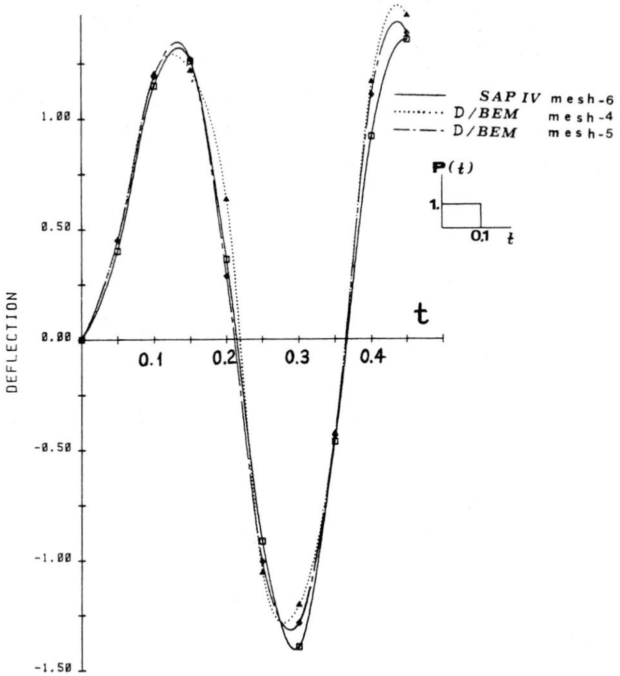

Fig. 7. History of vertical central deflection of clamped, square shallow spherical shell subjected to a vertical impulsive force at its crown

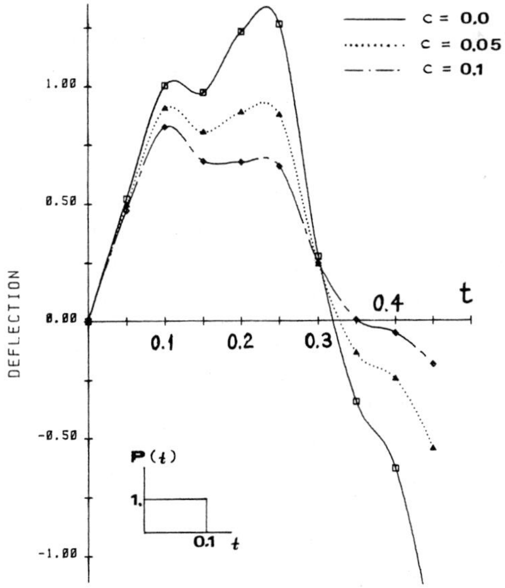

Fig. 8. History of vertical central deflection of clamped circular shallow spherical shell subjected to a vertical impulsive force at its crown for various values of external viscous damping coefficient c

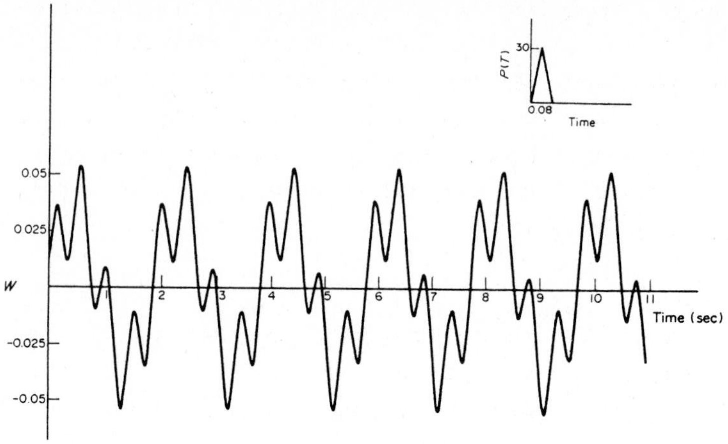

Fig. 9. Time variation of crown deflection due to a concentrated pulse at the crown for a clamped shallow spherical shell with a circular projection

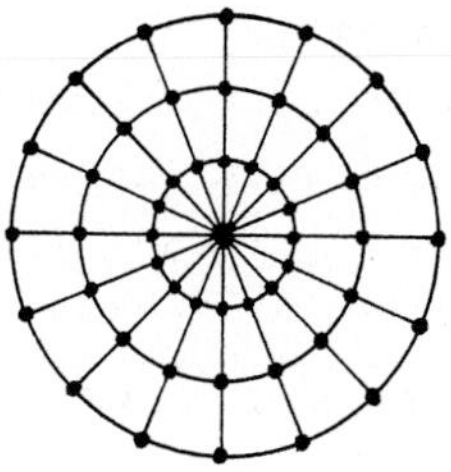

Fig. 10. Discretization mesh for the shell of Example 7

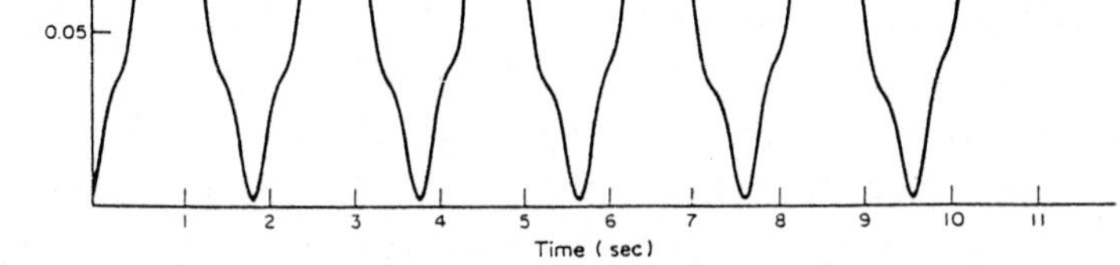

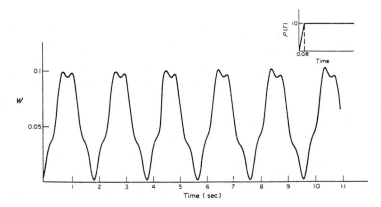

Fig. 11. Time variation of crown deflection due to a concentrated force P(t) at the crown for a clamped shallow spherical shell with a circular projection

its crown. Figures 9 and 11 show the time variation of vertical crown deflection for two different kinds of transient load as computed in Zhang and Atluri [14] by the time domain D/BEM in conjunction with a discretization involving linear boundary elements and bilinear quadrilateral interior elements. Fig. 10 shows the discretization mesh, which involves 99 interior degrees of freedom.

Conclusions

As a result of the preceding developments, the following concluding remarks can be made:

1. Two general direct boundary element methodologies for static analysis of homogeneous, isotropic and linearly elastic, thin, shallow shells of arbitrary planform and boundary conditions have been presented. These are the BEM employing the shallow shell fundamental solution in the context of a displacement or lateral displacement - membrane stress function formulation and the D/BEM employing the fundamental solution of a flat plate in bending and stretching. In addition, the D/BEM employing the static fundamental solution of a flat plate in bending and stretching as applied to free and forced vibration problems of shallow shells has also been presented. Forced vibrations are treated either in the time domain with the aid of a time marching scheme or in the complex frequency domain with the aid of the Laplace transform.
2. For static analysis BEM essentially requires only a discretization of the perimeter of the shallow shell, while in D/BEM both the perimeter and the interior domain have to be discretized. However, the high complexity of the shallow shell fundamental solution renders this method inefficient and only for the special cases of spherical or cylindrical shells with simpler fundamental solutions BEM may be useful. D/BEM is more efficient in spite of the increased discretization because of the simplity of the plate fundamental solution employed. D/BEM is also an efficient method for dynamic analysis of shallow shells.
3. The D/BEM appears to be similar to the Galerkin FEM in its final form. However, it does not require the trial

functions for displacements to be C^1 continuous, as it is the case with FEM, it is much simpler than the FEM and provides results of comparable accuracy with a discretization involving a much smaller number of degrees of freedom.

4. The use of Laplace transform in forced vibration analysis by the D/BEM reduces the problem to a static-like form with obvious advantages in formulation and computer implementation over the time domain approach. In addition, it permits an easier treatment of internal viscoelastic damping than do time domain formulations. However, time domain approaches in the D/BEM framework are more efficient and in addition they can be easily extended to nonlinear problems, while Laplace transformed techniques are restricted to linear problems.

Acknowledgements

The author is grateful to his former student Dr. C.P. Providakis for helpful discussions and technical assistance. Many thanks are also due to Mrs. H. Alexandridis-Balis for her excellent typing of this chapter.

References

1. Beskos, D.E.: Boundary element methods in dynamic analysis. Appl. Mech. Rev. 40 (1987) 1-23.

2. Beskos, D.E.: Dynamic analysis of beams, plates and shells, in: Boundary element methods in structural analysis. D.E. Beskos (ed.). New York: ASCE 1989. pp. 139-161.

3. Beskos, D.E. : Dynamic analysis of plates and shallow shells by the D/BEM, in: Advances in the theory of plates and shells. G.Z. Voyiadjis and D. Karamanlidis (eds). Amsterdam: Elsevier Science 1990. pp. 177-196.

4. Stern, M.: Static analysis of beams, plates and shells, in: Boundary element methods in structural analysis. D.E. Beskos (ed.). New York: ASCE 1989. pp. 41-64.

5. Manolis, G.D.; Beskos, D.E.: Boundary element methods in elastodynamics. London: Unwin Hyman 1988.

6. Simmonds, J.; Bradley, M.: The fundamental solution for a shallow shell with an arbitrary quadratic midsurface. J. Appl. Mech. 43 (1976) 286-290.

7. Matsui, T.; Matsuoka, O.: The fundamental solution in the theory of shallow shells. Int. J. Solids Struct. 14 (1978) 971-986.

8. Newton, D.A.; Tottenham, H.: Boundary value problems in thin shallow shells of arbitrary plan form. J. Engng. Math. 2 (1968) 211-223.

9. Tottenham, H.: The boundary element method for plates and shells, in: Developments in boundary element methods - 1, P.K. Banerjee and R. Butterfield (eds). London: Applied Science 1979. pp. 173-205.

10. Tosaka, N. ; Miyake, S. : A boundary integral equation formulation for elastic shallow shell bending problems, in: Boundary elements. C.A. Brebbia, T. Futagami and M. Tanaka (eds). Berlin: Springer-Verelag 1983. pp. 527-538.

11. Gospodinov, G.: The boundary element method applied to shallow spherical shells, in: Boundary elements VI. C.A. Brebbia (ed.). Berlin: Springer-Verlag 1984. pp. 3.65-3.77.

12. Lu, X.; Yao, Z.; Du, Q.: A boundary element method for the analysis of shallow spherical shells, in: Theory and applications of boundary element methods. M. Tanaka and Q. Du (eds). Oxford: Pergamon Press 1987. pp. 233-239.

13. Forbes, D.J.; Robinson, A.R.: Numerical analysis of elastic plates and shallow shells by an integral equation method. Structural research series report No 345. Urbana: University of Illinois 1969.

14. Zhang, J.D.; Atluri, S.N.: A boundary/interior element method for quasi-static and transient response analyses of shallow shells. Comput. Struct. 24 (1986) 213-223.

15. Zhang, J.D.; Atluri, S.N.: Nonlinear quasi-static and transient response analysis of shallow shells: formulations and interior/boundary element algorithms, in: Recent applications in computational mechanics. D.L. Karabalis (ed.) New York: ASCE 1986. pp. 43-65.

16. Wang, Y.C.; Ye, J.Q.; Wang, Z.H.: Spline boundary element method for shallow thin shells, in: Boundary elements. Q. Du (ed.). Oxford: Pergamon Press 1986. pp. 375-382.

17. Ye, J.Q.: A new approach for the bending problem of shallow shell by the boundary element method. Appl. Math. Modelling 12 (1988) 467-470.

18. Antes, H.: On boundary integral equations for circular cylindrical shells, in: Boundary element methods. C.A. Brebbia (ed.). Berlin: Springer-Verlag 1981. pp. 224-238.

19. Tepavitcharov, A.D.: Fundamental solutions and boundary integral equations in the bending theory of shallow spherical shells, in: Boundary elements VII. C.A. Brebbia and G. Maier (eds). Berlin: Springer-Verlag 1985. pp. 4.53-4.62.

20. Hadjikov, L.M.; Marginov, S.; Bekyarova, P.T.: Cubic spline boundary element method for circular cylindrical shells, in: Boundary elements VII. C.A. Brebbia and G. Maier (eds). Berlin: Springer-Verlag 1985. pp. 4.93-4.102.

21. Peng, X.L.; He, G.Q.: Computation of fundamental solutions of the boundary element method for shallow shells. Appl. Math. Modelling 10 (1986) 185-189.

22. Lei, X.Y.; Huang, M.K.: Boundary element method for shallow spherical shell bending problems involving shear deformation, in: Boundary elements IX, Vol. 2: stress analysis applications. C.A. Brebbia, W.L. Wendland and G. Kuhn (eds). Berlin: Springer-Verlag 1987. pp. 69-79.

23. Miyake, S. ; Yamazaki, H.; Yokayama, K.; Tosaka, N.: Boundary element analysis of shallow spherical shell bending problems describing with displacement vector components, in: Advances in boundary elements, vol. 3: stress analysis. C.A. Brebbia and J.J. Connor (eds). Berlin: Springer-Verlag 1989. pp. 303-315.

24. Fu, K.C. ; Harb, A.I.: Integral equation method for spherical shell under axisymmetric loads. J. Engng. Mech. ASCE. 116 (1990) 309-323.

25. Harb, A.I. ; Fu, K.C.: Analysis and optimal design of spherical shells under axisymmetric loads. J. Engng. Mech. ASCE 116 (1990) 324-342.

26. Tepavitcharov, A.; Gospodinov, G.: The boundary integral equation method applied to shallow membrane shells of positive Gaussian curvature. Appl. Math. Modelling 8 (1984) 179-187.

27. Simos, N.; Sadegh, A.M.: An indirect boundary integral equation for spherical shells, in: Betech 86. J.J. Connor and C.A. Brebbia (eds). Southampton: Computational Mechanics Publication 1986. pp. 539-553.

28. Mukherjee, S.; Poddar, B.: An integral equation formulation for elastic and inelastic shell analysis, in: Boundary elements. Q.Du (ed.). Oxford: Pergamon Press 1986. pp. 353-366.

29. Poddar, B.; Mukherjee, S.: An integral equation analysis of inelastic shells. Comput. Mech. 4 (1989) 261-275.

30. Providakis, C.P.; Beskos, D.E.: Forced vibrations of plates and shells by boundary - interior elements, in: Boundary elements IX, vol. 2: stress analysis applications. C.A. Brebbia, W.L. Wendland and G. Kuhn (eds). Berlin: Springer-Verlag 1987. pp. 97-109.

31. Providakis, C.P.; Beskos, D.E.: Dynamic analysis of shallow shells by boundary and interior elements, in: Proceedings of 12th Canadian congress of applied mechanics, vol. 1.

M.A. Erki and J. Kirkhope (eds). Ottawa: Carleton University 1989. pp. 190-191.

32. Providakis, C.P.; Beskos, D.E.: Free and forced vibrations of shallow shells by boundary and interior elements. Comp. Meth. Appl. Mech. Engng. to appear.

33. Conway, H.D.; Leissa, A.W.: Application of the point matching method to shallow spherical shell theory. J. App. Mech. 29 (1962) 745-747.

34. Nash, W.A.; Tai, I.H.; O'Callaghan, M.J.A.; Quinlan, P.M.: Statics and dynamics of elastic bodies - a new approach, in: Proceedings of international symposium on innovative numerical analysis in applied engineering science, Versailles, France. T.A. Cruse et al (eds). Senlis: CETIM 1977. pp. 8.3-8.8

35. Vlasov, V.Z.: General theory of shells and its applications in engineering. English translation NASA TT F-99, 1964 of original Russian, 1949.

36. Reissner, E.: Stresses and small displacements analysis of shallow shells - II. J. Math. Phys. 25 (1946) 279-300.

37. Møllmann, H.: Introduction to the theory of thin shells. Chichester: John Wiley & Sons 1981.

38. Abramowitz, M.; Stegun, I.S.; eds: Handbook of mathematical functions. New York: Dover 1972.

39. Chaudonneret, M.: On the discontinuity of the stress vector in the boundary integral equation method for elastic analysis, in: Recent advances in boundary element methods. C.A. Brebbia (ed.) London: Pentech Press 1978. pp. 185-194.

40. Howell, G.C.; Doyle, W.S.: An assessment of the boundary integral equation method for in-plane elastostatic problems. Appl. Math. Modelling 6 (1982) 245-256.

41. Smith, B.T.; Boyle, J.M.; Dongarra, J.J.; Garbow, B.S.; Ikebe, Y.; Klema, V.C.; Moler, C.B.: Matrix eigen-system routines - EISPACK guide. Berlin: Springer-Verlag 1976.

42. Durbin, F.: Numerical inversion of Laplace transform: an efficient improvement to Dubner and Abate's method. Computer J. 17 (1974) 371-376.

43. Narayanan, G.V.; Beskos, D.E.: Numerical operational methods for time dependent linear problems. Int. J. Num. Meth. Engng. 18 (1982) 1829-1854.

44. Pan, H.H.: Vibrations of viscoelastic plates. J. Mecan. 5 (1966) 355-374.

45. Tsuboi, Y.: Shell structures (in Japanese)., Tokyo: Maruzen 1965.

46. Wan, F.Y.M.: Membrane and bending stresses in shallow spherical shells. Techn. Rept. 317. Lincoln Laboratory. Cambridge: Massachusetts Institute of Technology 1964.

47. Reissner, E. : On axisymmetrical vibrations of shallow spherical shells. Q. Appl. Math. 13 (1955) 279-290.

48. Bathe, K.J.; Wilson, E.L.; Paterson, F.E.: SAP IV, a structural analysis program for static and dynamic response of linear systems. Rept. No EERC 73-11. Berkeley: University of California 1973.

49. Kalnins, A. : Free nonsymmetric vibrations of shallow spherical shells, in: Proceedings of 4th U.S. national congress on applied mechanics. New York: ASME 1963. pp. 225-233.

Large Deformation Analysis of Plates and Shells

S. N. ATLURI and D. S. PIPKINS

Center for Computational Mechanics
Georgia Tech, Atlanta, GA 30332-0356, USA

Summary

The Field/Boundary Element method is used to solve problems involving static and dynamic analysis of thin elastic plates and shallow shells undergoing finite delections. The method is developed through the use of the weak form of the appropriate governing differential equations and boundary conditions. The resulting equations are then linearized and incremental solution strategies are discussed. In the case of problems involving limit points, a procedure which is a variation of an arc-length method is described. Numerical results of both plate and shallow shell problems are given to demonstrate the computational efficiency of the method.

Introduction

This chapter deals with the Field/Boundary Element formulation for the static and dynamic analysis of thin elastic plates and shallow shells undergoing finite deflections. The term *Field* refers to the fact that, in contrast to usual BEM formulations, the equations derived for the non-linear plate and shell problems involve not only boundary integrals but also domain integrals. The reason for the appearance of the domain integrals is the non-existence of a fundamental solution to the governing differential equations of the non-linear problem. Thus, the usual reduction in dimensionality, as is the case for linear problems for which the fundamental solution is known, is lost in the non-linear case.

However, for some structural mechanics problems, the Field/Boundary Element method posseses certain benefits over other numerical schemes such as the Finite Element Method, despite the appearance of the domain integrals. In particular, the Finite Element formulation of plate and shell problems is plagued by the requirement of C^1 continuity of the trial functions for transverse displacements in and across each element. Extensive research aimed at the development of C^0 elements for the plate and shell problem has met with difficulties from spurious zero energy modes[1]. In contrast, the Field/Boundary Element formulation of the plate and shell problem is free of such continuity requirements.

The majority of work dealing with the large deflection analysis of plates using integral equations was done in the 1980's. In 1982, Tanaka[2] presented a formulation utilizing a stress function to solve the von Karman equations, which govern the plate problem. About the same time Kamiya and Sawaki published two papers on integral equation solutions of finite deflection plate problems, one utilizing Berger's equation[3], and the other von Karman's equations[4]. The formulation in [4] did not utilize a stress function but was in terms of the primary displacements, in-plane and transverse. In [5] Ye and Liu also present an integral equation formulation of von Karman's equations in terms of primary displacement variables. O'Donoghue[6] gives results which include dynamic effects and implements control theory within the framework of the Field/Boundary Element method. Parralleling this development of finite deflection formulations for plates was that of shallow shells. Zhang and Atluri [20], [34] combined a Field/Boundary Element formulation with an arc-length algorithm to perform a post-buckling analysis. Tosaka and Miyake also presented works in this area[7]-[9] which traced the equilibrium paths of the shallow shells through and beyond their limit points. Zhang and Atluri considered dynamic effects in the shallow shell problem in[10] and [34], and along with O'Donoghue looked at applications of control theory[11]. Other contributions in the large deflection analysis of plates and shallow shells utilizing Boundary Elements are in references[12]-[29].

Governing Equations

The formulation of the Field/Boundary Element method for the shallow shell problem will be based on Reissner's shallow shell theory[30]. By letting the curvature terms go to zero in this shallow shell theory, the von Karman equations for large deflection of thin flat plates are obtained. For this reason, and in the interest of conciseness, the Field/Boundary Element representation of the von Karman plate theory will not be derived explicitly, but will be treated as a special case of the shallow shell problem.

Consider a shallow shell, as in figure 1, of constant thickness, h, whose mid-surface is described by $z = z(x_1, x_2)$, where x_1 and x_2 are cartesian coordinates. The projection of the shell mid-surface on the x_1-x_2 plane is labeled Ω and it's boundary, which is piecewise smooth, is called Γ. The equations which govern the finite deflection of a shallow shell of this type may be written as:

$$N_{\alpha\beta,\beta} + b_\alpha - \rho\ddot{u}_\alpha = 0 \tag{1}$$

$$D\nabla^4 w + \frac{N_{\alpha\beta}}{R_{\alpha\beta}} - (b_3 - \rho\ddot{w}) = f_3 + (N_{\alpha\beta} w_{,\beta})_{,\alpha} \tag{2}$$

where w is the transverse deflection of the shell mid-surface, $N_{\alpha\beta}$ are the in-plane stress resultants, u_α the in-plane displacement components, b_α the body forces and f_3 is the load normal to the shell midsurface. The terms $R_{\alpha\beta}$ represent the radii of curvature of the undeformed shell and are defined such that:

$$R_{\alpha\beta} = \frac{-1}{z_{,\alpha\beta}} \tag{3}$$

The material parameters are; the distributed mass, ρ, the bending rigidity, D, which can be expressed in terms of Young's Modulus, E, and Poisson's Ratio, ν; as in classical plate theory. In the above equations, and throughout this chapter, the commas represent differentiation with respect to position and superposed dots represent temporal differentiation.

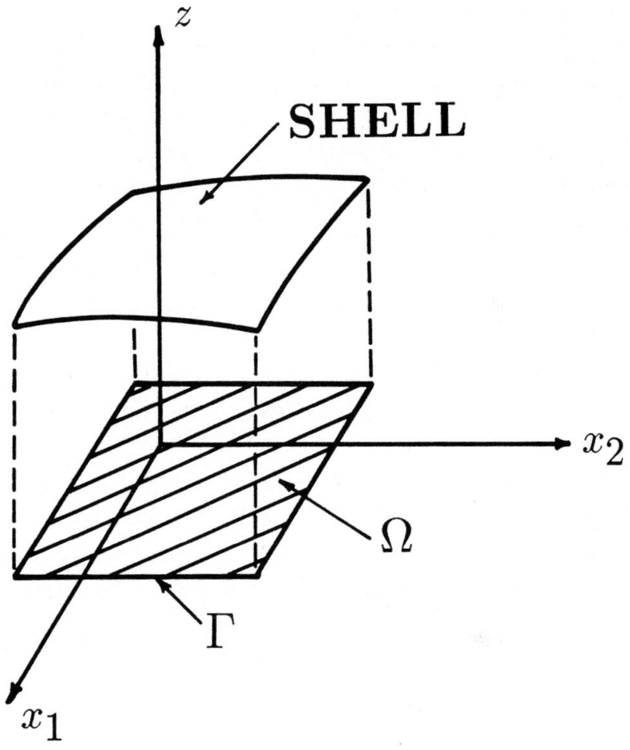

Fig. 1. Shell geometry

It is often acceptable to ignore the in-plane inertia term of equation (1). If this is the case, a stress function, Ψ, can be introduced for the in-plane stress resultants, $N_{\alpha\beta}$, such that:

$$N_{xx} = \Psi_{,yy} \tag{4}$$

$$N_{yy} = \Psi_{,xx} \tag{5}$$

$$N_{xy} = -\Psi_{,xy} \tag{6}$$

The equations governing the deformation of the shallow shell can then be written[9]:

$$\frac{1}{Eh}\nabla^4\Psi = -w_{,xx}w_{,yy} + (w_{,xy})^2 + \frac{1}{R}\nabla^2 w \tag{7}$$

$$D\nabla^4 w = w_{,xx}\Psi_{,yy} - 2w_{,xy}\Psi_{,xy} + w_{,yy}\Psi_{,xx} - \frac{1}{R}\nabla^2\Psi + f_3 - \rho\ddot{w} \tag{8}$$

Here, for simplicity, the body forces have been neglected and the shell is assumed to be a spherical cap of radius R. By using the stress function, the two in-plane equilibrium equations represented by equation (1) are reduced to a single equation of fourth order. Also, it should be noted that equations (7) and (8) are of similar form. However, the use of the stress function causes considerable difficulty in the implementation of the in-plane displacement boundary conditions. For this reason, equations (1) and (2) will be used to formulate the Field/Boundary Element method for the shallow shell. For formulations using the stress function, see references [2] and [9].

It remains to give the boundary conditions for the present problem. The correct interpretation of these boundary conditions is essential in correctly formulating the integral equations for the shallow shell problem. On the boundary, Γ, the in-plane boundary conditions are:

$$u_\alpha = \overline{u}_\alpha \qquad \text{on } \Gamma_u \tag{9}$$

$$N_{\alpha\beta}n_\beta = \overline{P}_\alpha \qquad \text{on } \Gamma_t \tag{10}$$

where n_β are the direction cosines of the unit outward normal to the boundary, Γ, and the quantities with an overbar are prescribed displacements, $\overline{u}_\alpha$, and tractions, $\overline{P}_\alpha$. The out of plane boundary conditions are:

$$w = \overline{w}\ , \quad \Psi_n = \overline{\Psi}_n\ , \quad \Psi_s = \overline{\Psi}_s \qquad \text{on } \Gamma_u \tag{11}$$

$$Q_n = \overline{Q}_n\ , \quad M_n = \overline{M}_n\ , \quad M_s = \overline{M}_s \qquad \text{on } \Gamma_t \tag{12}$$

where the symbols with an overbar again represent prescribed quantities. In equations (11) and (12) the subscript n refers to the normal to the boundary and s the tangent. The variables Ψ_n and Ψ_s represent rotations about the tangent, s, and normal, n, respectively. The moments corresponding to these rotations are M_n and M_s. The quantity Q_n represents the transverse shear. The relationships between the primary displacements(u_α, w) and the boundary variables introduced in equations (10)-(12) are:

$$N_{11} = C(u_{1,1} + \nu u_{2,2}) + C(\frac{1}{R_{11}} + \frac{\nu}{R_{22}})w + \frac{C}{2}[(w_{,1})^2 + \nu(w_{,2})^2] \tag{13}$$

$$N_{22} = C(u_{2,2} + \nu u_{1,1}) + C(\frac{1}{R_{22}} + \frac{\nu}{R_{11}})w + \frac{C}{2}[(w_{,2})^2 + \nu(w_{,1})^2] \tag{14}$$

$$N_{12} = \frac{C}{2}(1-\nu)(u_{1,2} + u_{2,1}) + C(\frac{1-\nu}{R_{12}})w + \frac{C}{2}(1-\nu)w_{,1}w_{,2} \tag{15}$$

$$\Psi_n = w_{,n} \tag{16}$$

$$\Psi_s = w_{,s} \tag{17}$$

$$Q_n = -D(\nabla^2 w)_{,n} + N_{1n}w_{,1} + N_{2n}w_{,2} \tag{18}$$

$$M_n = -D[(n_1^2 + \nu n_2^2)w_{,11} + 2(1-\nu)n_1n_2w_{,12} + (n_2^2 + \nu n_1^2)w_{,22}] \tag{19}$$

$$M_s = D[(n_1n_2 - \nu n_1n_2)(w_{,11} - w_{,22}) - (n_1^2 - n_2^2)(1-\nu)w_{,12}] \tag{20}$$

where $C = \frac{Eh}{1-\nu^2}$ and in equation (18), $N_{1n} = N_{11}n_1 + N_{12}n_2$ and $N_{2n} = N_{12}n_1 + N_{22}n_2$. Finally, the initial conditions for the problem are specified by:

$$u_\alpha(x_\beta, 0) = u_{\alpha 0}(x_\beta) \qquad \text{at } t = 0 \tag{21}$$

$$\dot{u}_\alpha(x_\beta, 0) = \dot{u}_{\alpha 0}(x_\beta) \qquad \text{at } t = 0 \tag{22}$$

$$w(x_\beta, 0) = w_0(x_\beta)\,, \qquad \dot{w}(x_\beta, 0) = \dot{w}_0(x_\beta) \qquad \text{at } t = 0 \tag{23}$$

with $(\,\cdot\,)_0$ representing prescribed initial conditions.

Integral Equation Formulation

In classical BEM formulations the Betti reciprocal theorem was the starting point in the formulation. This theorem is limited to linear elasticity, however particular forms of the reciprocal work theorem may be used in non-linear problems[31]. As BEM theory has developed it has been recognized that the problem formulation can be accomplished using a weighted residual scheme with a special test function, which is the method used in [6] and [10] and will be used here. The special test function is usually the fundamental or singular solution of the problem under consideration. However, as has been noted, the fundamental solution for the non-linear plate and shallow shell problem is not known. In this situation a fundamental solution which satisfies the highest order differential operator appearing in the governing equations, is the usual choice for the test function.

First, the integral equations for the in-plane equilibrium equations (1) will be derived. The weighted residual statement of equation (1) and associated boundary conditions (9,10) is:

$$\int_{\Omega}(N_{\alpha\beta,\beta}+b_\alpha-\rho\ddot{u}_\alpha)u^\star_\alpha d\Omega=\int_{\Gamma_t}(P_\alpha-\overline{P}_\alpha)u^\star_\alpha d\Gamma+\int_{\Gamma_u}(\overline{u}_\alpha-u_\alpha)P^\star_\alpha d\Gamma \tag{24}$$

For convenience, the in-plane stress resultants are broken up into linear, curvature-dependent and non-linear parts:

$$N_{\alpha\beta}=N^l_{\alpha\beta}+C\kappa_{\alpha\beta}w+N^{(n)}_{\alpha\beta} \tag{25}$$

where

$$N^l_{11}=C(u_{1,1}+\nu u_{2,2})\,,\quad N^l_{22}=C(u_{2,2}+\nu u_{1,1})\,,\quad N^l_{12}=\frac{C}{2}(1-\nu)(u_{1,2}+u_{2,1}) \tag{26}$$

$$\kappa_{11}=\frac{1}{R_{11}}+\frac{\nu}{R_{22}}\,,\quad \kappa_{22}=\frac{1}{R_{22}}+\frac{\nu}{R_{11}}\,,\quad \kappa_{12}=\frac{1-\nu}{R_{12}} \tag{27}$$

$$N^{(n)}_{11}=\frac{C}{2}[(w_{,1})^2+\nu(w_{,2})^2]\,,\quad N^{(n)}_{22}=\frac{C}{2}[(w_{,2})^2+\nu(w_{,1})^2]\,,\quad N^{(n)}_{12}=\frac{C}{2}(1-\nu)w_{,1}w_{,2} \tag{28}$$

The insertion of this decomposition of the in-plane stress resultants into equation (24) and the application of the divergence theorem results in:

$$\begin{aligned}&\int_{\Gamma}N^l_{\alpha\beta}n_\beta u^\star_\alpha d\Gamma-\int_{\Omega}N^l_{\alpha\beta}u^\star_{\alpha,\beta}d\Omega+\int_{\Omega}C(\kappa_{\alpha\beta}w)_{,\beta}u^\star_\alpha d\Omega+\int_{\Omega}N^{(n)}_{\alpha\beta,\beta}u^\star_\alpha d\Omega\\&+\int_{\Omega}(b_\alpha-\rho\ddot{u}_\alpha)u^\star_\alpha d\Omega=\int_{\Gamma_t}(P_\alpha-\overline{P}_\alpha)u^\star_\alpha d\Gamma+\int_{\Gamma_u}(\overline{u}_\alpha-u_\alpha)P^\star_\alpha d\Gamma\end{aligned} \tag{29}$$

Since the material is linear elastic and isotropic, we have:

$$N^l_{\alpha\beta}u^\star_{\alpha,\beta}=N^\star_{\alpha\beta}u_{\alpha,\beta} \tag{30}$$

where the definition of $N^\star_{\alpha\beta}$ is apparent. Using the relation (30) in equation (29) and once again applying the divergence theorem, the following is obtained:

$$\begin{aligned}&\int_{\Omega}N^\star_{\alpha\beta,\beta}u_\alpha d\Omega-\int_{\Omega}C(\kappa_{\alpha\beta}w)u^\star_{\alpha,\beta}d\Omega-\int_{\Omega}N^{(n)}_{\alpha\beta}u^\star_{\alpha,\beta}d\Omega\\&+\int_{\Omega}(b_\alpha-\rho\ddot{u}_\alpha)u^\star_\alpha d\Omega+\int_{\Gamma}\hat{P}_\alpha u^\star_\alpha d\Gamma-\int_{\Gamma}\hat{u}_\alpha P^\star_\alpha d\Gamma=0\end{aligned} \tag{31}$$

where $\hat{P}_\alpha=\overline{P}_\alpha$ on Γ_t and $\hat{P}_\alpha=P_\alpha$ on Γ_u;

and $\hat{u}_\alpha=\overline{u}_\alpha$ on Γ_u and $\hat{u}_\alpha=u_\alpha$ on Γ_t.

The fundamental solution to be used is the one obtained from solving the infinite domain plane stress problem:

$$N^{\star}_{\alpha\beta,\beta} + \delta(x_\mu - \xi_\mu)\delta_{\alpha\theta}e_\theta = 0 \tag{32}$$

where $\delta(x_\mu - \xi_\mu)$ is the Dirac delta function, $\delta_{\alpha\theta}$ is the Kronecker delta and e_θ denotes that the direction of the application of the point load is along the x_θ direction. The solution of (32) will be denoted as $u^{\star}_{(\theta)\alpha}$. Physically, $u^{\star}_{(\theta)\alpha}$ is the displacement along the x_α direction in a plane infinite body at x_μ, due to a unit load in the x_θ direction applied at ξ_μ. This fundamental solution can be written[10]:

$$u^{\star}_{(\theta)\alpha}(x_\mu, \xi_\mu) = \frac{-1}{8\pi G}[(3-\nu)\ln r\delta_{\theta\alpha} - (1+\nu)r_{,\theta}r_{,\alpha}] \tag{33}$$

where $G = \frac{E}{2(1+\nu)}$. The traction, $P^{\star}_{(\theta)\alpha}$, corresponding to $u^{\star}_{(\theta)\alpha}$ is written using equation (10) and recalling that $N^{\star}_{(\theta)\alpha\beta}$ is defined by equation (30).

$$P^{\star}_{(\theta)\alpha}(x_\mu, \xi_\mu) = \frac{-h}{4\pi r}[(1-\nu)(n_\theta r_{,\alpha} - n_\alpha r_{,\theta}) + \{(1-\nu)\delta_{\theta\alpha} + 2(1+\nu)r_{,\theta}r_{,\alpha}\}r_{,\beta}n_\beta] \tag{34}$$

Here, $r = |x_\mu - \xi_\mu|$ is the distance between the load point ξ_μ and field point x_μ. Now, by using the properties of the Dirac delta function, the following result is attained:

$$\int_\Omega N^{\star}_{\alpha\beta,\beta}u_\alpha d\Omega = -\int_\Omega \delta(x_\mu - \xi_\mu)\delta_{\alpha\theta}e_\theta u_\alpha d\Omega = -u_\theta(\xi_\mu) \tag{35}$$

This result is only valid for ξ_μ located in the domain, Ω. If ξ_μ is on the boundary, special considerations are necessary due to the singular nature of the boundary integrals[33]. Thus, using (35) in (31) if $\xi_\mu \in \Omega$, or the results given in [33] if $\xi_\mu \in \Gamma$, the following integral equations for the in-plane displacements are established:

$$\begin{aligned} \gamma_{\theta j}u_j(\xi_\mu) = &-\int_\Omega C(\kappa_{\alpha\beta}w)u^{\star}_{(\theta)\alpha,\beta}d\Omega - \int_\Omega N^{(n)}_{\alpha\beta}u^{\star}_{(\theta)\alpha,\beta}d\Omega \\ &+\int_\Omega (b_\alpha - \rho\ddot{u}_\alpha)u^{\star}_{(\theta)\alpha}d\Omega + \int_\Gamma \hat{P}_\alpha u^{\star}_{(\theta)\alpha}d\Gamma - \int_\Gamma \hat{u}_\alpha P^{\star}_{(\theta)\alpha}d\Gamma \end{aligned} \tag{36}$$

where for $\xi_\mu \in \Omega$, $\gamma_{\theta j} = \delta_{\theta j}$ and for $\xi_\mu \in \Gamma$:

$$\gamma_{11} = \frac{1}{4\pi}[2\alpha\pi + (1+\nu)\frac{\sin(2\alpha\pi)}{2}] \tag{37}$$

$$\gamma_{22} = \frac{1}{4\pi}[2\alpha\pi - (1+\nu)\frac{\sin(2\alpha\pi)}{2}] \tag{38}$$

$$\gamma_{12} = \gamma_{21} = -\sin^2(\alpha\pi) \tag{39}$$

Here $\alpha\pi$ is the inner angle of the boundary curve at ξ_μ as shown in figure 2. Also, note that the boundary integrals in (36) are to be interpreted in a Cauchy Principal Value sense when $\xi_\mu \in \Gamma$. Equation (36) represents two equations for the in-plane displacements, u_α. Note the presence of the domain integral term due to the non-linearity in the problem. This appearance of the domain integral is the characteristic of the Field/Boundary Element method.

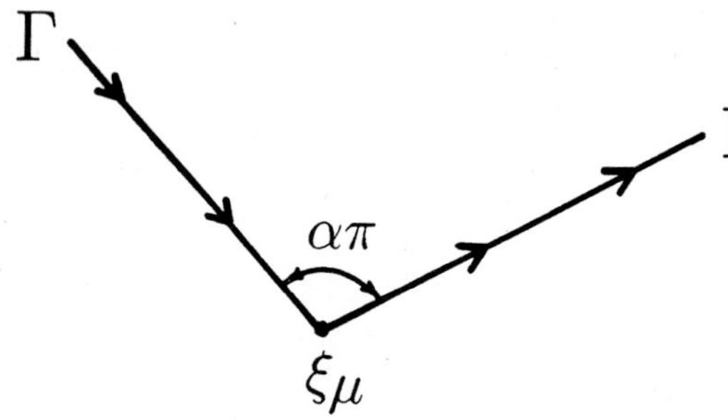

Fig. 2. Interior angle at a boundary node

The formulation of the boundary integral equations for the transverse displacement proceeds in a similar manner as that of the in-plane displacements. The first step being the writing of the weighted residual statement:

$$\begin{aligned}\int_\Omega (D\nabla^4 w + \frac{N_{\alpha\beta}}{R_{\alpha\beta}} - (b_3 - \rho\ddot{w}) - f_3 - (N_{\alpha\beta}w_{,\beta})_{,\alpha})w^\star d\Omega = \int_{\Gamma_u} (w - \overline{w})Q_n^\star d\Gamma \\ + \int_{\Gamma_u} (\overline{\Psi}_n - \Psi_n)M_n^\star d\Gamma + \int_{\Gamma_u} (\overline{\Psi}_s - \Psi_s)M_s^\star d\Gamma + \int_{\Gamma_t} (M_n - \overline{M}_n)\Psi_n^\star d\Gamma \\ + \int_{\Gamma_t} (M_s - \overline{M}_s)\Psi_s^\star d\Gamma + \int_{\Gamma_t} (\overline{Q}_n - Q_n)w^\star d\Gamma \qquad (40)\end{aligned}$$

where the definitions of $\Psi_n^\star$, $\Psi_s^\star$, $M_n^\star$ and $M_s^\star$ are identical to equations (16),(17),(19) and (20). However, $Q_n^\star$ is defined:

$$Q_n^\star = -D(\nabla^2 w^\star)_{,n} \qquad (41)$$

This difference in Q_n and $Q_n^\star$ arises because the fundamental solution, $w^\star$(for which a specific choice is made shortly), is for the linear plate bending problem in which the terms in equation (18) involving in-plane stress resultants are not retained.

Before proceeding, some explanation of the residual form of the boundary conditions as given by (40) is necessary. It is well known, that because of the Kirchhoff hypothesis in plate theory, a proper statement of the boundary conditions requires the introduction of a modified shear term, and at corners a jump term involving the twisting moment M_s. However, in the Boundary Element formulation it proves instructive to develop these Kirchhoff type boundary conditions by starting from the weighted residual statement given by (40).

By successive applications of the divergence theorem, the following transformations of domain integral terms of (40) can be found.

$$\int_\Omega D(\nabla^4 w)w^\star d\Omega = \int_\Omega D(\nabla^4 w^\star)w d\Omega + \int_\Gamma (M_n\Psi_n^\star + M_s\Psi_s^\star)d\Gamma - \int_\Gamma (\Psi_n M_n^\star + \Psi_s M_s^\star)d\Gamma$$
$$+ \int_\Gamma D[(\nabla^2 w)_{,n}]w^\star d\Gamma - \int_\Gamma D[(\nabla^2 w^\star)_{,n}]w d\Gamma \qquad (42)$$

$$\int_\Omega (N_{\alpha\beta}w_{,\beta})_{,\alpha} w^\star d\Omega = -\int_\Omega N_{\alpha\beta}w_{,\beta}w^\star_{,\alpha} d\Omega + \int_\Gamma N_{\alpha\beta}w_{,\beta}w^\star n_\alpha d\Gamma \qquad (43)$$

$$\int_\Omega \frac{N^l_{\alpha\beta}}{R_{\alpha\beta}} w^\star d\Omega = -\int_\Omega C u_\alpha(\kappa_{\alpha\beta}w^\star)_{,\beta} d\Omega + \int_\Gamma C\kappa_{\alpha\beta}u_\alpha n_\beta w^\star d\Gamma \qquad (44)$$

Using these transformations in (40) gives:

$$\int_\Omega D(\nabla^4 w^\star)w d\Omega + \int_\Omega N_{\alpha\beta}w_{,\beta}w^\star_{,\alpha} d\Omega - \int_\Omega C u_\alpha(\kappa_{\alpha\beta}w^\star)_{,\beta} d\Omega + \int_\Gamma C\kappa_{\alpha\beta}\hat{u}_\alpha n_\beta w^\star d\Gamma$$
$$+ \int_\Omega (C\frac{\kappa_{\alpha\beta}}{R_{\alpha\beta}}w)w^\star d\Omega + \int_\Omega \frac{N^{(n)}_{\alpha\beta}}{R_{\alpha\beta}} w^\star d\Omega - \int_\Omega (b_3 - \rho\ddot{w} + f_3)w^\star d\Omega = -\int_\Gamma \hat{w}Q_n^\star d\Gamma$$
$$+ \int_\Gamma \hat{\Psi}_n M_n^\star d\Gamma + \int_\Gamma \hat{\Psi}_s M_s^\star d\Gamma - \int_\Gamma \hat{M}_n\Psi_n^\star d\Gamma - \int_\Gamma \hat{M}_s\Psi_s^\star d\Gamma + \int_\Gamma \hat{Q}_n w^\star d\Gamma \qquad (45)$$

where ($\hat{}$) again implies a quantity is either prescribed or unknown on the boundary, $\Gamma = \Gamma_t \cup \Gamma_u$. Equation (45) needs to be modified slightly in order that a proper statement of the Kirchhoff type boundary conditions is made. Consider the terms:

$$\int_\Gamma M_s^\star \hat{\Psi}_s d\Gamma - \int_\Gamma \hat{M}_s \Psi_s^\star d\Gamma \qquad (46)$$

Integrating these two terms by parts and supposing, for illustration purposes, Γ to have two corners as shown in figure 3, gives:

$$-\int_\Gamma M^\star_{s,s}\hat{w} d\Gamma + \int_\Gamma \hat{M}_{s,s}w^\star d\Gamma + M_s^\star\hat{w}|_{1+}^{2-} + M_s^\star\hat{w}|_{2+}^{1-} - \hat{M}_s w^\star|_{1+}^{2-} - \hat{M}_s w^\star|_{2+}^{1-} \qquad (47)$$

or

$$-\int_\Gamma M^\star_{s,s}\hat{w} d\Gamma + \int_\Gamma \hat{M}_{s,s}w^\star d\Gamma - \sum_{i=1}^{k}\langle M_s^\star\rangle|_i\hat{w} + \sum_{i=1}^{k}\langle \hat{M}_s\rangle|_i w^\star \qquad (48)$$

where k is the number of corner points and as implied by (47), $\langle\cdot\rangle$ represents the jump in twisting moment across a corner. Using this manipulation of the boundary conditions, equation (45) becomes:

$$\int_\Omega D(\nabla^4 w^\star) w d\Omega + \int_\Omega N_{\alpha\beta} w_{,\beta} w^\star_{,\alpha} d\Omega - \int_\Omega C u_\alpha (\kappa_{\alpha\beta} w^\star)_{,\beta} d\Omega + \int_\Gamma C \kappa_{\alpha\beta} \hat{u}_\alpha n_\beta w^\star d\Gamma$$
$$+ \int_\Omega (C \frac{\kappa_{\alpha\beta}}{R_{\alpha\beta}} w) w^\star d\Omega + \int_\Omega \frac{N^{(n)}_{\alpha\beta}}{R_{\alpha\beta}} w^\star d\Omega - \int_\Omega (b_3 - \rho \ddot{w} + f_3) w^\star d\Omega = - \int_\Gamma \hat{w} V^\star_n d\Gamma$$
$$+ \int_\Gamma \hat{\Psi}_n M^\star_n d\Gamma - \int_\Gamma \hat{M}_n \Psi^\star_n d\Gamma + \int_\Gamma \hat{V}_n w^\star d\Gamma - \sum_{i=1}^{k} \langle M^\star_s \rangle |_i \hat{w} + \sum_{i=1}^{k} \langle \hat{M}_s \rangle |_i w^\star \quad (49)$$

where V_n and $V^\star_n$ are Kirchhoff or effective shear forces. It should be remembered that due to the non-linear nature of the present problem, V_n and $V^\star_n$ are defined differently.

$$V_n = -D(\nabla^2 w)_{,n} + M_{s,s} + N_{1n} w_{,1} + N_{2n} w_{,2} \quad (50)$$

$$V^\star_n = -D(\nabla^2 w^\star)_{,n} + M^\star_{s,s} \quad (51)$$

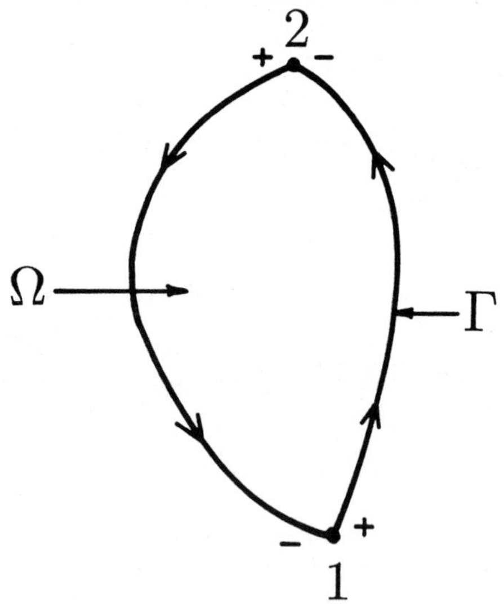

Fig. 3. Corner Points

The fundamental solution, $w^\star$, is taken as the solution of an infinite plate subjected to a unit point load. This problem is governed by the equation:

$$\nabla^4 w^\star = \delta(x_\mu - \xi_\mu) \quad (52)$$

whose solution is:

$$w^{\star}(x_{\mu}, \xi_{\mu}) = \frac{1}{8\pi} r^2 \ln r \tag{53}$$

Physically, $w^{\star}$, is the transverse deflection at x_{μ} due to a unit point load at ξ_{μ} which acts normal to the plate. Again, $r = |x_{\mu} - \xi_{\mu}|$ is the distance between the load point and field point. The expressions for $\Psi_n^{\star}$, $M_n^{\star}$, $M_s^{\star}$ and $V_n^{\star}$ are[32]:

$$\Psi_n^{\star} = \frac{1}{8\pi}(1 + 2\ln r) r \cos\beta \tag{54}$$

$$M_n^{\star} = -D[\frac{1+\nu}{4\pi}(1 + \ln r) + \frac{1-\nu}{8\pi}\cos 2\beta] \tag{55}$$

$$M_s^{\star} = D\frac{1-\nu}{8\pi}\sin 2\beta \tag{56}$$

$$V_n^{\star} = D[-\frac{\cos\beta}{4\pi r}\{2 + (1-\nu)\cos 2\beta\} + \frac{1-\nu}{4\pi R}\cos 2\beta] \tag{57}$$

where, as shown in figure 4, β is the angle from the radius direction, r, to the outward normal and R represents the radius of curvature of the boundary.

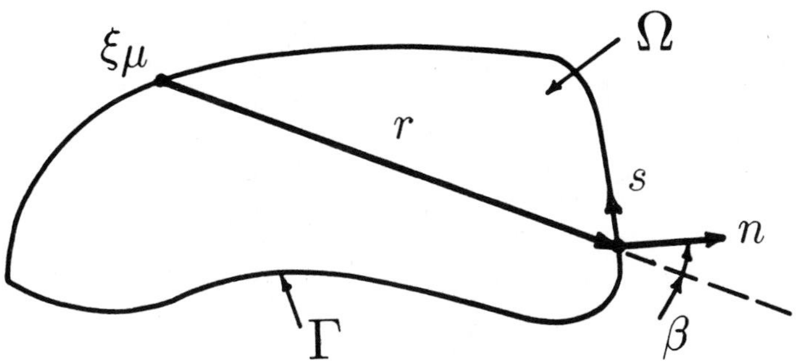

Fig. 4. The definition of the angle, β

Again, the properties of the Dirac delta function are used in the transformation:

$$\int_{\Omega} D(\nabla^4 w^{\star}) w d\Omega = \int_{\Omega} D[\delta(x_{\mu} - \xi_{\mu})] w d\Omega = D w(\xi_{\mu}) \tag{58}$$

This result is valid only for $\xi_{\mu} \in \Omega$. If $\xi_{\mu} \in \Gamma$ a derivation which is documented in [32] is necessary due to the discontinuous nature of the kernal functions. Considering $\xi_{\mu} \in \Gamma$, an integral expression for the transverse displacement is written as:

$$D\frac{\alpha}{2}w(\xi_\mu) = -\int_\Omega N_{\alpha\beta}w_{,\beta}w^\star_{,\alpha}d\Omega + \int_\Omega Cu_\alpha(\kappa_{\alpha\beta}w^\star)_{,\beta}d\Omega - \int_\Gamma C\kappa_{\alpha\beta}\hat{u}_\alpha n_\beta w^\star d\Gamma$$
$$-\int_\Omega(C\frac{\kappa_{\alpha\beta}}{R_{\alpha\beta}}w)w^\star d\Omega - \int_\Omega \frac{N^{(n)}_{\alpha\beta}}{R_{\alpha\beta}}w^\star d\Omega + \int_\Omega(b_3 - \rho\ddot{w} + f_3)w^\star d\Omega - \int_\Gamma \hat{w}V^\star_n d\Gamma$$
$$+\int_\Gamma \hat{\Psi}_n M^\star_n d\Gamma - \int_\Gamma \hat{M}_n \Psi^\star_n d\Gamma + \int_\Gamma \hat{V}_n w^\star d\Gamma - \sum_{i=1}^{k}\langle M^\star_s\rangle|_i\hat{w} + \sum_{i=1}^{k}\langle \hat{M}_s\rangle|_i w^\star \tag{59}$$

where $\alpha\pi$ is the inner angle on the boundary curve at ξ_μ as shown in figure 2. Further, the boundary integrals in (59) are interpreted in the Cauchy Principal Value sense. Also, it is to be noted that if ξ_μ is at a corner point, then the contribution of that corner to the summations in (59) is to be ignored. As expected, equation (59) contains domain integrals due to the problem non-linearities. In passing, it is noted that this Field/Boundary Element formulation is free of the C^1 continuity requirement inherent in the Finite Element Method.

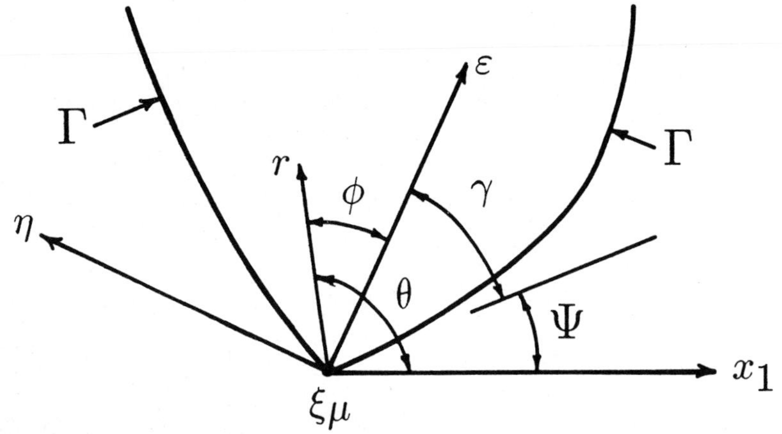

Fig. 5. The (ε, η) coordinate system

As for the linear plate bending problem, one equation at each boundary point is insufficient to solve a well posed problem. The second integral equation needed is formulated using a fundamental solution which is basically a directional derivative of $w^\star$ in a fixed direction ε that makes an angle $\psi+\gamma$ with the $x_1(\theta = 0)$ direction(see figure 5). A local ε-η coordinate system is introduced at ξ_μ and a new polar coordinate system (r, ϕ) with respect to the ε-η

coordinate system is formed(see figure 5). The appropriate fundamental solution denoted $w^{\star\star}$ is given by:

$$w^{\star\star} = \frac{1}{2\pi} r \ln r \cos\phi \tag{60}$$

The expressions for $\Psi_n^{\star\star}$, $M_n^{\star\star}$, $M_s^{\star\star}$ and $V_n^{\star\star}$ are:

$$\Psi_n^{\star\star} = \frac{1}{2\pi}[\cos\phi\cos\beta + \ln r\cos(\phi+\beta)] \tag{61}$$

$$M_n^{\star\star} = D[-\frac{(1+\nu)\cos\phi}{2\pi r} + \frac{(1-\nu)\sin\phi}{2\pi r}\sin 2\beta] \tag{62}$$

$$M_s^{\star\star} = D\frac{(1-\nu)\sin\phi}{2\pi r}\cos 2\beta \tag{63}$$

$$V_n^{\star\star} = \frac{D}{2\pi r^2}\{\cos(\beta-\phi)[2+(1-\nu)\cos 2\beta] + 2(1-\nu)\sin\phi\cos\beta\sin 2\beta\} \\ -D\frac{(1-\nu)}{\pi r R}\sin\phi\sin 2\beta \tag{64}$$

Using the procedure described in [32], a second independent integral equation is established for $\xi_\mu \in \Gamma$ and is given by:

$$\begin{aligned} D[\alpha_\varepsilon w_{,\varepsilon}|_{\xi_\mu} + \alpha_\eta w_{,\eta}|_{\xi_\mu}] = &-\int_\Omega N_{\alpha\beta} w_{,\beta} w_{,\alpha}^{\star\star} d\Omega + \int_\Omega C u_\alpha (\kappa_{\alpha\beta} w^{\star\star})_{,\beta} d\Omega \\ &- \int_\Gamma C\kappa_{\alpha\beta}\hat{u}_\alpha n_\beta w^{\star\star} d\Gamma - \int_\Omega (C\frac{\kappa_{\alpha\beta}}{R_{\alpha\beta}} w) w^{\star\star} d\Omega - \int_\Omega \frac{N_{\alpha\beta}^{(n)}}{R_{\alpha\beta}} w^{\star\star} d\Omega \\ &+ \int_\Omega (b_3 - \rho\ddot{w} + f_3) w^{\star\star} d\Omega - \int_\Gamma \{\hat{w} - \hat{w}(\xi_\mu)\} V_n^{\star\star} d\Gamma + \int_\Gamma \hat{\Psi}_n M_n^{\star\star} d\Gamma \\ &- \int_\Gamma \hat{M}_n \Psi_n^{\star\star} d\Gamma + \int_\Gamma \hat{V}_n w^{\star\star} d\Gamma - \sum_{i=1}^{k} \langle M_s^{\star\star}\rangle|_i \{\hat{w} - \hat{w}(\xi_\mu)\} + \sum_{i=1}^{k} \langle \hat{M}_s\rangle|_i w^{\star\star} \end{aligned} \tag{65}$$

where again the boundary integrals are in the sense of the Cauchy Principal Value and if ξ_μ is at a corner the contribution of that corner to the summations is ignored. The coefficients in (65) are:

$$\alpha_\varepsilon = -\alpha - \frac{\nu}{2\pi}[\sin 2\gamma + \sin 2(\alpha\pi - \gamma)] \tag{66}$$

$$\alpha_\eta = -\frac{\nu}{2\pi}[\cos 2\gamma - \cos 2(\alpha\pi - \gamma)] \tag{67}$$

Note that if $\xi_\mu \in \Gamma$ is a regular boundary point, and ε is oriented along the outward normal, then the two terms on the left hand side of (65) collapse to $-w_{,n}(\xi_\mu)$. A difficulty is encountered at the corner points. This is because the normal vector may be discontinuous at these points, and as a result, there are three unknowns corresponding to the out of plane equations. The problem may be circumvented with two judicious choices of ε-η axes which allow the formation of two independent equations at a corner point using equation (65). One choice is the ε_1 axis which bisects the exterior angle. In this case, $\gamma = \gamma_1 = (2+\alpha)\frac{\pi}{2}$ which gives $\alpha_{\eta_1} = 0$ and $\alpha_{\varepsilon_1} = \alpha_1 = -\alpha - \frac{\nu}{\pi}\sin\alpha\pi$. The ε_2 axis is now taken perpendicular to ε_1 so that $\gamma = \gamma_2 = (\alpha-1)\frac{\pi}{2}$ which yields $\alpha_{\varepsilon_2} = \alpha_2 = -\alpha + \frac{\nu}{\pi}\sin\alpha\pi$ and $\alpha_{\eta_2} = 0$. It can be verified that this selection of axes leads to the following convenient expressions involving the normal derivatives on either side of the corner[32].

$$\alpha_1 w_{,\varepsilon_1}|_{\xi_\mu} = -\frac{\alpha + \frac{\nu}{\pi}\sin\alpha\pi}{2\sin(\frac{\alpha\pi}{2})}[w_{,n}|_{\xi_\mu^+} + w_{,n}|_{\xi_\mu^-}] \tag{68}$$

$$\alpha_2 w_{,\varepsilon_2}|_{\xi_\mu} = -\frac{\alpha - \frac{\nu}{\pi}\sin\alpha\pi}{2\cos(\frac{\alpha\pi}{2})}[w_{,n}|_{\xi_\mu^+} - w_{,n}|_{\xi_\mu^-}] \tag{69}$$

By using this procedure to obtain two independent equations at a corner from equation (65) and making use of equation (59), three equations are established at corner points. In addition, it is necessary to take into account some results of an asymptotic analysis of the solution at corner points[32]. With this special consideration at corner points, equations (36), (59) and (65) are sufficient to solve a well posed problem of the finite deflections of plates and shallow shells.

Incremental Approach and Solution Strategy

The equations (36), (59) and (65) are essentially four coupled equations which solve the large deflection problem for plates and shallow shells. As these equations are non-linear, it is necessary to solve them incrementally. In order to facilitate an incremental approach the equations (36), (59) and (65) are first linearized as in [1] and [20].

Consider first equation (36) which governs the in-plane motion of the shallow shell. By introducing increments in the known and unknown variables of the form:

$$u_j^{K+1} = u_j^K + \Delta u_j \tag{70}$$

equation (36) can be expressed in incremental form as:

$$\begin{aligned} \gamma_{\theta j}(u_j^K + \Delta u_j) = &-\int_\Omega C[\kappa_{\alpha\beta}(w^K + \Delta w)]u^\star_{(\theta)\alpha,\beta}d\Omega \\ -\int_\Omega (N_{\alpha\beta}^{(n)K} + \Delta N_{\alpha\beta}^{(n)})u^\star_{(\theta)\alpha,\beta}d\Omega &+ \int_\Omega [(b_\alpha^K + \Delta b_\alpha) - \rho(\ddot{u}_\alpha^K + \Delta\ddot{u}_\alpha)]u^\star_{(\theta)\alpha}d\Omega \\ &+ \int_\Gamma (\hat{P}_\alpha^K + \Delta\hat{P}_\alpha)u^\star_{(\theta)\alpha}d\Gamma - \int_\Gamma (\hat{u}_\alpha^K + \Delta\hat{u}_\alpha)P^\star_{(\theta)\alpha}d\Gamma \end{aligned} \tag{71}$$

In this incremental equation and the ones to follow it is to be understood that the quantities $(\,\cdot\,)^K$ are known and the incremental variables $\Delta(\,\cdot\,)$ are the unknowns during each iteration. In equation (71) the incremental quantities involving the non-linear in-plane stress resultants can be expressed in terms of the kinematic variable, w, and its increments by:

$$\Delta N_{11}^{(n)} = C[w_{,1}^K \Delta w_{,1} + \nu w_{,2}^K \Delta w_{,2}] \tag{72}$$

$$\Delta N_{22}^{(n)} = C[w_{,2}^K \Delta w_{,2} + \nu w_{,1}^K \Delta w_{,1}] \tag{73}$$

$$\Delta N_{12}^{(n)} = C\frac{1-\nu}{2}[w_{,1}^K \Delta w_{,2} + w_{,2}^K \Delta w_{,1}] \tag{74}$$

where quantities involving products of incremental terms have been ignored. Using these relations for $\Delta N_{\alpha\beta}^{(n)}$ and the definition of $N_{\alpha\beta}^{(n)}$ as given in equation (28), it can be shown that:

$$\int_\Omega N_{\alpha\beta}^{(n)K} u_{(\theta)\alpha,\beta}^{\star} d\Omega = \frac{1}{2}\int_\Omega N_{(\theta)\alpha\beta}^{\star} w_{,\alpha}^K w_{,\beta}^K d\Omega \tag{75}$$

$$\int_\Omega \Delta N_{\alpha\beta}^{(n)} u_{(\theta)\alpha,\beta}^{\star} d\Omega = \int_\Omega N_{(\theta)\alpha\beta}^{\star} w_{,\alpha}^K \Delta w_{,\beta} d\Omega \tag{76}$$

Using these two transformations, the final incremental expression for the in-plane equations is:

$$\begin{aligned}\gamma_{\theta j}(u_j^K + \Delta u_j) = &-\int_\Omega C[\kappa_{\alpha\beta}(w^K + \Delta w)]u_{(\theta)\alpha,\beta}^{\star} d\Omega - \frac{1}{2}\int_\Omega N_{(\theta)\alpha\beta}^{\star} w_{,\alpha}^K w_{,\beta}^K d\Omega \\ &- \int_\Omega N_{(\theta)\alpha\beta}^{\star} w_{,\alpha}^K \Delta w_{,\beta} d\Omega + \int_\Omega [(b_\alpha^K + \Delta b_\alpha) - \rho(\ddot{u}_\alpha^K + \Delta\ddot{u}_\alpha)]u_{(\theta)\alpha}^{\star} d\Omega \\ &+ \int_\Gamma (\hat{P}_\alpha^K + \Delta\hat{P}_\alpha)u_{(\theta)\alpha}^{\star} d\Gamma - \int_\Gamma (\hat{u}_\alpha^K + \Delta\hat{u}_\alpha)P_{(\theta)\alpha}^{\star} d\Gamma\end{aligned} \tag{77}$$

The introduction of incremental quantities into equations (59) and (65) which govern the transverse motion of the shell yields:

$$\begin{aligned}D\frac{\alpha}{2}(w^K + \Delta w) = &-\int_\Omega [N_{\alpha\beta}^K w_{,\beta}^K + N_{\alpha\beta}^K \Delta w_{,\beta} + \Delta N_{\alpha\beta} w_{,\beta}^K] w_{,\alpha}^{\star} d\Omega \\ &+ \int_\Omega C(u_\alpha^K + \Delta u_\alpha)(\kappa_{\alpha\beta} w^{\star})_{,\beta} d\Omega - \int_\Gamma C\kappa_{\alpha\beta}(\hat{u}_\alpha^K + \Delta\hat{u}_\alpha)n_\beta w^{\star} d\Gamma \\ &- \int_\Omega [C\frac{\kappa_{\alpha\beta}}{R_{\alpha\beta}}(w^K + \Delta w)]w^{\star} d\Omega - \int_\Omega \frac{(N_{\alpha\beta}^{(n)K} + \Delta N_{\alpha\beta}^{(n)})}{R_{\alpha\beta}} w^{\star} d\Omega \\ &+ \int_\Omega [(b_3^K + \Delta b_3) - \rho(\ddot{w}^K + \Delta\ddot{w}) + (f_3^K + \Delta f_3)]w^{\star} d\Omega - \int_\Gamma (\hat{w}^K + \Delta\hat{w})V_n^{\star} d\Gamma \\ &+ \int_\Gamma (\hat{\Psi}_n^K + \Delta\hat{\Psi}_n)M_n^{\star} d\Gamma - \int_\Gamma (\hat{M}_n^K + \Delta\hat{M}_n)\Psi_n^{\star} d\Gamma + \int_\Gamma (\hat{V}_n^K + \Delta\hat{V}_n)w^{\star} d\Gamma \\ &- \sum_{i=1}^{k}\langle M_s^{\star}\rangle|_i(\hat{w}^K + \Delta\hat{w}) + \sum_{i=1}^{k}\langle\hat{M}_s^K + \Delta\hat{M}_s\rangle|_i w^{\star}\end{aligned} \tag{78}$$

and,

$$
\begin{aligned}
D[\alpha_\varepsilon(w^K_{,\varepsilon} + \Delta w_{,\varepsilon})|_{\xi_\mu} + \alpha_\eta(w^K_{,\eta} + \Delta w_{,\eta})|_{\xi_\mu}] &= \int_\Omega C(u^K_\alpha + \Delta u_\alpha)(\kappa_{\alpha\beta} w^{**})_{,\beta} d\Omega \\
- \int_\Omega [N^K_{\alpha\beta} w^K_{,\beta} + N^K_{\alpha\beta}\Delta w_{,\beta} + \Delta N_{\alpha\beta} w^K_{,\beta}] w^{**}_{,\alpha} d\Omega &- \int_\Gamma C\kappa_{\alpha\beta}(\hat{u}^K_\alpha + \Delta\hat{u}_\alpha) n_\beta w^{**} d\Gamma \\
- \int_\Omega [C\frac{\kappa_{\alpha\beta}}{R_{\alpha\beta}}(w^K + \Delta w)] w^{**} d\Omega &- \int_\Omega \frac{(N^{(n)K}_{\alpha\beta} + \Delta N^{(n)}_{\alpha\beta})}{R_{\alpha\beta}} w^{**} d\Omega \\
&+ \int_\Omega [(b^K_3 + \Delta b_3) - \rho(\ddot{w}^K + \Delta\ddot{w}) + (f^K_3 + \Delta f_3)] w^{**} d\Omega \\
- \int_\Gamma [(\hat{w}^K + \Delta\hat{w}) - (\hat{w}^K|_{\xi_\mu} + \Delta\hat{w}|_{\xi_\mu})] V^{**}_n d\Gamma &+ \int_\Gamma (\hat{\Psi}^K_n + \Delta\hat{\Psi}_n) M^{**}_n d\Gamma \\
&- \int_\Gamma (\hat{M}^K_n + \Delta\hat{M}_n)\Psi^{**}_n d\Gamma + \int_\Gamma (\hat{V}^K_n + \Delta\hat{V}_n) w^{**} d\Gamma \\
- \sum_{i=1}^{k} \langle M^{**}_s\rangle|_i [(\hat{w}^K + \Delta\hat{w}) - (\hat{w}^K|_{\xi_\mu} + \Delta\hat{w}|_{\xi_\mu})] &+ \sum_{i=1}^{k} \langle \hat{M}^K_s + \Delta\hat{M}_s\rangle|_i w^{**}
\end{aligned}
\tag{79}
$$

where again, products of incremental quantities are ignored. Note that the terms involving increments of the in-plane stress resultants should be interpreted as increments in the corresponding kinematic variables by using equations (25) and (72)-(74). Also, observe that the incremental equations (77)-(79) contain equilibrium constraints(terms with the K superscript) at the Kth state which must be satisfied for the iterative procedure to converge.

The next step in the solution process is the discretization of the boundary and the interior into elements in terms of the incremental variables. On the boundary Δw, $\Delta\Psi_n$, ΔM_n, ΔV_n, Δu_α, and ΔP_α are interpolated in terms of nodal values of each one dimensional element. In the interior Δw, $\Delta\ddot{w}$, Δu_α, and $\Delta\ddot{u}_\alpha$ are interpolated over each two dimensional element. Observing that the incremental equations (77)-(79) contain first derivatives of the increments of u_α and w, the interpolation functions for these displacement variables in the interior should be at least linear so that they make contributions to the domain integrals. However, they need not satisfy the C^1 continuity requirement across element interfaces as do conventional Finite Elements.

Using equations (77)-(79), four equations can be written for each boundary node(five if a corner node) and three equations at each interior node. A general representation of this system of equations is:

$$
\mathbf{K}\Delta u + \mathbf{M}\Delta\ddot{u} = \Delta f \tag{80}
$$

where Δu is a vector of nodal unknowns (which in general may be either forces or displacements), $\Delta\ddot{u}$ is a vector of nodal accelerations, and Δf is a vector which includes the incremental boundary condition and force vectors as well as the equilibrium constraints at the Kth state. The definitions of the **K** and **M** matrices may be deduced from the integral equations (77)-(79). The **K** matrix is analagous to the tangent stiffness matrix of Finite Element schemes. However, in the spirit of Boundary Elements, it is in general fully populated and unsymmetric. Likewise, the matrix **M** in dynamic problems will have a similar structure to the **K** matrix.

The solution of equation (80) is accomplished by applying the loads and boundary conditions in increments. For dynamic problems these increments correspond to time steps.Within each load increment or time step, an iterative procedure is used to solve the equations because of the dependency of the **K** matrix upon the current deformation state. The updating of this matrix during each cycle of iteration corresponds to a full Newton-Raphson scheme. If the matrix is updated only at the beginning of each load increment then a modified Newton-Raphson scheme is obtained. A comparison of these two methods of iteration in [6], chose in favor of the full Newton-Raphson method based on the observations that the size of the **K** matrix is not as large as that required for an equivalent Finite Element modeling of a given problem and the method converged rapidly to the solution for the problems tested. For dynamic problems it is necessary to choose a suitable time stepping algorithm. For instance, the Newmark beta method has been implemented successfully in references [6],[10],[19], and [34].

A problem of special interest is that involving the post-buckling analysis of the shallow shell. Due to the presence of a limit point, the Newton-Raphson iteration is not sufficient, but must be used in combination with an arc-length method. In [20] and [34] a displacement control form of the arc-length method is implemented succesfully. As is pointed out in [34], since the unknown vector in the Field/Boundary Element problem has both displacement and force components, all components of the unknown vector should not be included in the displacement control algorithm. This contrasts the implementation of the arc-length method based on displacement control in the popular displacement based Finite Element formulations, where all components of the unknown vector are displacements.

Numerical Examples

The following examples are taken from references [6] and [34]. They include quasi-static and dynamic analysis of plates and shallow shells.

Example 1. Consider a thin plate subjected to a uniformly distributed transverse load $\overline{P}$. The plate is assumed to be square and simply supported(Figure 6). Also, the in -plane displacements are taken to be zero on the boundaries. The thickness ratio is $\frac{h}{a} = \frac{1}{160}$, Poisson's ratio is 0.316 and Young's modulus $30x10^6$ psi. A linear interpolation was used for the boundary variables, while in the interior the unknowns are also linearly interpolated. The central deflection, using a $4x4$ mesh to model one quadrant(due to symmetry) is given in figure 7 where it is compared to the series solution of Levy[35].

Example 2. The buckling of a plate subjected to a uniaxial compression in one direction, and a small load normal to the plane of the plate to induce buckling is solved using the Field/Boundary Element Method. The plate is simply supported and two edges have prescribed displacements, while the other two sides are free in the sense that self-equilibrating loads are applied to maintain the straight edges. Use is made of the same mesh and interpolations as in example 1. The central deflection is plotted in figure 8 as a function of the average compressive stress on the sides with prescribed displacements. The results again agree quite well with Levy's series solution.

Example 3. To demonstrate the snap-through analysis of the shallow shell using Field/Boundary Elements, consider the square based spherical shallow shell shown in figure 9. The solution using the present method agrees with that obtained analytically by Licester[36] and with Finite Elements by Bathe and Lo[37], Bathe[38], Bergan[39] and Shatt[40]. These Finite Element solutions used from 80 to 206 degrees of freedom. The Field/Boundary Element solution utilized 64 degrees of freedom.

Example 4. The circular spherical shallow shell with hinged edges shown in figure 10 is subjected to an initial upward velocity of 15.0 at its crown. This loading corresponds to an upward point impulse applied at the crown of the shell. The value of R in this example is 15.0 and that of h is 0.3. The deflection of the crown as a function of time is shown in figure 11.

Example 5. The circular spherical shallow shell of Example 4 is again used. In this example an initial upward velocity distribution of $v = 3\cos(\frac{r\pi}{10})$ is applied to the shell, where r is the distance from the center of the base plane Ω. The variation of the crown deflection with time is shown in figure 12.

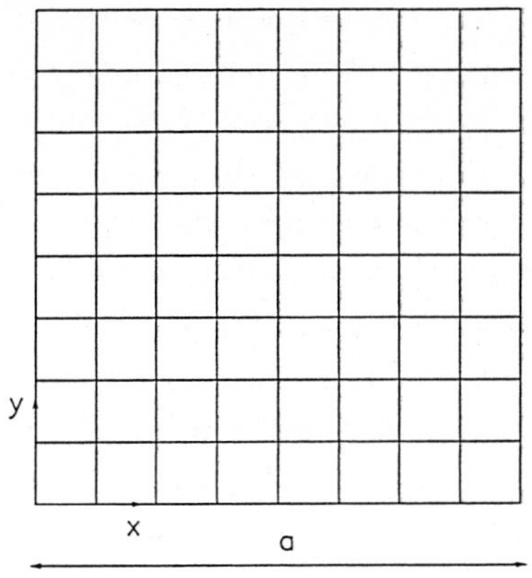

a = 16"

h = 0.1"

E = 30×10^6 psi.

ν = 0.316

Fig. 6. Simply supported square plate

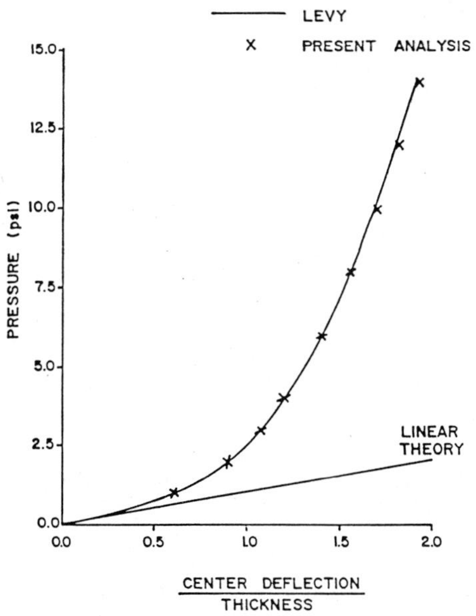

Fig. 7. Central deflection of square plate under transverse load

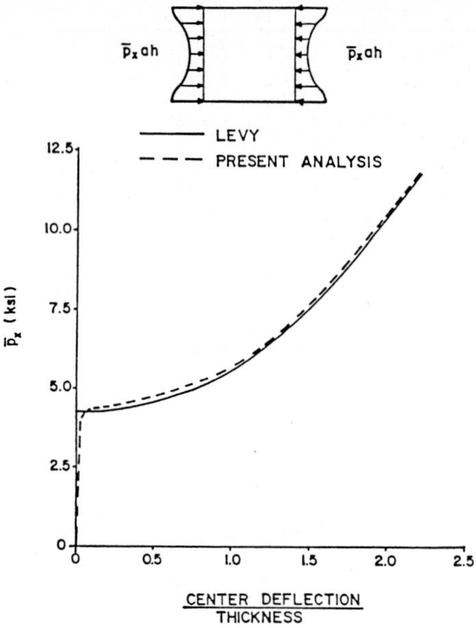

Fig. 8. Post-buckling deflection of square plate

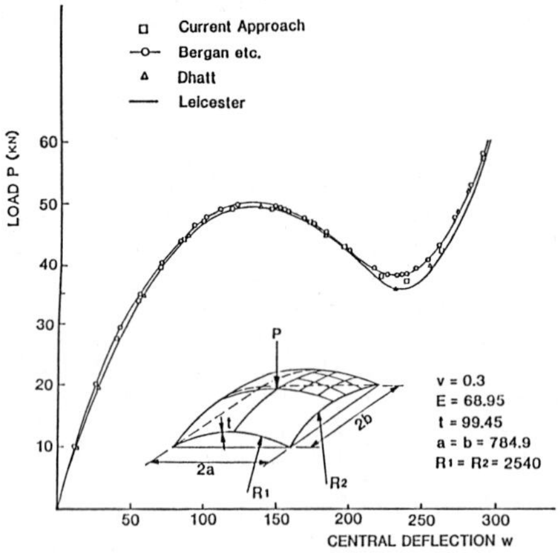

Fig. 9. Snap-through analysis of a shallow spherical shell

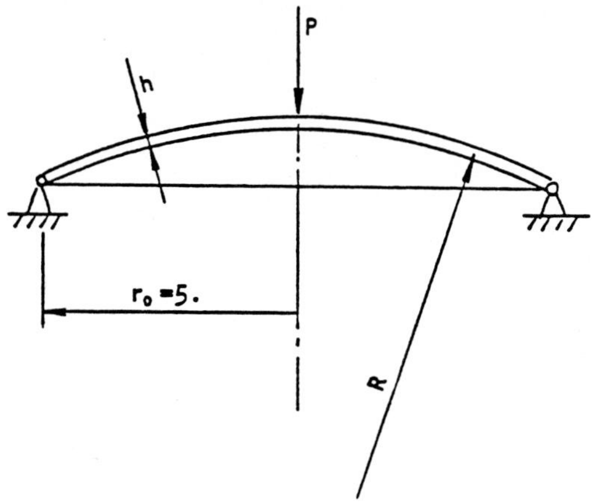

Fig. 10. Cross-section of a circular spherical shallow shell

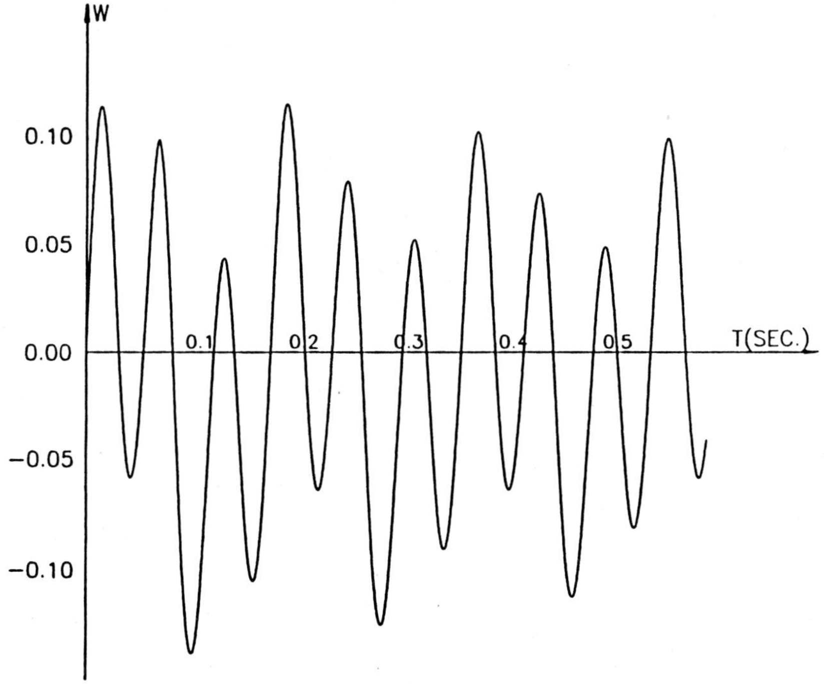

Fig. 11. Crown deflection of a shallow shell subjected to an initial velocity of 15.0 at the crown

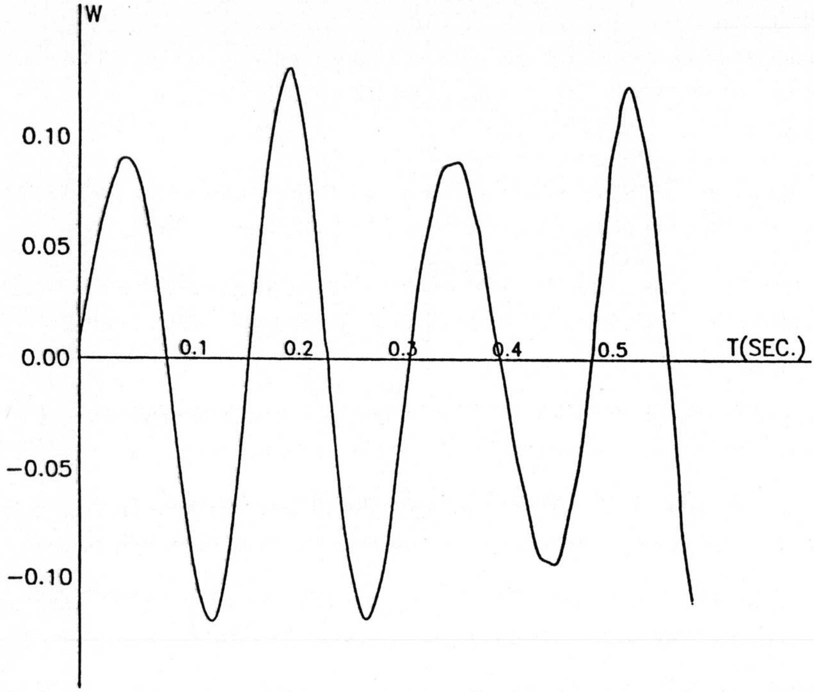

Fig. 12. Crown deflection of a shallow shell subjected to an initial velocity distribution of $v = 3\cos\left(\frac{r\pi}{10}\right)$

Acknowledgements

These results were obtained during the course of investigations supported by the Air Force Office of Scientific Research. This support is gratefully acknowledged.

References

1. O'Donoghue, P.E.; Atluri S.N.: Field/Boundary element approach to the large Deflection of thin flat plates. Comp. & Struc. 27, 3, (1987) pp. 427-435.

2. Tanaka M.: Integral equation approach to small and large displacements of thin elastic plates. Boundary Element Methods in Engineering. Berlin: Springer 1982 pp. 526-539.

3. Kamiya, N.; Sawaki, Y.: An integral equation approach to finite deflection of elastic plates. Int. J. Non-Lin. Mech. 17, 3, (1982) pp. 187–194.

4. Kamiya, N.; Sawaki, Y.: Integral equation formulation for non-linear bending of plates-formulation by weighted residual method. ZAMM. 62 (1982) pp. 651-655.

5. Ye, T.Q.; Liu, Y.J.: Finite deflection analysis of elastic plate by the boundary element method. Appl. Math. Modelling. 9 (1985) pp. 183-188.

6. O'Donoghue, P.E.: Boundary integral equation approach to the nonlinear response control of large space structures; alternating technique applied to multiple flaws in three dimensional bodies. Ph. D. Thesis, Georgia Inst. of Tech., Atlanta, GA(1985).

7. Tosaka, N.; Miyake, S.: Large deflection analysis of shallow spherical shell using an integral equation method. Proceedings of Int. Conf. on Boundary Elements, Beijing, China(1986).

8. Tosaka, N.; Miyake, S.: Nonlinear analysis of elastic shallow shells by boundary element method. Boundary Elements VII. Berlin: Springer pp 4-43 to 4-52, 1985.

9. Tosaka, N.; Miyake, S.: Geometrically nonlinear analysis of shallow spherical shell using an integral equation method. Boundary Elements VIII. Berlin: Springer pp 537-546, 1986.

10. Zhang, J.D.; Atluri, S.N.: Nonlinear quasi-static and transient response analysis of shallow shells: formulations and interior/boundary element algorithms. Boundary Elements. Du Qinghua, (Ed.) Oxford: Pergamon Press pp. 87-109, 1986.

11. Atluri, S.N.; O'Donoghue, P.E.; Zhang, J.D.: Analysis and control of finite deformations of plates and shells: formulations and interior/boundary element algorithms. Finite Element Analysis of Shells: Formulations and Algorithms. Hughes T.J.; Hinton, E. (ed.) Swansea, UK: Pine-Ridge Press 1986.

12. Kamiya, N.; Sawaki, Y.; Nakamura, Y.; Fukui, A.: An approxiamte finite deflection analysis of a heated elastic plate by the boundary element method. Appl. Math. Modelling 6 (1982) 23-27.

13. Kamiya, N.; Sawaki, Y.; Nakamura, Y.: Non-linear bending analysis of heated sandwich plates and shells by the boundary element method. Res. Mech. 8 (1983) 29-38.

14. Kamiya, N.; Sawaki, Y.; Nakamura, Y.: Postbuckling analysis by the boundary element method. Engng. Anal. 1 (1984) 40-44.

15. Kamiya, N.; Sawaki, Y.: Boundary element analysis of non-linear bending of sandwich plates and shallow shells. Developments in Boundary Element Methods Banerjee, P.K.; Watson, J.O. (Eds.) London: Elsevier Applied Science 4 (1986) 121-148.

16. Sladek, J.; Sladek, V.: The BIE analysis of the Berger equation. Ing. Archiv. 53 (1983) 385-397.

17. Kamiya, N.; Sawaki, Y.; Nakamura, Y.: Finite and postbuckling deformations of heated plates and shallow shells. Boundary Elements. Brebbia,C.A.; Futagami, T.; Tanaka, M. (Eds.) Berlin: Springer-Verlag 1983, 507-516.

18. Ye, T.Q.; Liu, Y.J.: Finite deflection analysis of heated elastic plates by the boundary element method. Boundary Elements. Du, Q. (Ed.) Oxford: Pergamon Press 1986, 367-374.

19. Zhang, J.D.; Atluri, S.N.: Non-linear quasi-static and transient response analysis of shallow shells: Formulations and interior/boundary element algorithms. Recent Applications in Computational Mechanics. Karabalis,D.L. (Ed.) New York: ASCE 1986, 43-65.

20. Zhang, J.D.; Atluri, S.N.: Postbuckling analysis of shallow shells by the field/boundary element method. Int. J. Num. Meth. Engng. 26 (1988) 571-587.

21. Katsikadelis, J.T.; Nerantzaki, M.S.: Large deflections of thin plates by the boundary element method. Boundary Elements X. Brebbia, C.A. (Ed.) Berlin: Springer-Verlag 1988, 435-456.

22. Kamiya, N.: Geometrically non-linear analysis of elastic plates by the boundary element method. Advanced Boundary Element Methods. Cruse, T.A. (Ed.) Berlin: Springer-Verlag 1988, 189-196.

23. Kamiya, N.; Sawaki, Y.: Finite deflections of plates. Topics in Boundary Element Research. Brebbia, C.A. (Ed.) Berlin: Springer- Verlag 1984, 204-224.

24. Tanaka, M.: Large deflection analysis of thin elastic plates. Developments in Boundary Element Methods. Banerjee, P.K.; Mukherjee, S. (Ed.) London: Elsevier Applied Science 1984, 115-136.

25. Ye, T.Q.; Liu, Y.: Finite deflection analysis of heated elastic plates by the boundary element method. Boundary Elements. Du, Q. (Ed.) Oxford: Pergamon Press1986, 367-374.

26. Tosaka, N.; Miyake, S.: Large Deflection analysis of shallow spherical shells using an integral equation method. Boundary Elements. Du Q. (Ed.) Oxford: Pergamon Press 1986, 59-66.

27. Tosaka, N.; Miyake, S.: Integral equation analysis of geometrically non-linear problems of elastic bodies. Theory and Applications of Boundary Element Methods. Tanaka, M.; Du, Q. (Eds.) Oxford: Pergamon Press 1982, 251-260.

28. Feng, Z.N.; Li, Z.F.: Applications of boundary element method in bending problem of thin plates with large deflection. Boundary Elements. Du, Q. (Ed.) Oxford: Pergamon Press 1986, 411-418.

29. Nerantzaki, M.S.; Katsikadelis, J.T.: A Green's function method for large deflection analysis of plates. Acta Mechanica. 75 (1988) 211-225.

30. Reissner, E.: Stresses and small displacement analysis of shallow spherical shells-II. J. Math. Physics. 25 (1946) 279-300.

31. Swedlow, J.L.; Cruse, T.A.: Formulation of boundary integral equations for three-dimensional elasto-plastic flow. Int. J. Solids Structures. 7 (1971) 1673-1683.

32. Stern, M.: A General boundary integral formulation for the numerical solution of plate bending problems. Int. J. Solids Structures. 15 (1979) 769-782.

33. Atluri, S.N.; Grannell, J.J.: Boundary element (BEM) and combination of BEM-FEM. Report No. GIT-ESM-SA-78-16, Center for the Advancement of Computational Mechanics, Georgia Inst. of Tech., 1978.

34. Zhang, J.D.: Nonlinear dynamic analysis and optimal control of shallow shells by field/boundary element approach. Ph. D. Thesis, Georgia Inst. of Tech., Atlanta, GA (1987).

35. Levy, S.: Bending of rectangular plates with large deflections. NACA Technical Report 737, pp. 139-157, 1942.

36. Licester, R.H.: Finite deformation of shallow shells. Proceedings ASCE, 94 (1968) 1409-1423.

37. Bathe, K.J.; Lo, L.W.: A simple and effective element for analysis of general shell structures. Comp. & Struct. 13 (1981) 673-681.

38. Bathe, K.J.; Dvorkin, E.N.: A Continuum mechanics based four-node shell element for general non-linear analysis. Engineering Computations. 1 (1984).

39. Bergan, P.G. et. al.: Solution techniques for non-linear finite element problems. Int. J. Num. Meth. Engg. 12 (1978) 1677-1696.

40. Shatt, G.S.: Instability of thin shells by the finite element method. IASS Symposium for Folded Plates and Prismatic Structures, Vienna, 1970.

Inelastic Analysis of Plates and Shells

S. MUKHERJEE

Department of Theoretical and Applied Mechanics
Cornell University
Ithaca, NY 14853, USA

B. PODDAR

Department of Mechanical Engineering
University of Miami
Coral Gables, FL 33124, USA

Summary

This chapter presents applications of the boundary element method to inelastic analysis of plates and shells. For the analysis of inelastic plate problems, three different formulations are compared. In addition, thermal stresses, membrane effects, large deformation analysis and instability analysis are also considered for the plate problems. The shell formulation is derived by transforming the general 3-D BEM equations to the appropriate curvilinear coordinates and taking advantage of the shell thinness. Numerical results are presented for several plate and shell problems.

Introduction

The subject of this chapter is static inelastic analysis of plates and shells. For the most part, small deformations are considered here. Thus, material nonlinearities (plasticity and viscoplasticity) are included, while geometrical nonlinearities are not (except in one section).

Following a discussion of the governing differential equations for analysis of inelastic plate deformation, three different integral formulations (called A, B and C respectively) are presented here. Formulation A, an older formulation, uses $\dot{w}$, $\frac{\partial \dot{w}}{\partial n}$, $\nabla^2 \dot{w}$ and $\frac{\partial}{\partial n}(\nabla^2 \dot{w})$ (where w is the transverse displacement of a plate and **n** is an unit normal on the boundary of the mid-section of the plate) as primary boundary variables in the governing integral equations. More attractive are the more recent formulations B or C, where the shearing force, bending moment and twisting moment, the physical quantities of interest in plate bending, appear as primary boundary variables. These formulations are quite versatile in that boundary conditions such as free edges can now be modeled efficiently.

Representative numerical results are presented for elastic-plastic problems from formulations B and elastic-viscoplastic problems from formulation C. This is followed by a discussion of more complex plate deformation problems including the effects of thermal stresses, membrane effects, large deformations and instability.

The remaining part of the chapter is devoted to analysis of (small) elasto-viscoplastic deformation of shells. The lack of explicit Green's functions for deformation of shells of arbitrary shape has long been a stumbling block against efficient boundary element analysis of general shells. This chapter presents a novel approach to try and get around this difficulty. The integral model is derived by projection of the appropriate 3-D elasto-viscoplastic BEM equations onto the shell space and making appropriate assumptions regarding the displacement variation through the shell thickness and load specification on the edges of the shell. Numerical results, for representative examples of elastic and inelastic deformation of axisymmetric shells, are presented at the end of the chapter.

Governing Differential Equations for Plate Bending

The analytical formulation for small elastic-plastic (or elastic-viscoplastic) bending of thin, laterally loaded Kirchoff plates closely follows the elastic analysis discussed in Timoshenko and Woinowsky-Krieger [1]. The plate is thin, of arbitrary shape, of uniform thickness h and is loaded laterally by a load of intensity q per unit area. The only deflection of the plate is the transverse deflection w and this is assumed to be small compared to the thickness of the plate. Membrane effects (in-plane deflections) are neglected for the present. Thus, the middle plane of the plate is a plane of symmetry and is a neutral surface for the bending problem under consideration. The total in-plane strains in the plate are assumed to remain proportional to the distance from the neutral surface even in the presence of inelastic deformation. The formulation is carried out in terms of the time rates of change of the relevant variables.

Let the mid-surface of the undeformed flat plate be the $x_1 - x_2$ plane with w the deflection in the normal x_3 direction. The total strain rates $\dot{\varepsilon}_{ij}$ are assumed to be linearly decomposable into elastic and nonelastic strain rates. Also, the total strain rates must be compatible. Thus, for $i, j = 1, 2$

$$\dot{\varepsilon}_{ij} = \dot{\varepsilon}_{ij}^{(e)} + \dot{\varepsilon}_{ij}^{(n)} = x_3 \dot{\kappa}_{ij} \tag{1}$$

where $\dot{\kappa}_{ij} = -\dot{w}_{,ij}$ denote the principal curvatures and twist of the plate mid-surface with respect to the x_1 and x_2 axes, respectively.

The stress rates are related to the elastic strain rates by Hooke's law for plane stress, i.e.,

$$\begin{aligned} \dot{\sigma}_{11} &= \frac{E}{1-\nu^2}[\dot{\varepsilon}_{11}^{(e)} + \nu\dot{\varepsilon}_{22}^{(e)}] \\ \dot{\sigma}_{22} &= \frac{E}{1-\nu^2}[\dot{\varepsilon}_{22}^{(e)} + \nu\dot{\varepsilon}_{11}^{(e)}] \\ \dot{\sigma}_{12} &= 2G\,\dot{\varepsilon}_{12}^{(e)} \end{aligned} \tag{2}$$

in terms of the Young's modulus E, the shear modulus G and the Poisson's ratio ν of the isotropic homogeneous plate material.

The rates of the bending and twisting moments are defined as $(i, j = 1, 2)$

$$\dot{M}_{ij} = \int_{-\frac{h}{2}}^{\frac{h}{2}} \dot{\sigma}_{ij} x_3 dx_3 \tag{3}$$

The rate equilibrium equation for a plate element is

$$\dot{M}_{ij,ij} = -\dot{q} \tag{4}$$

Substituting Equations (1), (2) and (3) into the equilibrium Equation (4) results in the governing partial differential equation for the deflection rate

$$\nabla^4 \dot{w} = \frac{\dot{q}}{D} + \frac{12}{h^3} f^{(n)}(x_1, x_2, t) \equiv g(x_1, x_2, t) \tag{5}$$

where ∇^4 is the biharmonic operator in two dimensions,

$$D = \frac{Eh^3}{12(1-\nu^2)}$$

and

$$f^{(n)} = \frac{\partial^2}{\partial x_1^2} \int_{-\frac{h}{2}}^{\frac{h}{2}} (\dot{\varepsilon}_{11}^{(n)} + \nu \dot{\varepsilon}_{22}^{(n)}) x_3 dx_3 + \frac{\partial^2}{\partial x_2^2} \int_{-\frac{h}{2}}^{\frac{h}{2}} (\dot{\varepsilon}_{22}^{(n)} + \nu \dot{\varepsilon}_{11}^{(n)}) x_3 dx_3$$

$$+ 2(1-\nu) \frac{\partial^2}{\partial x_1 \partial x_2} \int_{-\frac{h}{2}}^{\frac{h}{2}} \dot{\varepsilon}_{12}^{(n)} x_3 dx_3$$

In view of what is to follow, it is useful to examine Equations (2) and (3) a little further. Equation (3), with $i = j = 1$ for example, can be written as

$$\dot{M}_{11} = \int_{-\frac{h}{2}}^{\frac{h}{2}} \frac{E}{1-\nu^2} [\dot{\varepsilon}_{11} + \nu \dot{\varepsilon}_{22}] x_3 dx_3 - \int_{-\frac{h}{2}}^{\frac{h}{2}} \frac{E}{1-\nu^2} [\dot{\varepsilon}_{11}^{(n)} + \nu \dot{\varepsilon}_{22}^{(n)}] x_3 dx_3 \equiv \dot{M}'_{11} - \dot{M}_{11}^{(n)} \tag{6}$$

where the first term is defined as $\dot{M}'_{11}$ and the second as the nonelastic moment rate $\dot{M}_{11}^{(n)}$. Of course, the primed moment M'_{11} reduces to the physical moment M_{11} for purely elastic problems. The quantities $\dot{M}'_{22}$, $\dot{M}'_{12}$, $\dot{M}_{22}^{(n)}$ and $\dot{M}_{12}^{(n)}$ can be defined from Equation (3) in analogous fashion.

The boundary conditions for plate bending problems involve the quantities w and $\frac{\partial w}{\partial n}$ as well as the moments and shearing forces on the plate boundary. As in Equation (6) above, one can decompose the physical bending moment M_{nn}, shearing force V_n and twisting moment M_{nt} at a boundary point, as

$$\dot{M}_{nn} = \dot{M}'_{nn} - \dot{M}^{(n)}_{nn}, \quad \dot{V}_n = \dot{V}'_n - \dot{V}^{(n)}_n \quad \text{and} \quad \dot{M}_{nt} = \dot{M}'_{nt} - \dot{M}^{(n)}_{nt} \tag{7}$$

The primed quantities, for a regular point on the plate boundary ∂B, are

$$\begin{aligned} \dot{M}'_{nn}(s) &= n_i \dot{M}'_{ij} n_j = -D\left[\nabla^2 - (1-\nu)\frac{\partial^2}{\partial \tau^2}\right]\dot{w} \\ \dot{M}'_{nt}(s) &= n_i \dot{M}'_{ij} \tau_j = -D(1-\nu)\frac{\partial^2 \dot{w}}{\partial n \partial \tau} \\ \dot{V}'_n(s) &= n_i \dot{M}'_{ij,j} + \frac{\partial \dot{M}'_{nt}}{\partial s} = -D\left[\frac{\partial}{\partial n}\nabla^2 + (1-\nu)\frac{\partial}{\partial s}\frac{\partial^2}{\partial n \partial \tau}\right]\dot{w} \end{aligned} \tag{8}$$

where s is a curvilinear coordinate which is measured along the plate boundary. Also, $\mathbf{n}$ is the unit outward normal and τ is the unit counter-clockwise tangent vector to the plate boundary. The nonelastic quantities $\dot{M}^{(n)}_{nn}$ etc. are defined as

$$\begin{aligned} \dot{M}^{(n)}_{nn}(s) &= n_i \dot{M}^{(n)}_{ij} n_j \\ \dot{M}^{(n)}_{nt}(s) &= n_i \dot{M}^{(n)}_{ij} \tau_j \\ \dot{V}^{(n)}_n(s) &= n_i \dot{M}^{(n)}_{ij,j} + \frac{\partial \dot{M}^{(n)}_{nt}}{\partial s} \end{aligned} \tag{9}$$

It should also be noted here that with the above definitions, the nonelastic term from Equation (5) can be written as in Moshaiov and Vorus [2] as

$$\frac{12}{h^3} f^{(n)} = \frac{1}{D}\dot{M}^{(n)}_{ij,ij} \tag{10}$$

where, as before, the range of i and j is 1, 2.

Integral Equations

Over the years, three distinct integral formulations, for the above problem, have appeared in the literature. These are described below as formulations A, B and C respectively.

Formulation A

This formulation has been presented in Morjaria and Mukherjee [3]. It is a direct formulation in terms of the boundary values of $\dot{w}$, $\frac{\partial \dot{w}}{\partial n}$, $\nabla^2 \dot{w}$ and $\frac{\partial}{\partial n}(\nabla^2 \dot{w})$. Two coupled integral equations, for these quantities, have been derived. These are

$$\alpha\pi\nabla^2\dot{w} - \int_B (\ln r) g\, dA = \int_{\partial B}\left[\frac{\partial}{\partial n}(\ln r)\nabla^2\dot{w} - \ln r\frac{\partial}{\partial n}(\nabla^2\dot{w})\right]ds \tag{11}$$

$$4\alpha\pi\dot{w} - \int_B (r^2 \ln r) g\, dA = \int_{\partial B} \left[\frac{\partial}{\partial n}[\nabla^2(r^2\ln r)]\dot{w} - \nabla^2(r^2 \ln r)\frac{\partial \dot{w}}{\partial n} + \frac{\partial}{\partial n}(r^2 \ln r)\nabla^2\dot{w} - r^2 \ln r \frac{\partial}{\partial n}(\nabla^2 \dot{w}) \right] ds \tag{12}$$

Here B is the mid-surface of the plate which is bounded by ∂B. The value of α is 1 if the source point is on the boundary ∂B where it is locally smooth and α equals 2 if the source point is inside the plate.

Boundary conditions for clamped or simply supported plates can be written as

Clamped plate: $w = \dfrac{\partial w}{\partial n} = 0$ on ∂B

Simply supported plate: $w = \nabla^2 w = 0$ on ∂B

For these cases, Equations (11) and (12) (with $\alpha = 1$) can be used to solve for the unspecified boundary quantities. Once all four quantities are determined on ∂B, Equation (12), with $\alpha = 2$, can be used to obtain $\dot{w}$ at a point inside the plate. Curvature rates inside and on the boundary of the plate can be determined by using Equations given in [3].

One of the major drawbacks of this approach is that moments and shearing forces do not appear as primary boundary variables. Thus, boundary conditions such as free surfaces cannot be handled by this approach. Other disadvantages of this early formulation are the lack of jump terms at corners of the plate and that $f^{(n)}$ in Equation (5) must be determined from second derivatives of integrals which are typically only known numerically. These difficulties are overcome in the formulations described below.

Formulation B

This formulation was first presented for the elastic-plastic case by Moshaiov and Vorus [2]. This formulation uses $\dot{w}$, $\dfrac{\partial \dot{w}}{\partial n}$, $\dot{M}_{nn}$, $\dot{V}_n$ and $\dot{M}_{nt}$ (at corners), so that general plate boundary conditions can now be dealt with. Jump terms at corners appear and derivatives in $f^{(n)}$ are avoided. The elastic-plastic formulation presented in [2] is a generalization of an elastic plate formulation that was derived independently by Stern [4] and Bezine [5]. The first elastic-plastic plate equation for a point P_o on ∂B where it is locally smooth, has the form $(i, j = 1, 2)$

$$0.5D\dot{w}(P_o) = \int_{\partial B} \left[w_1^s \dot{V}_n - \dot{w} V_n(w_1^s) + M_{nn}(w_1^s) \frac{\partial \dot{w}}{\partial n} - \dot{M}_{nn} \frac{\partial w_1^s}{\partial n} \right] ds$$

$$+ \sum_{i=1}^{m} \left\{ [\,|w_1^s \dot{M}_{nt}|\,]_{Q_i} - [\,|\dot{w} M_{nt}(w_1^s)|\,]_{Q_i} \right\}$$

$$- \int_B (\dot{M}_{ij}^{(n)} w_{1,ij}^s - w_1^s \dot{q}) dA \qquad (13)$$

where $w_1^s = (\frac{1}{8\pi}) r^2 \ln r$,

in terms of the distance r between a source point p (or P) and a field point q (or Q). Points on ∂B are denoted by capital and those inside B by lower case letters. The quantities w_1^s, $\frac{\partial w_1^s}{\partial n}$, $V_n(w_1^s)$, $M_{nn}(w_1^s)$, $M_{nt}(w_1^s)$ and $w_{1,ij}^s$ are two-point functions. All derivatives in these functions are taken at a field point Q. The quantities $M_{nn}(w_1^s)$, $M_{nt}(w_1^s)$ and $V_n(w_1^s)$ are obtained from Equation (8) by replacing $\dot{w}$ by w_1^s and taking field point derivatives. Quantities multiplying these functions in Equation (13), such as $\dot{w}$, $\frac{\partial \dot{w}}{\partial n}$, $\dot{V}_n$ and $\dot{M}_{nn}$, are all calculated at a field point. Finally, Q_i, $i = 1, m$ are the locations of m corners on ∂B and a jump in a variable at a corner point is defined as

$$[\,|\,.\,|\,]_{Q_i} = [\,.\,]_{Q_i^+} - [\,.\,]_{Q_i^-}$$

As in the case of formulation A, a second integral equation is needed to solve the problem since Equation (13) has four boundary quantities, two of which are typically prescribed on ∂B. Moshaiov and Vorus [2], following Stern [4], derive an equation for the normal derivative of $\dot{w}$ at a regular point P_o on ∂B. Also, they use $\dot{w} - \dot{w}(P_o)$ in their equation, instead of $\dot{w}$, in order to deal with the strong $(O(\frac{1}{r^2}))$ singularity of $V_n(w_2^s)$. Here $w_2^s = \frac{\partial w_1^s}{\partial n_p}$. The resulting equation is

$$-D\frac{\partial \dot{w}(P_o)}{\partial n_p} = \int_{\partial B} \left[w_2^s \dot{V}_n - (\dot{w} - \dot{w}(P_o)) V_n(w_2^s) + M_{nn}(w_2^s) \frac{\partial \dot{w}}{\partial n} - \dot{M}_{nn} \frac{\partial w_2^s}{\partial n} \right] ds$$

$$+ \sum_{i=1}^{m} \left\{ \left[|w_2^s \dot{M}_{nt}| \right]_{Q_i} - \left[|(\dot{w} - \dot{w}(P_o)) M_{nt}(w_2^s)| \right]_{Q_i} \right\}$$

$$- \int_B (\dot{M}_{ij}^{(n)} w_{2,ij}^s - w_2^s \dot{q}) dA \qquad (14)$$

Stern [4] discusses the situation if P_o lies at a corner of ∂B. Also, equations for the rate of curvature inside the plate are given in [2].

As mentioned before, the primary boundary variables in this problem can be directly used for plate problems. Thus, for example, one has

Clamped plate: $w = \dfrac{\partial w}{\partial n} = 0$ on ∂B

Simply supported plate: $w = M_{nn} = 0$ on ∂B

Free edge: $V_n = M_{nn} = 0$ on ∂B

Of course, some of these quantities can be prescribed instead of being zero in some problems. Also, the above boundary conditions can apply on any portion of the boundary ∂B. Another important advantage of this formulation is that $\dot{M}_{ij}^{(n)}$, rather than its second partial derivatives, appear in Equations (13) and (14).

As usual, Equations (13) and (14) must be used to solve for the unspecified boundary conditions on ∂B. Once all the boundary variables have been determined, $\dot{w}$ and curvatures inside the plate can be obtained from the appropriate internal equations.

Formulation C

This formulation, for elastic-plastic (or elastic-viscoplastic) problems has been presented by Song and Mukherjee [6] and is an extention of earlier work on elastic plates by Du, Yao and Song [7] (see, also, Song and Mukherjee [8]). Here, the tangential derivative of $\dot{w}$ is added to the list of primary boundary variables and a third independent integral equation is added to the two from formulation B. The inclusion of $\dfrac{\partial \dot{w}}{\partial \tau}$ as a primary variable makes the three equation scheme even more versatile than formulation B, in that plate corners, where the edges meeting at a corner have different boundary conditions, such as a clamped edge meeting a free edge, can now be modeled in an elegant manner [8].

The three integral equations, for the elastic-plastic problem, can be written in compact form as ($k = 1, 2, 3$, i or $j = 1, 2$)

$$\int_{\partial B}\left[w_k^s \dot{V}_n - \dot{w} V_n(w_k^s) + M_{nn}(w_k^s)\frac{\partial \dot{w}}{\partial n} - \dot{M}_{nn}\frac{\partial w_k^s}{\partial n}\right] ds$$

$$+ \sum_{i=1}^{m}\left\{\left[\,| w_k^s \dot{M}_{nt} |\,\right]_{Q_i} - \left[\,| \dot{w} M_{nt}(w_k^s) |\,\right]_{Q_i}\right\} - \int_B (\dot{M}_{ij}^{(n)} w_{k,ij}^s - w_k^s \dot{q})\, dA = 0 \qquad (15)$$

Now $w_3^s = \dfrac{\partial w_1^s}{\partial \tau_P}$ and w_1^s and w_2^s are the same as before.

An important feature of this formulation is that the free terms in Equation (15) have been formally included in the term $\int_{\partial B} \dot{w} V_n(w_k^s) ds$. This formulation contains hypersingular integrals. Singular integrals are evaluated indirectly in this work [6, 8] through the use of particular solutions.

The equation at an internal point p has $D\dot{w}(p)$ equaling everything on the left of the equal sign, with $k = 1$, in Equation (15). Curvature rates at an internal point are obtained by differentiating $\dot{w}(p)$ twice under the integral sign. The resulting equation, for $p \in B$, has the form $(i, j, k, l = 1, 2)$

$$D\dot{w}_{,ij} = \int_{\partial B} \left[w^s_{1,ij}\dot{V}_n - \dot{w}V_n(w^s_{1,ij}) + M_{nn}(w^s_{1,ij})\frac{\partial \dot{w}}{\partial n} - \dot{M}_{nn}\frac{\partial w^s_{1,ij}}{\partial n} \right] ds$$

$$+ \sum_{k=1}^{m} \left\{ w^s_{1,ij}[\,|\dot{M}_{nt}|\,]_{Q_k} - \dot{w}[\,|M_{nt}(w^s_{1,ij})|\,]_{Q_k} \right\} + \int_B \dot{q} w^s_{1,ij} dA$$

$$- \lim_{\eta \to 0} \int_{B - B_\eta} w^s_{1,ijkl}\dot{M}^{(n)}_{kl} dA - I_{ijkl}\dot{M}^{(n)}_{kl} \qquad (16)$$

where the derivatives with respect to x_i and x_j are taken at the source point p and rest are taken at a field point. Since the fourth derivatives of w^s_1 are $\frac{1}{r^2}$ singular, this differentiation must be carried out with care. The free terms above are obtained by using the method outlined by Bui [9] and B_η is a circle of small radius η, centered at the source point p. The integral over $B - B_\eta$ in the above expression yields the principal value of the integral as $\eta \to 0$.

The coefficients I_{ijkl} $(i, j, k, l = 1, 2)$ of the free terms can be shown to be (Moshaiov and Vorus [2]),

	I_{ijkl}
(a) All four indices are equal	3/8
(b) Any two indices are equal and the other two are equal to a different number	1/8
(c) Any three indices are equal and the fourth index equals a different number	0

The integrals

$$\lim_{\eta \to 0} \int_{B - B_\eta} w^s_{1,ijkl}\dot{M}^{(n)}_{kl} dA$$

over triangular internal cells, can be obtained in closed form. An example is shown in [6].

Numerical Treatment and Examples

Some numerical results from formulations B and C are presented in this section.

Constitutive model

Elastic-plastic results are presented below from formulation B (Moshaiov and Vorus [2]). A Prandtl-Reuss constitutive model with a Von Mises yield surface and linear strain hardening is used here. Elastic-viscoplastic results from formulation C (Song and Mukherjee [6]) are also presented below. In this case, as hyperbolic sine law has been used. This has the form

$$\dot{\varepsilon}_{ij}^{(n)} = \frac{3}{2} A e^{-C/T} \frac{\sinh(B\sigma)}{\sigma} S_{ij} \tag{17}$$

where A, B and C are material constants, T is the temperature in ^oK, S_{ij} is the deviatoric stress tensor and σ is the stress invariant which is defined as

$$\sigma = \sqrt{\frac{3}{2} S_{ij} S_{ij}} \tag{18}$$

Discretization of integral equations

Moshaiov and Vorus [2] use straight boundary segments on ∂B and internal cells in the domain ∂B. The variables of interest, i.e. $\dot{V}_n$, $\dot{M}_{nn}$, $\frac{\partial \dot{w}}{\partial n}$ and $\dot{w}$ are assumed to be piecewise constant on the boundary elements, while $\dot{M}_{xx}^{(n)}$, $\dot{M}_{yy}^{(n)}$, $\dot{M}_{xy}^{(n)}$, and $\dot{q}$ are assumed to be piecewise constant over the internal cells. For the sake for simplicity, the authors only consider cases with no corner effects. The solution is obtained by marching forward in load increments δq and iterating, if necessary, at each load step [2].

Song and Mukherjee [6] also use piecewise straight boundary elements but use Hermite polynomials for shape functions for the boundary variables. The nonelastic moment rates in Equation [6] are evaluated by 9 point Gaussian integration through the plate thickness. These moment rates and $\dot{q}$ are assumed to be piecewise constant on the internal cells that subdivide the plate midsurface B. A march forward scheme in real time is used to obtain the time histories of the variables of interest. Due to the nature of the constitutive model used (Equation (17)), the integrand in the domain integral in Equation (15) is known at time t once the complete solution is known at that time (see, also, Mukherjee [10]) for further discussion of elastic-viscoplastic problems solved by the boundary element method). Thus, iterations are not necessary within each time step. Automatic time step control, however, is employed. Details are available in [6] and [10].

The values of the material and geometrical parameters used in [2] and [6] are available elsewhere.

Results of sample problems from [2] and [6] are presented below. Moshaiov and Vorus [2] give results for a clamped square plate of linear strain hardening material subjected to a uniform load. The boundary of the plate is subdivided into 4x10 straight boundary elements of equal length. The domain of the plate is divided into 12x12 square cells of equal size. Each domain element has 10 integration points through the thickness for calculating the plastic moments.

The results of the calculations are given in Figures 1 and 2. The load versus central deflection curve in Figure 1 shows characteristic elastic-plastic behavior and shows good agreement with the finite element results of Owen and Figueiras [11]. Figure 2 indicates the spread of plasticity through the plate volume at a load near the limit load. The numbers inside the domain cells indicate the level of plasticity through the thickness and correspond to the number of integration points at which yielding is reached. Blank cells are elastic.

Moshaiov and Vorus also present numerical results for a simply supported and a clamped circular plate subjected to uniform load, in [2]. They do not, however, present any numerical results for plates with free edges in their paper [2].

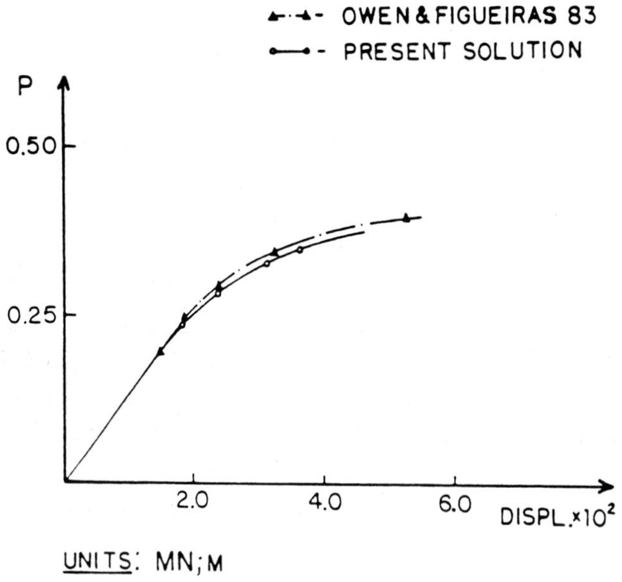

Figure 1. Central deflection versus load for a clamped square plate (from Moshaiov and Vorus [2]).

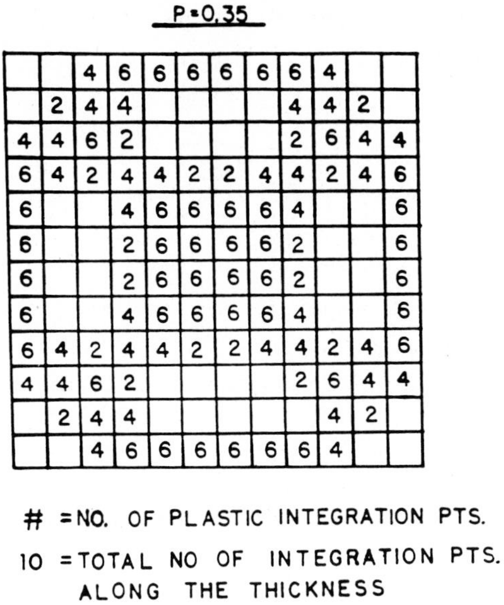

Figure 2. Elastic-plastic boundaries for a clamped square plate (from Moshaiov and Vorus [2]).

Corresponding results for square plates, from Song and Mukherjee, are shown in Figures 3, 4 and 5. In each case the loading is uniform and increases in time at a constant rate. The square plates are divided into 20 equal boundary elements and 25 equal size square cells (Figure 3). Figure 3 shows the load versus central deflection for a fully clamped plate, and one with two opposite edges clamped and the other two simply supported. The corresponding redistribution of stress, through the thickness at point B in Figure 3, is shown in Figure 4. This figure shows the characteristic transition of the stress from linear elastic to nonlinear elastic-viscoplastic. Results for a cantilevered square plate are also given in [6]. Finally, Figure 5 shows load-deflection curves for a clamped square plate with a square cutout. This time 16 equal boundary elements are used on the boundary ACDEFG in Figure 5, and 12 uniform cells are used to divide the region enclosed within this boundary.

Thus, the results presented in [6], from formulation C, include combinations of all the important boundary conditions - clamped, simply supported and free edges - together with corners of a general nature. Global equilibrium checks have been carried out for these

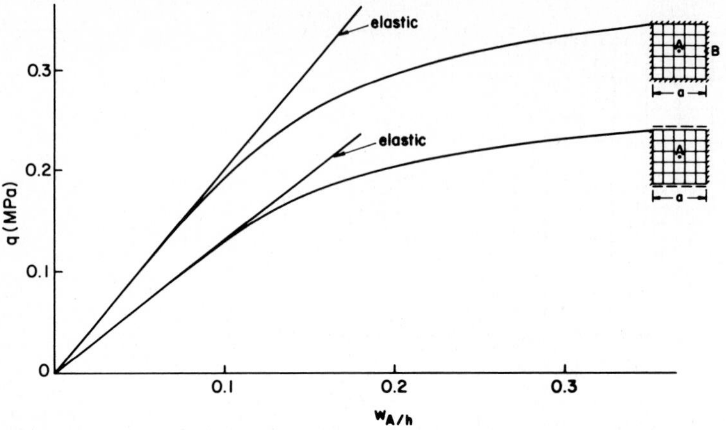

Figure 3. Central deflection versus load for a clamped square plate and a plate with two edges clamped and two simply supported (from Song and Mukherjee [6]).

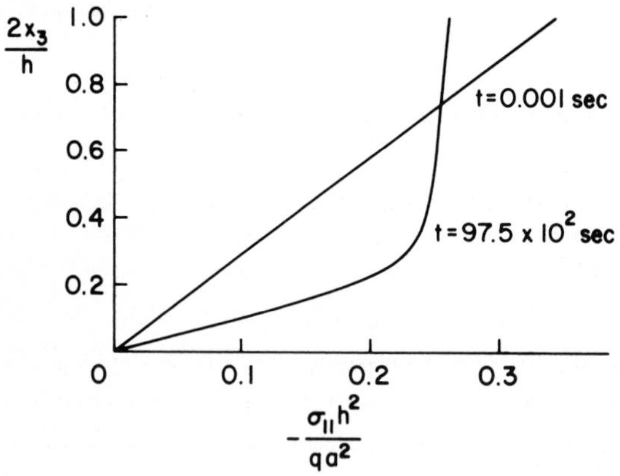

Figure 4. Redistribution of stress at a point B (of Figure 3) of the clamped square plate (from Song and Mukherjee [6]).

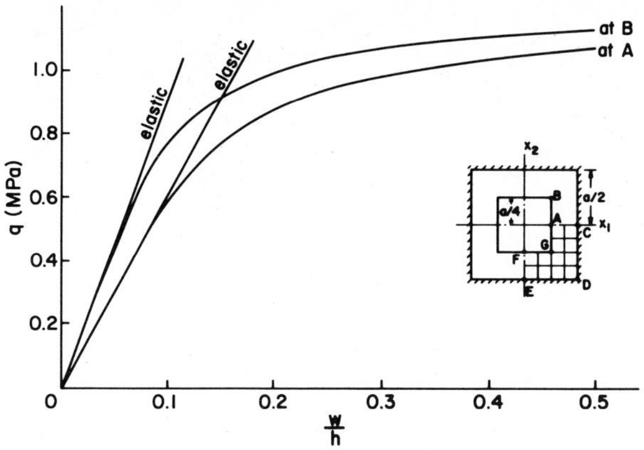

Figure 5. Loads as functions of displacements at points A and B of a clamped square plate with a square cutout (from Song and Mukherjee [6]).

problems in order to check the accuracy of the numerical solutions. These are satisfied within around 0.06%. Details are available in [6].

Additional Topics in Nonlinear Analysis of Plates

Thermal stresses and membrane effects

Moshaiov and Vorus [12] present an extention of formulation B above to include thermal loading, variable material properties and membrane effects. Their main motivation here is to model the line heating method, which is used to bend plates in shipyards. Of course, the formulation is general and can be used to solve thermo-elasto-plastic bending problems for plates.

In [12], the authors present an extention of their earlier formulation B, to include membrane effects and thermal loads, and variation of Young's modulus E and shear modulus G through the thickness (x_3 direction) of the plate. The material properties are assumed to be constant in the in-plane (x_1 and x_2) directions in the plate. The resulting equation, for a point p inside the plate, has the form

$$\overline{D}\dot{w}(p) = \int_{\partial B} \left[w_1^s \dot{V}_n - \dot{w} V_n(w_1^s) + M_{nn}(w_1^s)\frac{\partial \dot{w}}{\partial n} - \dot{M}_{nn}\frac{\partial w_1^s}{\partial n} \right] ds$$

$$+ \sum_{i=1}^{m} \left\{ [\,|\, w_1^s \dot{M}_{nt} \,|\,]_{Q_i} - [\,|\, \dot{w} M_{nt}(w_1^s) \,|\,]_{Q_i} \right\}$$

$$- \int_B (\dot{M}_{ij}^{(I)} w_{1,ij}^s - w_1^s \dot{q}) dA - \int_B \dot{M}^{(TC)} w_{1,kk}^s dA \qquad (19)$$

where

$$\dot{M}_{11}^{(I)} = \dot{M}_{11}^{(n)} - \dot{M}_{11}^{(c)} - \overline{E}_3(\dot{\overline{\varepsilon}}_{11}^{(e)} + \nu\dot{\overline{\varepsilon}}_{22}^{(e)}) - \overline{E}_3(\dot{\overline{\varepsilon}}_{11}^{(n)} + \nu\dot{\overline{\varepsilon}}_{22}^{(n)})$$

$$\dot{M}_{22}^{(I)} = \dot{M}_{22}^{(n)} - \dot{M}_{22}^{(c)} - \overline{E}_3(\dot{\overline{\varepsilon}}_{22}^{(e)} + \nu\dot{\overline{\varepsilon}}_{11}^{(e)}) - \overline{E}_3(\dot{\overline{\varepsilon}}_{22}^{(n)} + \nu\dot{\overline{\varepsilon}}_{11}^{(n)})$$

$$\dot{M}_{12}^{(I)} = \dot{M}_{12}^{(n)} - \dot{M}_{12}^{(c)} - \overline{G}_3\dot{\overline{\varepsilon}}_{12}$$

where the midplane strain rates are denoted by bars on them.

The moment corrections due to material property variations are

$$\dot{M}_{11}^{(c)} = \int_{-\frac{h}{2}}^{\frac{h}{2}} \frac{\dot{E}}{1-\nu^2}(\varepsilon_{11}^{(e)} + \nu\varepsilon_{22}^{(e)}) x_3 dx_3$$

$$\dot{M}_{22}^{(c)} = \int_{-\frac{h}{2}}^{\frac{h}{2}} \frac{\dot{E}}{1-\nu^2}(\varepsilon_{22}^{(e)} + \nu\varepsilon_{11}^{(e)}) x_3 dx_3$$

$$\dot{M}_{12}^{(c)} = \int_{-\frac{h}{2}}^{\frac{h}{2}} 2\dot{G}\,\varepsilon_{12}^{(e)} x_3 dx_3$$

The thermal moment rates are

$$\dot{M}^{(T)} = \int_{-\frac{h}{2}}^{\frac{h}{2}} \frac{E}{1-\nu^2}\dot{\varepsilon}^T x_3 dx_3$$

and $\dot{M}^{(TC)} = \dot{M}^{(T)} - \overline{\varepsilon}_3(1+\nu)\dot{\varepsilon}^T$.

Finally, the averaged material properties are defined as

$$\overline{E}_3 = \int_{-\frac{h}{2}}^{\frac{h}{2}} \frac{E}{1-\nu^2} x_3 dx_3$$

$$\overline{G}_3 = \int_{-\frac{h}{2}}^{\frac{h}{2}} 2Gx_3 dx_3$$

$$\overline{D} = \int_{-\frac{h}{2}}^{\frac{h}{2}} \frac{E}{1-\nu^2} x_3^2 dx_3$$

In order to solve the problem, one also needs two equations, for the boundary values of $\dot{w}$ and for the boundary slope. These are available in [12].

The coupling between bending and in-plane quantities requires, in general, separate equations for solving of the in-plane problem. This can also be carried out by using the boundary element method [10, 13].

Moshaiov and Vorus [12] present numerical solutions for a simplified problem where zero in-plane stresses are assumed. They consider thermo-elastic-plastic plate bending due to thermal loads - in particular, plate bending due to line heating. These numerical solutions are available in [12].

Large deflections and instability analysis

Okada, Fujimoto and Abe [14] present an application of the boundary element method to elasto-plastic instability analysis of thin plates undergoing large deflections. Both geometric and material nonlinearities are included in the analysis. Of course, membrane effects must be included in large deformation analysis of plates. A plasticity constitutive model is used to model inelastic behavior.

The authors start with the usual equilibrium and kinematic equations. The kinematic equations, in view of geometric nonlinearities, has the form $(i, j = 1, 2)$

$$\dot{\varepsilon}_{ij} = \dot{u}_{i,j} + \frac{1}{2}\frac{d}{dt}(w_{,i}w_{,j}) - x_3\dot{w}_{,ij}$$

where u_i are the inplane displacement components. Following a weighted residual approach, the authors in [14] derive two coupled boundary integral equations, one for the inplane and the other for transverse displacements. The inplane equations have the standard terms for planar boundary element analysis [10] but also include a domain integral that involves the transverse displacement. The equation for $\dot{w}$ is an extended version of the equations presented earlier in this chapter. Again, equations are derived for the boundary values of $\dot{w}$ and $\frac{\partial \dot{w}}{\partial n}$.

The resulting equations are quite complicated. They are discretized in the usual way, with piecewise constant unknowns on the boundary elements and on the internal cells. An iterative scheme is used to solve the discretized equations.

Three numerical examples are presented in [14]. The first example is concerned with buckling of a simply supported thin elastic plate subjected to shearing stresses. The accuracy of the results, for a sufficiently fine discretization, is excellent. The second example is concerned with elastic instability analysis of a thin square plate which is subjected to a compressive force, with uniform displacements, on opposite sides. The other two sides of the plate are free. The post buckling displacements agree very well with a finite element analysis.

Finally, the last example considers elasto-plastic instability analysis of a thin simply supported square plate. Two loading cases, uniform compressive, and uniform shearing, are considered here.

Introduction to Inelastic Analysis of Shells

Applications of the boundary element method in shell analysis have so far been very limited. The primary reason for this is that while Green's functions exist for certain special situations (e.g. for cylindrical shells (Sanders and Simmonds [15]), they are not known for arbitrary shells. Tottenham [16], and Newton and Tottenham [17] have presented some BEM formulations for shallow shells together with numerical results for shallow cylindrical or spherical shells, but there is no way to generalize this approach to attack boundary value problems for general shells.

Poddar and Mukherjee [18] present an integral equation approach for the analysis and determination of numerical solutions for the deformation of shells of arbitrary shape subjected to arbitrary loading. The mathematical model in this approach is derived by projection of the appropriate 3D BEM equations onto the shell space. This is done by transformation of the three-dimensional equations from the Cartesian to the appropriate curvilinear coordinates of the shell. Besides transforming the 3-D equations to the shell midsurface, some assumptions are made in order to take advantage of the shell being thin. In particular, these assumptions are mainly concerned with the specification of the load on the edges, and kinematic assumptions for the dependence of the displacements on the thickness coordinate of the shell.

A general shell is assumed to consist of a shell midsurface (S), which is described by only two curvilinear coordinates θ^α, a shell top surface (S^+), a shell bottom surface (S^-), and a shell edge (S_E) (Figure 6). In Poddar and Mukherjee [18], it is assumed that the shell is of uniform thickness, i.e., the surfaces S^+ and S^- are assumed to be parallel to the surface S.

In all the tensor expressions to follow, the following convention will be followed: all Greek indices for tensor quantities will have a range from 1 to 2, whereas all Latin indices will have a range from 1 to 3.

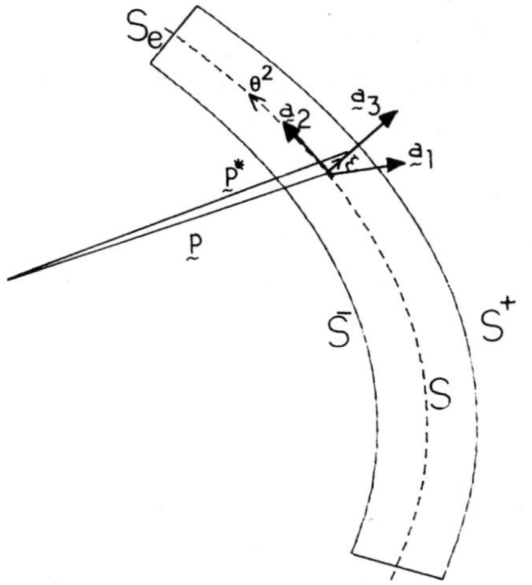

Figure 6. Geometry of the shell showing various surfaces and the shell midsurface basis (from Poddar and Mukherjee [18]).

The position vector of a point on the shell midsurface is given by

$$\mathbf{p} = x^i(\theta^\alpha)\mathbf{e}_i, \qquad \alpha = 1, 2 \tag{20}$$

where $\mathbf{e}_i$ are the components of the Cartesian basis.

The shell midsurface basis is defined as

$$\mathbf{a}_\alpha = \frac{\partial \mathbf{p}}{\partial \theta^\alpha}, \qquad \alpha = 1, 2$$

$$\mathbf{a}_3 = \frac{\mathbf{a}_1 \times \mathbf{a}_2}{|\mathbf{a}_1 \times \mathbf{a}_2|} \tag{21}$$

The shell midsurface basis is related to the Cartesian basis by the transformations

$$\mathbf{a}_i = \phi^j{}_i \mathbf{e}_j$$

$$\mathbf{e}_i = (\phi^{-1})^j{}_i \mathbf{a}_j \tag{22}$$

where the transformations (ϕ) and (ϕ^{-1}), of course, depend on the particular problem under consideration.

For a two point second rank tensor $\mathbf{A}(p,q)$, the transformation has to be carried out keeping in mind the fact that the two indices depend on different spatial locations p and q. Hence,

$$A^i{}_j \mathbf{e}_i(q)\mathbf{e}^j(p) = \overline{A}^i{}_j \mathbf{a}_i(q)\mathbf{a}^j(p) \tag{23}$$

where

$$\mathbf{e}_i(q) = (\phi^{-1}(q))^j{}_i \mathbf{a}_j(q)$$

$$\mathbf{e}^j(p) = (\phi(p))^j{}_i \mathbf{a}^i(p) \tag{24}$$

and a superscribed bar is used to denote quantities in the $\mathbf{a}_i$ basis. It is important to note that different functions ϕ must be used for the two locations p and q.

More detailed information on shell basis vectors, tensor transformation relationships and the procedure for obtaining the strain tensors $\overline{\varepsilon}_{\theta\nu}$, $\overline{\varepsilon}_{\theta 3}$ and $\overline{\varepsilon}_{33}$ in the shell midsurface basis, from the midsurface displacements $\overline{u}_\alpha$ and $\overline{u}_3$, is available in Poddar and Mukherjee [18], Dikmen [19], Flugge [20], and Naghdi [21].

Integral Equation Formulation for Inelastic Shells

The formulation for general shells consists of three parts - first the derivation of the governing integral equations in the shell coordinates, second, kinematic assumptions, and third, the approximations on the edge where only a limited number of boundary conditions are available for the shell.

Transformation of the 3-D BEM equations for general shells

The starting point for this analysis is an integral equation for the analysis of three-dimensional solids. The direct formulation in terms of tractions and displacements on the boundary is used here (Mukherjee [10]). The equation in Cartesian coordinates, using general tensor notation, has the form

$$\dot{u}_j(p) = \int_{\partial B} [U^i{}_j(p,Q)\dot{\tau}_i(Q) - T^i{}_j(p,Q)\dot{u}_i(Q)]\, dS_Q + \int_B 2GW^i{}_{jk}(p,q)\dot{\varepsilon}^{(n)k}{}_i(q)dv_q \tag{25}$$

where the components of the velocity and traction rate vectors are denoted as $\dot{u}_i$ and $\dot{\tau}_i$, respectively, and $U^i{}_j$, $T^i{}_j$, and $W^i{}_{jk} = U^i{}_{j\,||\,k}$ are the mixed components of the usual two-point kernels which are available in many references (e.g. Mukherjee [10]). The inelastic strain rate, $\dot{\varepsilon}^{(n)k}{}_i$, is obtained from an appropriate constitutive model. In the numerical simulations reported later, a viscoplastic type constitutive model, in particular, the model proposed by Anand [22], has been used. Also, p (or P) is a source point and q (or Q) is a field point (with the lower case letters denoting points inside the body B and upper case letters denoting points on its boundary ∂B). Unless otherwise indicated, the range of indices for the equations in this section is 1 to 3.

The next step is to transform Equation (25) from the Cartesian basis $\mathbf{e}_i$ to the shell midsurface basis, $\mathbf{a}_i$. The two point kernels in Equation (25) are transformed according to the transformation laws given by Equation (24).

The transformed Equation (25) becomes

$$\dot{\bar{u}}_j(p) = \int_{\partial B} [\bar{U}^i{}_j(p,Q)\dot{\bar{\tau}}_i(Q) - \bar{T}^i{}_j(p,Q)\dot{\bar{u}}_i(Q)]\, dS_Q + \int_B 2G\bar{W}^i{}_{jk}(p,q)\dot{\bar{\varepsilon}}^{(n)k}{}_i(q)dv_q \tag{26}$$

where

$$\begin{aligned}\dot{\bar{u}}_i(Q) &= (\phi(Q))^m{}_i \dot{u}_m(Q)\\ \dot{\bar{\tau}}_i(Q) &= (\phi(Q))^m{}_i \dot{\tau}_m(Q)\end{aligned} \tag{27}$$

and

$$\begin{aligned}\bar{U}^i{}_j(p,q) &= (\phi(p))^l{}_j(\phi^{-1}(q))^i{}_k U^k{}_l(p,q)\\ \bar{T}^i{}_j(p,q) &= (\phi(p))^l{}_j(\phi^{-1}(q))^i{}_k T^k{}_l(p,q)\\ \bar{W}^i{}_{jk}(p,q) &= (\phi(p))^l{}_j(\phi^{-1}(q))^i{}_m(\phi(q))^n{}_k W^m{}_{ln}(p,q)\end{aligned} \tag{28}$$

are the transformed components of the two point kernel tensors. Finally Equation (26) takes the explicit form

$$\begin{aligned}\dot{\bar{u}}_j(p) = {} & (\phi(p))^l{}_j \int_{\partial B} (\phi^{-1}(Q))^i{}_k U^k{}_l(p,Q)\dot{\bar{\tau}}_i(Q)\, dS_Q\\ & - (\phi(p))^l{}_j \int_{\partial B} (\phi^{-1}(Q))^i{}_k T^k{}_l(p,Q)\dot{\bar{u}}_i(Q)\, dS_Q\\ & + (\phi(p))^l{}_j \int_B 2G(\phi^{-1}(q))^i{}_m(\phi(q))^s{}_k W^m{}_{ls}(p,q)\dot{\bar{\varepsilon}}^{(n)k}{}_i(q)dv_q\end{aligned} \tag{29}$$

The integrals must be evaluated over the entire boundary of the shell which includes the surfaces S^+ and S^- which are parallel to the shell midsurface S, as well as the edges S_E of the shell (Figure (6)). The edge S_E is assumed to be normal to the shell midsurface S. The idea here is to initially solve for the unknowns on the shell boundary by using Equation (29) with $p \to P$ and treating the shell as a three-dimensional solid. Once this has been done, appropriate kinematic assumptions are made for the variation of velocities as a function of the thickness coordinate ξ of the shell and then the strain rates and stress rates are determined throughout the shell. The stress rate resultants can then be obtained by integrating the stress rates through the thickness of the shell.

Kinematic assumptions for the displacements

As discussed in Poddar [23], if starting from the displacements, one desires to obtain the strains, stresses, and then the moments accurately using purely kinematic assumptions, then the displacement must be at least quadratic in the thickness coordinate ξ in order to yield the correct moment.

The velocity field through the thickness is assumed to be

$$\dot{\bar{u}}_i = \dot{\tilde{\bar{u}}}_i + \xi \dot{\tilde{\bar{\delta}}}_i + \xi^2 \dot{\tilde{\eta}}_i \tag{30}$$

where a superposed $\tilde{}$ indicates that the corresponding quantity is a function of θ^1 and θ^2, the natural curvilinear coordinates of the shell midsurface (and not of ξ).

Usually, one solves for the displacement on the two boundaries of the shell. However, that is not enough to specify the quadratic displacement through the thickness completely. Hence, once the displacement vector on the boundary is known, displacement components are calculated at points on the shell midsurface. Knowing displacements at three points, it is easy to find $\tilde{\bar{u}}_i$, $\tilde{\bar{\delta}}_i$, and $\tilde{\eta}_i$ using Equation (30).

The above kinematic approximation for the velocities leads to an infinite series in ξ for the strains. Only terms up to quadratic in ξ are retained in subsequent analysis. With this assumption, the expression for the stresses is given as

$$\dot{\tau}_i = \dot{\bar{\sigma}}^j{}_i \bar{n}_j = A_i + B_i \xi + C_i \xi^2 - 2G \dot{\bar{\varepsilon}}^{(n)j}{}_i \bar{n}_j \tag{31}$$

where A_i, B_i, and C_i are unknown coefficients that correspond to a quadratic behavior of the total strain and $\dot{\bar{\varepsilon}}^{(n)j}{}_i$ is a non-linear distribution of inelastic strain which evolves in time.

Boundary conditions

In view of the quadratic velocity assumption (Equation (30)), each line in S_E, perpendicular to S, must have at least a midpoint node in addition to the nodes where this line intersects S^+ and S^-. Since S_E is part of the shell boundary, this requirement must be met at the outset.

Several situations might arise for the boundary conditions on an edge. If the tractions are prescribed on an edge, their values at the edge nodes are used in the integral equation and the displacements are obtained at these points. If, instead, the displacements are prescribed on an edge, the tractions are determined on the nodes through the integral equation and then their distribution is obtained from Equation (31). Mixed situations are taken care of in an analogous fashion.

A third situation can arise in which stress resultants are prescribed on S_E. This situation is handled by integrating Equation (31) to relate the unknown constants A_i, B_i and C_i to the stress resultants. However, the number of unknown constants (A_i etc.) exceed the number of stress resultants. Additional information is obtained from the shear tractions at the corners in order to specify the unknown constants completely. For example, the shear traction $\bar{\tau}_1$ on S^+ is equal to $\bar{\tau}_3(\xi{=}h/2)$ on S_E. More details of the approximations made for the stress resultant boundary conditions are given in Poddar and Mukherjee [18].

Numerical Results

Axisymmetric elastic problems

Poddar and Mukherjee [18] obtain the results from this formulation for a torus subjected to internal pressure. The radial displacement is shown in Figure 7 and shows good agreement with the finite element results from Zienkiewicz[24]. For the same torus, results are also obtained for several exact solutions to axisymmetric elastic problems. The correlation between the exact and computed solutions are uniformly excellent.

In order to verify the approximations for the edges, a problem of simply supported circular cylinder under internal pressure has also been solved in [18].

Axisymmetric inelastic problems

To avoid complications that could arise during time integration of some of the more detailed constitutive models (Mukherjee [10]), a simple inelastic constitutive model proposed by Anand [22] for Fe-0.05 weight percent carbon steel has been used by Poddar and Mukherjee [18]. Details of Anand's model, as well as the material parameters used in the simulation are given in Poddar [23].

Poddar and Mukherjee [18] give results for a circular cylinder of length 1000.0 mm with thickness 10.0 mm and midsurface radius 250.0 mm subjected to constant load rate test where the pressure linearly increases from 0.0 MPa to 2.0 MPa in 60 s. The cylinder is also subjected to an axial force, $p\pi r^2$, due to the capped ends. The displacement history of the midsurface of the cylinder, as a function of position and time, is shown in Figure 8. One half of the cylinder is shown here. The results of three different calculations are shown in this figure - this BEM, a FEM calculation for axisymmetric inelastic solids (Rajiyah and Mukherjee [26]), and a semi-analytical solution based on Love-Kirchhoff theory (Kollmann and Mukherjee [25]). The Love-Kirchhoff and FEM results, for t = 40

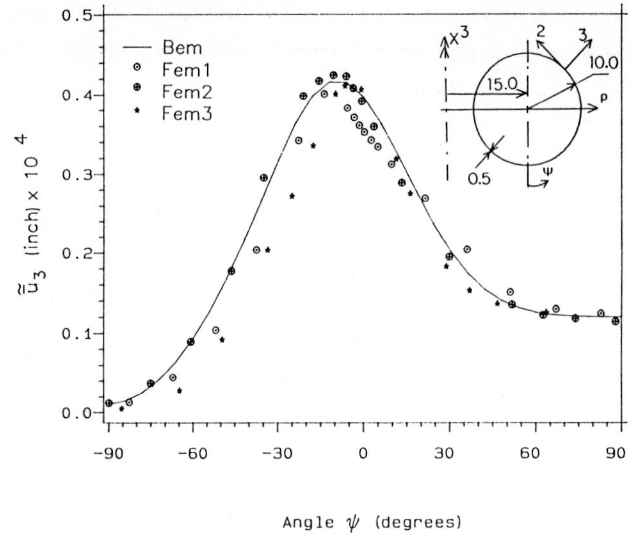

Figure 7. Variation of radial displacement with the angle ψ for a torus under internal pressure - p = 1 psi, dimensions of the inset are in inches (from Poddar and Mukherjee [18]).

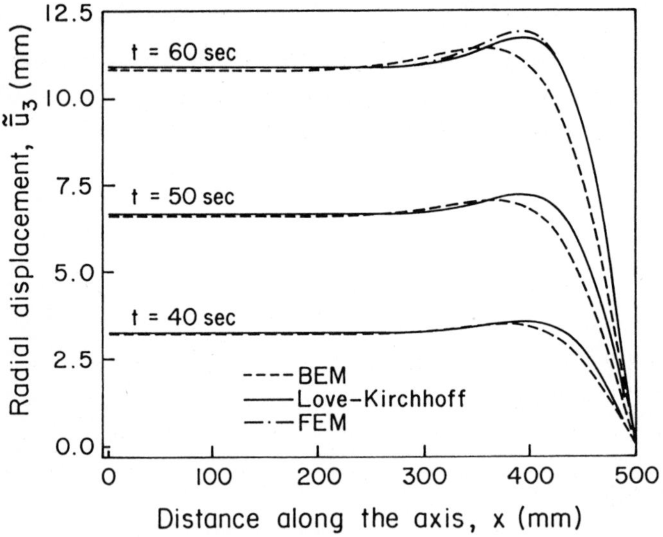

Figure 8. Radial displacement history for a simply supported cylinder under increasing internal pressure - p = 0.75 MPa, radius = 250.0 mm, thickness = 10.0 mm, length = 1000.0 mm (from Poddar and Mukherjee [18]).

and 50 s in Figure 8, coincide within plotting accuracy. Similar results for the redistribution of axial stress, at a location $x = 465$ mm (the length of the half cylinder is 500 mm), are given in Figure 9. Overall, the FEM results show better correlation with the Love-Kirchoff theory results than the BEM.

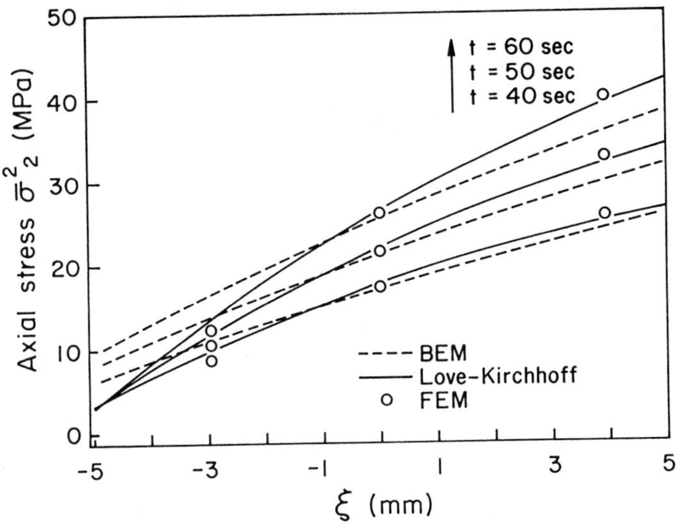

Figure 9. Axial stress history for a simply supported cylinder under increasing internal pressure - $p = 0.75$ MPa, radius = 250.0 mm, thickness = 10.0 mm, length = 1000.0 mm (from Poddar and Mukherjee [18]).

Acknowledgements

The research of Mukherjee, Poddar and Song, reported in this article, has been supported by NSF grant number MSM8609391 to Cornell University. Figures 1 and 2 have been reprinted with permission from the International Journal of Solids and Structures, Vol. 22, Moshaiov and Vorus, Elasto-plastic plate bending analysis by a boundary element method with initial plastic moments, 1986, Pergamon Press.

References

1. Timoshenko, S. P.; Woinowsky-Krieger, S.: Theory of plates and shells. New York: McGraw-Hill 1959.

2. Moshaiov, A.; Vorus, W. S.: Elasto-plastic plate bending analysis by a boundary element method with initial plastic moments. Int. J. Solids Structures 22 (1986) 1213-1229.

3. Morjaria, M.; Mukherjee, S.: Inelastic analysis of transverse deflection of plates by the boundary element method. J. Appl. Mech. 47 (1980) 291-296.

4. Stern, M.: A general boundary integral formulation for the numerical solution of plate bending problems. Int. J. Solids Structures 15 (1979) 769-782.

5. Bezine, G.: A boundary integral equation method for plate flexure with conditions inside the domain. Int. J. Num. Meth. Engng. 17 (1981) 1647-1657.

6. Song, G-S.; Mukherjee, S.: Boundary element method analysis of bending of inelastic plates with general boundary conditions. Comput. Mech. 5 (1989) 104-112.

7. Du, Q.; Yao, Z.; Song, G-S.: Solution of some plate bending problems using the boundary element method. Appl. Math. Modeling 8 (1984) 15-22.

8. Song, G-S.; Mukherjee, S.: Boundary element method analysis of bending of elastic plates of arbitrary shape with general boundary conditions. Eng. Anal. 3 (1986) 36-44.

9. Bui, H. D.: Some remarks about the formulation of three-dimensional thermoelasto-plastic problems by integral equations. Int. J. Solids Structures 14 (1978) 935-939.

10. Mukherjee, S.: Boundary element methods in creep and fracture. London: Elsevier Applied Science Publishers 1982.

11. Owen, D. R. J.; Figueiras, J. A.: Elasto-plastic analysis of anisotropic plates and shells by the semiloof element. Int. J. Num. Meth. Engng. 19 (1983) 521-539.

12. Moshaiov, A.; Vorus, W. S.: Thermo-elastic-plastic plate bending by a boundary element method with initial plastic moments. Connor, J. J.; Brebbia, C. A. (eds.): Betech 86. Southampton: Computational Mechanics (1986) 567-594.

13. Moshaiov, A.: Thermo-elastic-plastic plate bending by a boundary element method with initial plastic moments. Ph. D. Thesis, Department of Naval Architecture and Marine Engineering, The University of Michigan, Ann Arbor (1985).

14. Okada, H.; Fujimoto, M.; Abe, H.: Elastoplastic instability analysis of thin plates. Brebbia, C. A.; Futagami, T.; Tanaka, M. (eds.): Boundary elements. Berlin: Springer Verlag (1983) 589-597.

15. Sanders, J. L.; Simmonds, J. G.: Concentrated forces on shallow cylindrical shells. J. Appl. Mech. 37 (1970) 367-373.

16. Tottenham, H.: The boundary element method for plates and shells. Banerjee, P. K.; Butterfield, R. (eds.): Progress in Boundary Element Methods, vol. 2. England: Elsevier Applied Science Publishers (1979) 173-205.

17. Newton, D. A.; Tottenham, H.: Boundary value problems in thin shallow shells of arbitrary plan form. J. Engng. Math. II (1968) 211-223.

18. Poddar, B.; Mukherjee, S.; An integral equation analysis of inelastic shells. Comput. Mech. 4 (1989) 261-275.

19. Dikmen, M.: Theory of thin elastic shells. London: Pitman (1982).

20. Flugge, W.: Tensor analysis and continuum mechanics. Springer Verlag (1972).

21. Naghdi, P. M.: The theory of plates and shells. Flugge, W.; Truesdell, C. (eds.): Handbuch der Physik, Vol. VIa/2. Springer (1972).

22. Anand, L.: Constitutive equations for the rate-dependent deformation of metals at elevated temperatures. J. Engng. Mat. Tech. 104 (1982) 12-17.

23. Poddar, B.: An integral equation analysis of inelastic shells. Ph. D. Thesis. New York: Cornell University (1987).

24. Zienkiewicz, O. C.: The finite element method. UK: McGraw-Hill (1977).

25. Kollmann, F. G., and Mukherjee, S.: Inelastic deformation of thin cylindrical shells under axisymmetric loading. Ingenieur-Archiv 54 (1984) 355-367

26. Rajiyah, H. and Mukherjee, S.: A comparison of boundary element and finite element methods for inelastic axisymmetric problems with large strains and rotations. Nakazawa, S.; Willam, K.; Rebelo, N. (eds.): Advances in inelastic analysis, AMD Vol. 88 (1987) 199-222.

Stability Analysis of Plates and Shells

G. D. MANOLIS

Department of Civil Engineering
Aristotle University of Thessaloniki
GR-54006 Thessaloniki, Greece

Summary

This chapter presents an application of the direct boundary element method (BEM) to the classical stability analysis of thin (Kirchoff-type) plates, plate systems, and thin shallow shells. In particular, the case of the individual plate is treated in an exhaustive way, and material on orthotropic plates, on how to avoid volume integrals, on how to introduce experimental strain measurements in the formulation, and on the thermal buckling problem is also included. The single plate serves as a springboard for the problem of plate systems, where the membrane action must now be explicitly modeled. Shell stability requires coupling of both bending and membrane action in a nonlinear fashion, since it is known that the Euler load for shells overestimates the buckling loads that have been experimentally observed. Finally, extensions of the BEM formulation to include both material and geometric nonlinearities in the plate stability formulation are also discussed.

Introduction

Among the earliest formulations for the Euler buckling load of thin plates using the direct BEM is due to Sekiya and Katayama [1] and Tai et al [2]. In their work, the effect of the in-plane forces responsible for the buckling phenomenon is accounted for through the presence of an area integral. Their formulation, however, is restricted to cases where both transverse displacement and rotations are zero at the boundaries of the plate (i.e., clamped boundaries). An interesting by-product of their work is the expression of the kernel of the area integral in terms of surface strains that allows efficient use of experimentally obtained strain data in the computation of the buckling load.

Complete formulations that allow for any type of commonly encounted boundary conditions to be considered have since appeared, i.e., Bézine et al [3], Costa and Brebbia [4], and others [5,6]. As is expected, the boundary conditions in these papers are handled through the presence of boundary integrals, while area integrals are still necessary because the fundamental solutions used are for the biharmonic operator (pure bending behavior) only. Also, Bezine et al [3] give the modifications in the BEM formulation that are necessary for introducing an elastic foundation below the plate. In an effort to dispense with area integrations, Gospodinov and Ljutskanov [7], Manolis et al [5] and Kawabe [8] have all introduced special fundamental solutions of the governing differential equation that includes the effect of in-plane forces on bending. It was found [5,9], though, that the effort in numerically evaluating a fundamental solution that is now more complicated than the ordinary one for pure plate bending is often compensated by the extra effort in computing area integrals when the simpler fundamental solutions are used, at least for simple problems. Finally, Liu [10] has managed, through repeated integration by parts, to convert the area integral accounting for the in-plane forces to a surface integral only, while Jin [11] discusses fundamental solutions for the quarter plate and the plate sector that, depending on the boundary conditions, dispense with line integrals over part of the plate's surface.

The basic direct BEM formulation for thin plate stability has been extended to cover the case of structures assembled from simple plate components by Tanaka and Miyazaki [12,13]. This requires the introduction of local and global coordinate systems, but in order to be able to transform from the former to the latter system, the in-plane behavior must be modeled explicitly through an additional boundary integral equation. Other developments in the area of plate stability include orthotropic plates [14] where the key ingredient is a fundamental solution for orthotropic bending; the buckling of heated plates [15,16], where the Berger hypothesis is used to linearize the relation between deformation and temperature fields; and the introduction of elastoplastic material behavior [17,18] as well as of large deflections [19] in the stability analysis. The last improvement adds considerable power to the analysis procedure, because information on the post-buckling behavior of thin plates can now be obtained.

Finally, as far as the stability analysis of shallow shells is concerned, it is necessary to introduce geometric nonlinearities in the formulation, because the first critical (Euler) buckling load is not a realistic quantity. Actually, a thin shallow shell will invariably experience a dynamic snap-through to a new equilibrium configuration, at a load considerably lower than the Euler load, that may or may not be followed by a stiffening of the shell. As a result, the work of Zhang and Atluri [20,21] and of Tosaka and Miyake [22} considers a nonlinear, coupled strain-displacement relation in their formulation that leads to a coupled set of boundary integral equations for both bending and membrane action, that are subsequently solved numerically through the use of incremental/iterative schemes.

This chapter is structured as follows: First, the elastic stability problem for thin flat plates is formulated via the direct BEM, followed by numerical implementation aspects and by examples. Next, the formulation is extended to cover the buckling of plate structures, followed by material on the linearized thermal buckling of plates. Subsequently, the post-buckling analysis of thin, shallow shells is described and is illustrated by an example. The final section gives a brief description of the way material and geometric nonlinearities can be introduced in the BEM formulation so as to enable tracing of the post-buckling behavior of plates.

Plate Stability-Formulation

This section develops the direct BEM for stability analysis of a thin, Kirchoff-type plate exhibiting linear elastic material behavior, as shown in Fig. 1. The governing differential equation in cartesian coordinates is [23]

$$D\nabla^4 w = \lambda \, N_{ij} \, w_{,ij} = q \qquad (i,j=1,2) \tag{1}$$

where $w(x_1,x_2)$ is the transverse deflection. The flexural rigidity of the plate is $D = Eh^3 / 12(1-\nu)$, where E is the modulus of elasticity, ν is Poisson's ratio, and h is the plate thickness. Factor λ denotes proportional loading, while the contribution of the in-plane (membrane) forces $N_{ij}(x_1,x_2)$ can be viewed as equivalent to a lateral load q. Also, the summation convention is implied for repeated subscripts, commas indicate differentiation with respect to the planar coordinates x_1,x_2 and ∇^4 is the two-dimensional biharmonic operator. Finally, the membrane forces obey the following equilibrium equations:

$$N_{ij,j} = 0 \qquad (i,j=1,2) \tag{2}$$

Additional definitions for the sake of completeness include the generalized moments and shears per unit length, i.e.,

$$M_{ij} = -D\{(1-\nu)w_{,ij} + \nu \, w_{,kk}\delta_{ij}\} \quad \text{and} \quad Q_i = M_{ij,j} \tag{3}$$

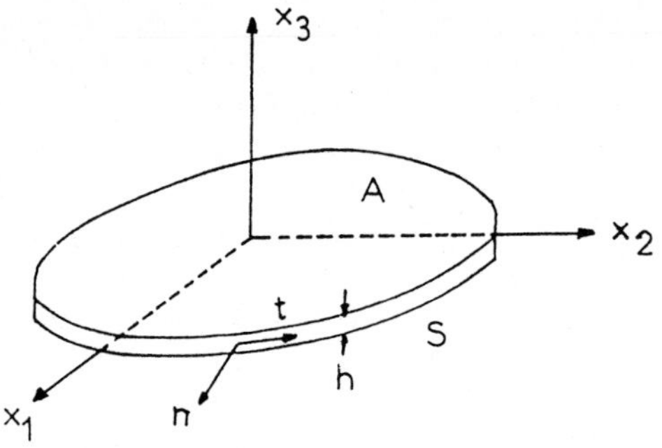

Fig. 1. Thin plate: Notation and coordinate system

respectively, where δ_{ij} is the Kronecker delta. It is now expedient to introduce local coordinate system (n,t), where n is the normal and t is the tangent to the plate's perimeter. Then, rotation θ, bending moment M, Kirchoff shear V and the jump in the twisting moment T_m at a corner m can be defined as

$$\theta = \frac{\partial w}{\partial n},\ M = \frac{\partial^2 w}{\partial n} + \nu \frac{\partial^2 w}{\partial t^2},\ V = \frac{\partial^3 w}{\partial n^3} + (2-\nu) \frac{\partial^3 w}{\partial n \partial t^2} \text{ and}$$

$$T_m = -D(1-\nu) \left[\!\left[\frac{\partial^3 w}{\partial n \partial t} \right]\!\right]_m \tag{4}$$

In the above, double brackets indicate a jump term due to the discontinuity in the normal and tangent vectors at corner m.

In order to derive a boundary integral equation representation for this problem, Betti's reciprocal theorem or the more general method of weighted residuals may be used [4]. Following the former path, we have, for two different elastic states, that

$$\iint q w^* \, dA + \int (V w^* - M \theta^*) dS + T_m w_m^* =$$

$$\iint q^* w dA + \int (V^* w - M^* \theta) dS + T^*_m w_m \tag{5}$$

where S is the plate's perimeter and A is its area. If the starred state is identified with the solution of Eqn. (1) for a unit point force $\delta(\xi_1, \xi_2)$ replacing q, i.e.,

$$w^*(r) = r^2(\ell n r^2 - 1)/(16\pi D) \tag{6}$$

where $r^2 = (x_1-\xi_1)^2 + (x_2-\xi_2)^2$, then Eqn. (5) becomes, through a limiting process,

$$c\, w(\xi_i) = \int (-wV^* + \theta M^* - M\theta^* + Vw^*)\, dS$$
$$- (w_m T_m^* - T_m w_m^*) + \lambda \iint N_{ij}\, w_{,ij}\, w^* dA \tag{7}$$

The above integrations are carried out with respect to field point x_i. If receiver point ξ_i is on S, then the jump term c is equal to the angle (as a fraction of 2π radians) subtended by the tangents on either side of ξ_i, which is equal to 0.5 for a smooth boundary. Also, the boundary integrals are then understood in a Cauchy principal-value sense. For ξ_i inside A, c is equal to unity. The remaining fundamental solutions θ^*, M^*, V^*, and T_m^* can be derived in view of the relations given by Eqn. (4) and the definition of w^* given by Eqn. (6) [5,6].

For solving a well-posed boundary-value problem, where two out of the four quantities w, θ, M and V are known at a point, an additional equation for the rotation is required. This can be obtained by differentiating Eqn. (7) with respect to the normal vector $\underline{n}$ at ξ_i, i.e.,

$$c\theta(\xi_i) = \int (-w\, V_n^* + \theta\, M_n^* - M\, \theta_n^* + V\, w_n^*)\, dS$$
$$- (w_m T_{mn}^* - T_m w_{mn}^*) + \lambda \iint N_{ij} w_{,ij}\, w_n^*\, dA \tag{8}$$

where subscript n denotes ∂/∂_n and should not be confused with a free index such as i,j, etc. The only problem still remaining, however, is evaluation of the derivatives of the transverse displacement in the interior of the plate required by the area integrals. To that purpose, the interior version (c=1.0) of Eqn. (7) is differentiated with respect to spatial coordinates ξ_1, ξ_2 to give

$$w_{,kl}(\xi_i) = \int (-w\, V^*_{,kl} + \theta\, M^*_{,kl} - M\theta^*_{,kl} + V\, w^*_{,kl})\, dS$$
$$- (w_m T^*_{m,kl} - T_m w^*_{m,kl}) + \lambda \iint N_{ij}\, w_{,ij}\, w^*_{,kl}\, dA \tag{9}$$

Equations (7)-(9) are sufficient for a complete solution of the classical plate stability problem, including buckling loads and shapes.

It should be mentioned at this point that it is possible to dispense with the area integrals by employing, for instance, a fundamental solution for the equation

$$D\nabla^4 w - \lambda N\nabla^2 w = \delta(\xi_1, \xi_2) \tag{10}$$

which corresponds to the case $N_{xx}=N_{yy}=N$, $N_{xy}=0$. In this case [5],

$$w^* = D\{\ln r + K_0(\sqrt{\lambda N r^2/D})\} / (2\pi\lambda N) \tag{11}$$

where K_o is the modified Bessel function of order zero. Other such fundamental solutions can be used [7,8] depending on what kind of in-plane force components are present. Alternatively, it is possible to avoid integration over certain parts of the plate's perimeter by employing specialized solutions for cases such as an infinite quarter plate with one edge clamped and the other simply supported, a semi-infinite plate sector with both edges simply supported, etc. [11].

Plate Stability-Numerical Implementation

A numerical solution of Eqs. (7)-(9) requires discretization of the plate's perimeter using line elements and of its interior using area elements (cells). The simplest possible scheme employs straight line elements and triangular or rectangular cells. The centroid of each element is then used as a node for collocating the values of the field variables w, θ, M and V. This implies, of course, that the field variables remain constant over an element. Alternatively, curved elements plus a representation of the field variables across an element using shape functions can be used [24]. In the most general case, the kernels of both line and area integrals consist of products of fundamental solutions times shape functions times determinant of the Jacobian transformation matrix and have to be integrated numerically. With line integrals, standard Gaussian quadrature is used for the nonsingular cases ($x_i \neq \xi_i$). For the singular cases ($x_i = \xi_i$), the resulting integrals are understood in a Cauchy principal value sense and log-weighted Gaussian quadrature or other special techniques can be used [24]. For added accuracy, elements may be divided into sub-elements whose number is increased as the distance between receiver and field points decreases [24]. Finally, standard Gaussian quadrature in two dimensions or quadrature formulas in triangular coordinates are used for rectangular and triangular area elements, respectively. In what follows, it is assumed that the plate's perimeter and its area contain N and M nodes, respectively.

At first, a system of boundary integral equations is generated by allowing the receiver ξ_i in Eqs. (7) and (8) to sequentially coincide with all nodes on the perimeter. The twisting moment T_m is not considered as part of the field variables. Instead, a finite difference approximation (see Eqn. (4)) is used to give

$$T_m = -D(1-\nu)\ 2\ (\theta_{p+1} - \theta_p)\ /(\Delta s_{p+1} + \Delta s_p) \tag{12}$$

where Δs_p is the length of the pth line elements. Thus, the twisting moment can be expressed in terms of the normal slopes θ at the two elements (p+1 and p) adjoining corner m [6]. Subsequently, the boundary integral equations are numerically integrated according to the way outlined before. Upon imposition of the boundary conditions and rearrangement, the following system of algebraic equations is obtained:

$$[A]\ \{X\} = [B]\ \{Y\} + \lambda[G]\ \{Z\} \tag{13}$$

In the above, {X} and {Y} are vectors of dimension 2N that respectively contain the unknown and prescribed values of the field variables, while {Z} is a vector of dimension 3M containing the unknown curvatures $w_{,ij}$. Also, [A], [B] and [G] are matrices whose coefficients are the integrated kernel products that were previously mentioned. The first two are of dimension 2N x 2N, while the third is of dimension 2N x 3M.

Next, the receiver in Eqn. (9) is allowed to coincide with all internal nodes, thus generating a new system of non-singular integral eqations that are numerically integrated and rearranged in the form

$$\{Z\} = [C]\ \{X\} + [D]\ \{Y\} + \lambda\ [H]\ \{Z\} \tag{14}$$

Again, [C], [D] and [H] are all matrices of dimensions corresponding to the vectors they multiply. By using Eqs. (13) and (14) to eliminate the unknowns {X}, the following equation is obtained

$$[F_1]\{Z\} = \lambda^{-1}(\{Z\} - [F_2]\{Y\}) \tag{15}$$

where

$$[F_1] = [C][A]^{-1}[G] + [H],$$
$$[F_2] = [C][A]^{-1}[B] + [D] \tag{16}$$

and λ are now the dimensionless eigenvalues (critical or buckling loads). In most cases, the boundary conditions are homogeneous, i.e, simply supported edges (w=M=0), clamped edges (w=θ=0) or free edges (M=V=0). Under such circumstances, Eqn. (15) degenerates to the classical Sturm-Liouville formulation

$$[F]\{Z\} = \lambda^{-1}\{Z\} \tag{17}$$

Any number of methods, direct or iterative, can then be used to recover the eigenvalues. The simplest approach is to find the roots of the determinant of $[F]-\lambda^{-1}[I]$, where [I] is the identity matrix. As far as the eigenvalues are concerned, it should be noted that since {Z} contains curvatures, it does not correspond to the buckled shape of the plate when λ is a critical load. The course of action taken here is to recover {Z} from the eigenvalue problem, find {X} from Eqn. (13), and then use Eqn. (7) with c=1.0 to numerically generate the transverse displacements at all interior nodes of the plate. A more efficient formulation [14] is to recast Eqn. (9) in terms of the fictitious load $q=N_{ij}\,w_{,ij}$.

This way, upon numerical processing of Eqn. (9), {Z} is of dimension M only.

Finally, for nonhomogeneous boundary conditions, it is best to introduce a modified field variable that obeys homogeneous boundary conditions, albeit at the cost of a more complicated differential operator, so as to work with the classical eigenvalue formulation of Eqn. (17). As an example, consider the common case of a plate on elastic foundation. For this problem, the term kw, k being the stiffness modulus of the supporting subgrade, is subtracted from the right-hand side of Eqn. (1). Equations (13) and (14) are still applicable with the understanding that {Y} is of dimension M and contains values of the transverse interior displacements. A third equation is generated from the interior (c=1) version of Eqn. (7), as previously discussed, in the form

$$\{Y\} = [E]\{X\} + \lambda[J]\{Z\} + [K]\{Y\} \tag{18}$$

Equations (13), (14) and (18) can now be used to eliminate both {X} and {Y}, resulting in an eigenvalue problem of the Sturm-Liouville form as in Eqn. (17). An iterative procedure is required, however, because when the transverse displacement is negative, contact between plate and subgrade is lost and reaction kw is taken as zero [3].

In order to avoid the curvatures $w,_{ij}$ in the stability formulation, Jin [11] proposed a finite difference scheme for them throughout the area of the plate. Thus,

$$\{Z\} = [L]\ \{W\} \tag{19}$$

where {W} is the vector of the internal transverse displacements and is of dimension M, while [L] is an operator matrix resulting from the finite difference scheme. The above equation can now be used to eliminate {Z} from the general system of Eqs. (13), (14) and (18). Further elimination of {X} and {Y} from the aforementioned system gives the classical stability formulation of Eqn. (17) in terms of the true eigenvectors (or modal shapes) {W}. The disadvantages of such an approach is that it requires an orthogonal grid for simple implementation and that accuracy is compromised as the edges are approached, because forward or backward finite differences must be employed. A more rigorous approach was previously followed by Liu [10], who used integration by parts in order to express the area integral in Eqn. (7) as

$$\iint N_{ij}\, w,_{ij}\, w^* \, dA = \int p_k (w,_k\, w^* - w\, w,^*_k) dS + \iint N_{ij}\, w\, w,^*_{ij}\, dA \tag{20}$$

where

$$p_k = N_{kl} n_l \tag{21}$$

are the tractions on the boundary. When the new Eqn. (7) is differentiated with respect to the normal at the receiver ξ_i to give Eqn. (8), only higher order derivatives of the starred state appear. This way, when Eqs. (7)-(9) are numerically processed, vector {Z} now contains the transverse displacements and rotations of the M interior nodes. Therefore, when Eqs. (13) and (14) (plus Eqn. (18) when $\{Y\} \neq 0$) are combined to produce the classical stability formulation, the resulting Eqn. (17) is again in terms of the true eigenvectors.

The present BEM formulation can also be combined with experimental strain measurements, as outlined in Tai et al [2]. In that case, the terms $w^*_{,ij}$ in Eqn. (20) correspond to surface strains, i.e.,

$$w^*_{,ij} = -2\, \epsilon^*_{ij}/h \tag{22}$$

where ϵ^*_{ij} is the strain tensor and h is the thickness of the plate. If the boundary conditions contain w=0 or if no in-plane external forces act at the edges of the plate (p_k=0), then the appropriate boundary integral equation is

$$c\, w(\xi_i) = \frac{\lambda h}{2} \iint N_{ij}\, \epsilon^*_{ij}\, w\, dA \tag{23}$$

The above equation can now be numerically solved for the buckling load λ, provided surface strain measurements are available.

Plate Stability - Examples

The buckling of a square plate under different edge conditions and for various in-plane loads is investigated in Costa and Brebbia [4]. In all cases, Poisson's ratio is taken as 0.30 and the first (critical) buckling load λ_c is normalized by the ratio $D\pi^2/L^2$, where L is the side length of the plate. Table I compares λ_c as obtained by the BEM for two meshes, namely case A that employs 36 single-noded line elements and 36 single-noded rectangular cells and case B that employs 36 line elements and 64 cells, with exact values [23] and with results obtained using the finite element method (FEM). All FEM results were obtained for a mesh of 36 rectangular, four noded plate elements with coupled bending and membrane action [25]. The notation used is SS for simple support, CS for clamped support and an x-edge (y-edge) is one whose normal is parallel to the x-axis (y-axis). It is observed that there is close agreement between all results tabulated. To further investigate the rate of convergence of the BEM versus that of the FEM, Fig. 2 plots the error in λ_c (as a percentage) versus number of total elements for the case of the

Table I - Buckling Load of a Square Plate

Load	Edge Support	Exact	FEM	BEM-A	BEM-B
$N_x \neq 0$, $N_y = N_{xy} = 0$	SS on all	4.00	4.00	4.19	4.13
	CS on all	10.07	10.09	10.92	10.51
	SS on y-edges, CS on x-edges,	7.80	--	8.82	8.01
$N_x = N_y \neq 0$, $N_{xy} = 0$	SS on all	2.00	2.00	2.08	2.05
	CS on all	5.33	5.31	5.50	5.43
$N_{xy} \neq 0$, $N_x = N_y = 0$	SS on all	9.34	9.31	9.80	9.67
	CS on all	14.71	14.73	15.10	14.90
	SS on y-edges, CS on x-edges	12.28	--	12.76	12.53

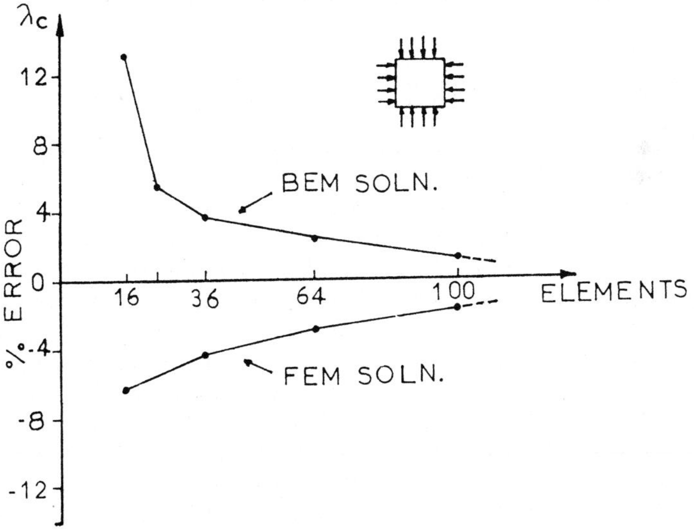

Fig. 2. Error versus mesh refinement for BEM and FEM

completely clamped square plate for $N_x=N_y\neq 0$ and $N_{xy}=0$. For this case, the BEM provides an upper bound solution for λ_c, while the FEM based on a displacement formulation [26] provides a lower bound.

The next example is drawn from Bézine et al [3], who investigated the buckling of a simply-supported rectangular plate with (unilateral) and without (bilateral) subgrade support. In all cases, Poisson's ratio is 0.30 and results are given in terms of the dimensionless variables x/a and y/b, where a and b are the plate's dimensions. Also, the perimeter is discretized into 48 line elements and 64 (when a/b=1) or 96 when (a/b>1) rectangular cells, all with a single node defined at their centroid. Table II lists the first buckling load λ_c normalized by the ratio b^2/D obtained by the BEM, along with the exact solution [23] for the classical (bilateral) buckling case. It is observed that the influence of the subgrade stiffness k (unilateral case) on λ_c is rather negligible, except for the case of the elongated plate (a/b=2) under normal in-plane load, where the difference between bilateral and unilateral buckling is around 13%. Finally, Fig. 3 plots the first buckling shape of the square, simply-supported plate under in-plane shearing forces. The buckling shape obtained for the same case but in the presence of the subgrade is almost identical.

Table II - Buckling Load of a Simply-Supported Plate

Load	a/b	Exact	BEM-Bilateral	BEM-Unilateral
$N_{xy}\neq 0$, $N_x=N_y=0$	1.0	92.8	96.5	96.8
$N_{xy}\neq 0$, $N_x=N_y=0$	1.5	70.1	72.1	73.8
$N_x\neq 0$, $N_y=N_{xy}=0$	1.5	42.7	43.7	45.1
$N_x\neq 0$, $N_y=N_{xy}=0$	2.0	39.9	40.3	45.5

Finally, the buckling of orthotropic plates can also be handled with the present formulation, since the fundamental solution of the governing differential equation for bending of such a plate, i.e.,

$$\nabla^4(Dw) = D_{11}\ \partial^4 w/\partial x^4 + 2(D_{12}+2D_{66})\ \partial^4 w/\partial x^2 \partial y^2 +$$

$$D_{22}\ \partial^4 w/\partial y^4 = q \qquad (24)$$

is known [14]. In the above, D_{11}, D_{12} D_{22} and D_{66} are flexural rigidities which can be calculated from the elastic modulii of the plate material. The same reference gives, as an example, the critical buckling load λ_c of a square graphite/epoxy plate, for simple supported edges and under uniaxial compression ($N_x \neq 0$), as equal to 0.119 10^3 D_{11}/a^2, where a is the plate's side and D_{11} =

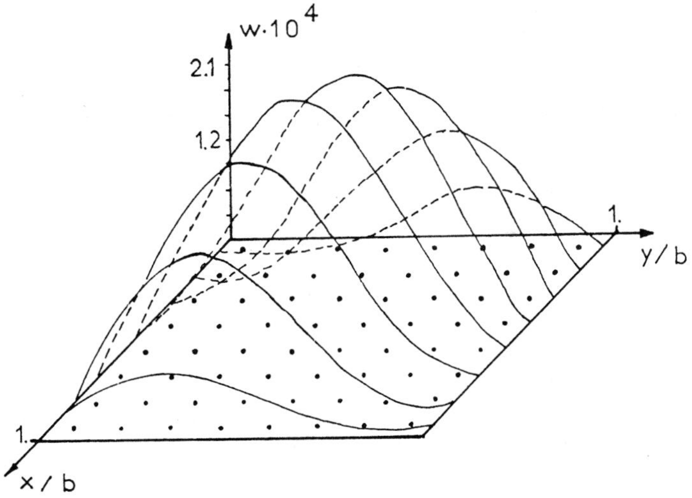

Fig. 3. Bialateral buckling deflections for simply-supported square plate under in-plane shearing force . are nodes inside the plate domain

0.862 10^3 N-m. This solution, which was obtained using 48 constant line elements and 49 constant cells, is in error by 2.9% when compared to the analytical solution [27].

Plate Structures

The procedure previously outlined can be extended to cover the buckling of plate structures. As shown in Fig. 4, it becomes necessary to distinguish between a global coordinate system (x_1, x_2, x_3) and a local one (x_1', x_2', x_3'), where coordinate x_3' is always perpendicular to the plane of the individual plate elements. Furthermore, the in-plane (membrane) action must be analyzed as a separate, plane stress state. The boundary integral equation for this case is well known [28] and can be expressed as

$$c_{ij}\, u_j(\xi_1, \xi_2) = \int \{p_j u^*_{ij} - u_j\, p^*_{ij}\} dS \qquad (i,j=1,2) \tag{25}$$

where u_i are the in-plane displacements, p_i are the corresponding tractions (see Eqn. (21)), and u^*_{ij}, p^*_{ij} are respectively the

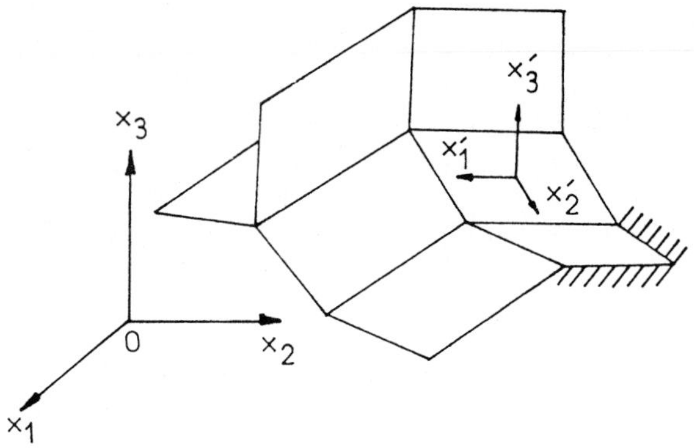

Fig. 4. Assembled plate structure

fundamental solutions in tensor form for the displacements and tractions corresponding to a unit point force in an infinitely extending, two dimensional elastic medium (Kelvin's solution). Also, c_{ij} is the jump term equal to $0.5\,\delta_{ij}$ for a smooth boundary, (ξ_1, ξ_2) is the receiver, and the perimeter integrations are done with respect to field point (x_1, x_2). Equation (25) is to be used with a local coordinate system. As far as the out-of-plane (bending) action is concerned, Eqs. (7)-(9) still hold true, but are also written for the local coordinate system.

Numerical solution of Eqs. (7)-(9) and (25) follows along the lines discussed in the previous section. In particular, the following systems of algebraic equations are obtained, prior to the imposition of boundary conditions, for a particular plate element:

$$[A_b'] \left\{ {w' \atop \theta} \right\} + [B_b'] \left\{ {V' \atop M} \right\} + \lambda \ [G_b'] \ \{Z'\} = 0 \tag{26}$$

$$\{Z'\} = [C_b'] \left\{ {w' \atop \theta} \right\} + [D_b'] \left\{ {V' \atop M} \right\} + \lambda [H_b'] \ \{Z'\} \tag{27}$$

$$[A_p'] \left\{ {u_1' \atop u_2'} \right\} + [B_p'] \left\{ {p_1' h \atop p_2' h} \right\} = 0 \tag{28}$$

In the above, vectors $[\ w', \theta]^T$, $[V', M]^T$, $[u_1', u_2']^T$ and $[p_1'h, p_2'h]^T$, where T denotes transpose, contain the nodal values of the obvious quantities at all N nodes of the perimeter. Vector $\{Z'\}$ contains the values of the curvatures $w'_{,ij}$ at all M interior nodes. Primes indicate local coordinates, while subscripts b and p in the matrices denote bending and in-plane action, respectively. The tractions p_1' and p_2' are multiplied by the plate thickness h so that their dimension is compatible with that of the shearing force V'. Note that all jump terms and the twisting moments (see Eqn. (12)) have been absorbed in the appropriate system matrices.

In order to derive a set of algebraic equations for the plate structure, the individual plate element system matrices must first be transformed from local to global coordinates and then appropriately superimposed. The nodal variables in global coordinates are $[u_1, u_2, u_3, \theta]$ for the generalized displacements and $[f_1, f_2, f_3, M]$ for the generalized forces, which are respectively related to their local coordinate counterparts $[u_1', u_2', w', \theta]$ and $[p_1'h, p_2'h, V', M]$ via the usual coordinate transformation matrix. Note that the curvatures $w'_{,ij}$ in $\{Z'\}$ are also transformed into global coordinates. Since slope θ and moment M are already defined as vector rotations normal to the plate's edges, no transformation is necessary for them as will be shown shortly [13]. The final form of the algebraic system is obtained by combining Eqs. (26) and (28), by augmenting Eqn. (27) to the same size as the previous combination, and by transforming to global coordinates, i.e.,

$$\begin{bmatrix} A_p & 0 \\ 0 & A_b \end{bmatrix} \begin{Bmatrix} u_1 \\ u_2 \\ \overline{u_3} \\ \theta \end{Bmatrix} + \begin{bmatrix} B_p & 0 \\ 0 & B_b \end{bmatrix} \begin{Bmatrix} f_1 \\ f_2 \\ \overline{f_3} \\ M \end{Bmatrix} + \lambda \begin{bmatrix} 0 \\ G_b \end{bmatrix} \{Z\} \tag{29}$$

and

$$\{Z\} = [\ 0 \ \ C_b\ ] \begin{Bmatrix} u_1 \\ u_2 \\ \overline{u_3} \\ \theta \end{Bmatrix} + [\ 0 \ \ D_b\ ] \begin{Bmatrix} f_1 \\ f_2 \\ \overline{f_3} \\ M \end{Bmatrix} + \lambda\ [H_b]\ \{Z\} \tag{30}$$

Along the interfaces between plate elements, compatibility of the generalized displacements and equilibrium of the generalized forces must be enforced in order to assemble the plate structure system equation from the individual plate element BEM equations. Assuming that m plates join along an edge, the compatibility conditions are

$$u_i^{(1)} = u_i^{(2)} = \ldots = u_i^{(m)} \text{ and } (\alpha\theta)^{(1)} = (\alpha\theta)^{(2)} = \ldots = (\alpha\theta)^{(m)} \qquad (i=1,2,3) \tag{31}$$

while equilibrium yields

$$f_i^{(1)} + f_i^{(2)} + \ldots = f_i^{(m)} = 0 \text{ and } (\alpha M)^{(1)} + (\alpha M)^{(2)} + \ldots (\alpha M)^{(m)} = 0 \qquad (i=1,2,3) \tag{32}$$

where the superscripts denote the plate elements. In the above equations, $\alpha^{(j)}$ and $\alpha^{(j+1)}$, j=1,2,...,m, are either both +1 or are +1 and -1, depending on whether the tangent vectors at the interface between j th and (j+1)th elements are in the same or opposite directions. Upon assemblage of the plate structure's system matrices, imposition of (homogeneous) global boundary conditions and rearrangement gives the classical eigenvalue problem of Eqn. (17).

The plate structure example of Fig. 5(a) is taken from Tanaka and Miyazaki [13]. The two rectangular plates are joined at right angles and have aspect ratios of b/a=0.5 and a/h=240. The top and bottom boundaries are fixed, while the vertical sides are free. The mesh used is shown in Fig. 5 and the predicted first buckling load is $\lambda_c b^2/(\pi^2 D) = 0.67$, which is 4.1% in error when compared with the analytical solution [23].

Thermal Buckling of Plates

The governing equation of a plate in the presence of a temperature field $T(x_i)$ is

$$D\nabla^4 w = D\beta^2\nabla^2 w - \nabla^2 M_T/(1-\nu) = \hat{q} \qquad (33)$$

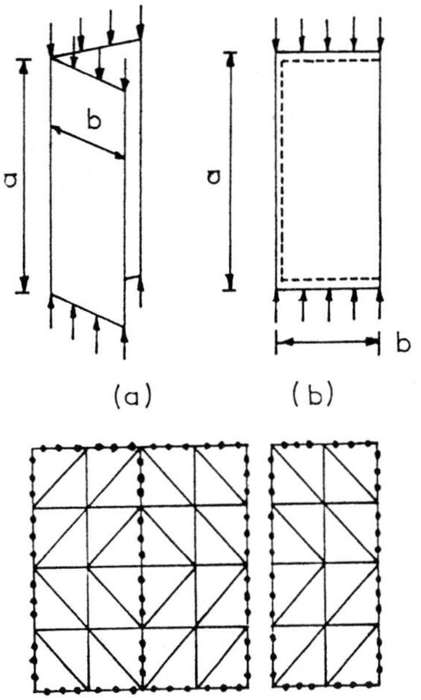

Fig. 5. Buckling problem of (a) assembled plate and (b) its equivalent single plate, with the discretization pattern shown below

where β is the Berger parameter [15,16]. Also, M_T is the thermal bending moment defined as

$$M_T = \int_{-h/2}^{h/2} E\,\alpha_T T z\,dz \qquad (34)$$

with α_T the thermal expansion coefficient of the plate. Eqn. (33) is an approximation in the sense that the Berger parameter results from a linearization procedure of the original nonlinear relation between the deformation and temperature fields. This approximation yields acceptable results provided that the in-plane displacements u_1 and u_2 are constrained on the plate boundary. Other admissible boundary conditions are combinations of w=0 with prescribed normal slopes and moments.

As before, the effect of the temperature field can be thought of as an equivalent lateral load $\hat{q}$. Therefore, Eqs. (7) through (9) are still usable, provided the area integrals there are replaced by

$$\iint \{ \beta^2 \nabla^2 w\, w^* - \frac{M_T}{1-\nu} \nabla^2 w^* \}\, dA , \tag{35}$$

$$\iint \{ \beta^2 \nabla^2 w\, w^*_n - \frac{M_T}{1-\nu} (\nabla^2 w^*)_n \}\, dA \tag{36}$$

and

$$\iint \{ \beta^2 \nabla^2 w\, w^*{,}_{kl}\, dA - M_T(\xi_1,\xi_2)/(1-\nu) , \tag{37}$$

respectively. In addition, the definitions of the normal moment M and the Kirchhoff shear V, Eqn. (4), need to be revised by the addition of the terms $-M_T/(1-\nu)$ and $-\frac{\partial}{\partial n}(M_T/(1-\nu)$, respectively. The thus revised Eqns. (7)-(9) can now be numerically processed following the procedures outlined previously. The magnitude of the Berger parameter can be estimated as [15,16]

$$\beta^2 = \frac{12}{h^2 A} \iint \{\frac{1}{2} (w^2{,}_1 + w^2{,}_2) - \frac{(1+\nu)}{Eh} N_T\} dA \tag{38}$$

where A is the area of the plate and the thermal in-plane force is

$$N_T = \int_{-h/2}^{h/2} E\, \alpha_T T dz \tag{39}$$

The numerical analysis procedure is now as follows: First, an initial estimate of the plate deflections is required. Next, β^2 is determined from Eqn. (38) followed by numerical solution of the boundary-value problem. Finally, the deflections in the interior of the plate are computed and compared with the initial guess. The whole process is repeated until the interior displacements converge. Two basic types of behavior are possible: (a) If the temperature field is such that a thermal bending moment results, then the plate gradually deforms (finite deflection mode) and (b) if no thermal bending moment appears, then the plate is liable to buckle due to the presence of the thermal in-plane force when a certain temperature is reached (buckling mode).

As an example, consider the axisymmetric deformations of a circular clamped plate of radius a given in Kamiya et al [16] under two temperature distributions,

$$T_B = \{T_0 + T_1 (1-(x_1^2 + x_2^2)/a^2 \} \tag{40}$$

and

$$T_F = T_B (1 + 2x_3/3h) \tag{41}$$

The first distribution corresponds to the buckling mode (BM), while the second one corresponds to the finite deflection mode (FDM). The plate is discretized using 32 constant line elements and 144 cells. Fig. 6 plots the normalized maximum plate deflection across the radius as a function of the initial temperature T_0, for three ratios of T_1/T_0, and for both modes. Also plotted are the results of a numerical solution of the governing equation using the Runge-Kutta-Gill method (RKGM). It is observed that agreement between the BEM and the RKGM is excellent.

Post-Buckling Analysis of Shallow Shells

Consider a shallow shell described by its midsurface $z=z(x_i)$ and exhibiting linear elastic material behavior. The von-Karman equations are [29]

$$D\nabla^4 w + N_{ij}/R_{ij} - b_3 = \lambda(N_{ij}\, w_{,j})_{,i} + q_3 \qquad (i,j=1,2) \tag{42}$$

for the out-of-plane (bending) equilibrium and

$$N_{ij,j} + b_i = 0 \qquad (i,j=1,2) \tag{43}$$

for the in-plane (membrane) equilibrium. In the above, $R_{ij} = 1/z_{,ij}$ are the radii of curvature of the undeformed shell, b_i are the body forces and q_3 is the load normal to the mid-surface. Eqs. (42) and (43) degenerate to their thin plate counterparts, Eqs. (1) and (2) respectively, if the curvature terms are taken as zero. In Eqn. (4), the definitions of the rotation θ and normal bending moment M remain unchanged, while the Kirchhoff shear V is redefined by the addition of the coupling terms ($-N_n \cdot \partial w/\partial n - N_t\, \partial w/\partial t$), where $N_n = N_j\, n_i\, n_j$ and $N_t = N_{ij}\, t_i\, t_j$. It is reminded here that n_i and t_i are the components of the normal and tangent vectors at the shell's perimeter. Furthermore, it becomes necessary to introduce the membrane stress-strain

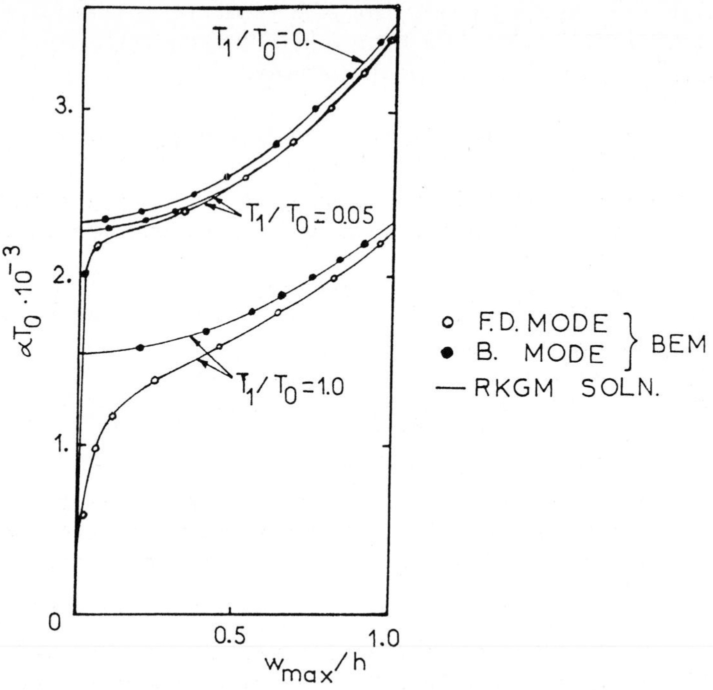

Fig. 6. Maximum deflections of circular clamped plate: ∘ ∘ Finite deflection mode (BEM); . . buckling mode (BEM); - - RKGM solution

relations as

$$N_{ij} = C\,\{\nu\epsilon_{kk}\delta_{ij} + (1-\nu)\,\epsilon_{ij}\} \quad (k=1,2) \tag{44}$$

where $C = Eh/(1-\nu^2)$ and

$$\epsilon_{ij} = 0.5\,(u_{i,j} + u_{j,i}) + 2w/R_{ij} + w_{,i}\,w_{,j} \tag{45}$$

are the membrane strain-displacement relations. The presence of nonlinear terms in the above equation, which give rise to finite deformations in the shell, is necessary because it has been found that the Euler loads do not agree with the experimentally obtained buckling loads for shell structures [30,31]. By combining the above two equations, the membrane forces may be written as

$$N_{ij} = N'_{ij} + C\,\kappa_{ij} + N''_{ij} \tag{46}$$

where

$$N'_{ij} = C\,\{\nu\, u_{k,k}\,\delta_{ij} + \tfrac{1}{2}\,(1-\nu)\,(u_{i,j} + u_{j,i})\} \tag{47}$$

is the linear part corresponding to a flat plate that is augmented by a coupling term due to the shell's curvature

$$\kappa_{ij} = \nu\,\delta_{ij}/R_{kk} + (1-\nu)/R_{ij} \tag{48}$$

and a nonlinear part

$$N''_{ij} = 0.5\,C\{\nu\delta_{ij}\,w_{,k}\,w_{,k} + (1-\nu)\,w_{,i}w_{,j}\}$$

Finally, the boundary conditions for bending action involve, as before, combinations of w, θ, M and V, while those of the in-plane action involve combinations of the displacements u_i and tractions p_i.

A general weighted residual formulation can be used to derive integral representations for the displacements. Details of this procedure can be found in Zhang and Atluri [20,21] and the final expressions are

$$\begin{aligned} c\,w\,(\xi_i) = &\int (\,-wV^* + \theta\,M^* - M\theta^* + Vw^*)\,dS \\ &- (w_m\,T_m^* - T_m\,w_m^*) + \iint (\lambda N'_{ij}w_{,ij} + b_3 + q_3)w^*dA \\ &- \frac{C}{D}\,\{\,\int \kappa_{ij}\,n_j\,u_i\,w^*\,dS - \iint u_i\,(\kappa_{ij}w^*)_{,j}\,dA \\ &+ \iint (\,(\kappa_{ij}\,w + N''_{ij})/R_{ij})\,w^*\,dA\,\} \end{aligned} \tag{49}$$

plus a similar equation for $\theta(\xi_i)$ with the fundamental solutions w^*, θ^*, M^* and V^* replaced by their derivatives with respect to the normal at ξ_i, i.e., w_n^*, θ_n^*, M_n^* and V_n^*, respectively. By comparing Eqn. (49) to Eqn. (7), it is noticed that the curvature of the shell plus the coupling of the bending and membrane displacements in the nonlinear expressions for the in-plane strains are responsible for the presence of the last three terms in the right-hand side of the former equation.

The necessary third integral equation for the in-plane displacements is

$$c_{ij}\, u_j(\xi_i) = \int \{ p_j\, u^*_{ij} - u_j\, p^*_{ij} \} dS + \iint b_j\, u^*_{ij}\, dA$$

$$- \iint \{ C\, \kappa_{jk}\, w + N''_{jk} \}\, u^*_{ij,k} dA \qquad (k=1,2) \qquad (50)$$

where u^*_{ij}, p^*_{ij} are the Kelvin solutions. Again, comparison of Eqn. (5)) with Eqn. (25) for the uncouple membrane behavior reveals that, with the exception of the contribution of the body forces b_j that is usually neglected, the curvature-induced nonlinear coupling of u_i and w is manifested by the presence of the last term in the right-hand side of the former equation. An alternative formulation and solution for the geometrically nonlinear problem of elastic shallow shells using complex variables can be found in Tosaka [22].

The above system of equations are numerically solved by discretizing the perimeter and area of the shell into line elements and cells, respectively, along the lines previously discussed. Zhang and Atluri [20,21] formulate an incremental scheme, whereby both load and prescribed boundary conditions are applied in small, yet finite increments. The presence of nonlinear terms in the strain-displacement law, Eqn. (45), necessitates the introduction of an iterative scheme to equilibrate the residual load vector present at the beginning of each load increment. A full Newton-Raphson algorithm has been used to produce solutions that converge rapidly.

An as example, consider the case of a shallow spherical shell with a square base and loaded by a point load at the crown, as shown in Fig. 7. The relevant material properties are E=69 kN/mm^2 and ν=0.3, while the geometrical data is a=b = 784.9 mm, h=99.45 mm and R_1=R_2 = 2540 mm. The BEM solution of Zhang and Atluri [21] employed a 3 x 3 mesh over one-quarter of the shell with a total of 21 nodes and 63 degrees-of-freedom. Excellent agreement is obtained between the BEM results and the analytical solution of Leicester [32], as shown in Fig. 7 that plots the load P versus deflection w_c at the crown. A snap-through is clearly observed at around w_c = 150mm (and at a value of ρ that is less than the Euler load), followed by a drop in the strength of the shell. Subsequently, at w_c around 250mm, the shell stiffens and exhibits sizeable post-buckling strength. It was noted in [21] that FEM solutions required between 100 to 200 degrees-of-freedom discretizations, depending on the particular shell finite element used, to produce results comparable with those obtained by the BEM.

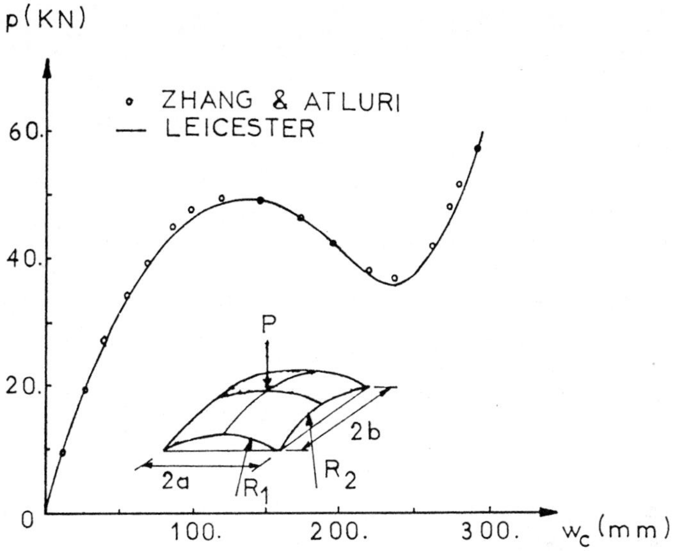

Fig. 7. Load-deformation diagram of square-based, shallow spherical shell: Post-buckling analysis

Nonlinear Stability Analysis of Plates

Two possible sources of nonlinearities arise in the stability analysis of plates, namely geometric and material nonlinearities. These two topics will only be briefly discussed in this section, since two other chapters have already been devoted to them.

In the case of geometric nonlinearities, the kinematic relation between strains and displacements for the membrane action is

$$\epsilon_{ij} = 0.5\ (u_{i,j} + u_{j,i} + w_{,i}\ w_{,j}) - z\ w_{,ij} \quad (i,j=1,2) \tag{51}$$

The similarity between Eqn. (51) and the shell kinematic relation, Eqn. (45), should be noticed because a similar approach can now be used. In particular, the linear and nonlinear coupling terms in the above equation require the addition of Eqn. (25) for the membrane action augmented by the term

$$- \iint N''_{jk}\ u^*_{ij,k}\ dA \quad (k=1,2) \tag{52}$$

where N''_{jk} is the nonlinear part of the membrane force, to the system of Eqs. (7)-(9). A combined incremental/iterative scheme corresponding to the total Lagrangian formulation, plus the usual discretization using elements, have been successfully used by O'Donoghue and Atluri [19] to solve problems such as the large deflections of a plate under uniform transverse load, the post-buckling deflection of a plate under normal in-plane loading, etc.

In the case of material nonlinearities, the governing differential equations for a plate, Eqs. (1) and (2), have to be written in rate (incremental) form. Actually, material and geometric nonlinearities can be combined by retention of the kinematic relation of Eqn. (51), written in rate form as well.

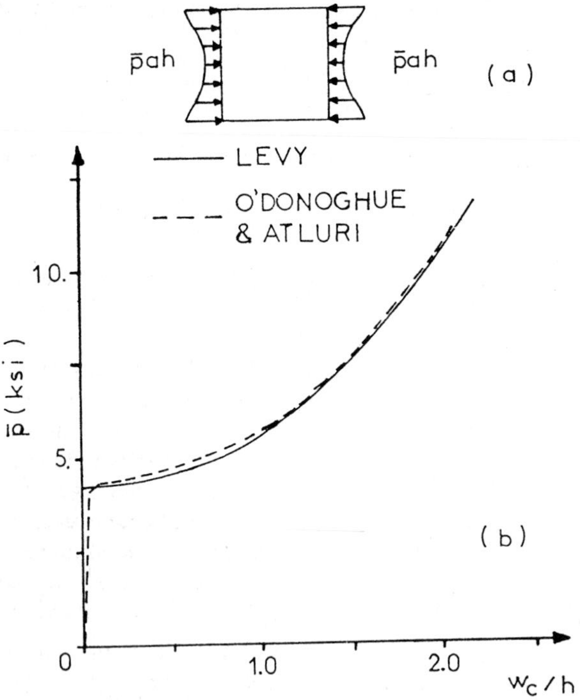

Fig. 8. Post-buckling deflections of a thin square plate

The integral equations (7)-(9) and (25) can again serve as the basis of a BEM solution, provided they are augmented by terms such as

$$\iint \dot{N}_{ij}\, w\, w^{*}{}_{,ij}\, dA \tag{53}$$

for Eqn. (7) and

$$-\frac{1}{2}\iint \left({}_{o}\!\int^{t} \sigma^{*}_{kij}\, dt\right) \dot{w}_{,i}\, \dot{w}_{,j}\, dA \tag{54}$$

for Eqn. (25), where dots indicate incremental variables, $\sigma^{*}{}_{kij}$ is Kelvin solution's for the stresses, and the deflections w may also contain an initial deflection component. The presence of stresses in the integral equation formulation requires specifying a stress-strain law, such as ideal plasticity or strain hardening plasticity. The usual boundary element discretization, in conjunction with incremental/iterative schemes, has been used by Okada et al [17] for problems such as the elasto-plastic instability of thin plates under compressive or shear in-plane loads, etc.

As an example, consider the large deformations of a square plate of side length a subjected to uniaxial compression along the mid-surface and with buckling induced by applying a small load in the transverse direction. The plate is simply supported, with displacements prescribed on two parallel sides and self-equilibrating loads applied on the other two sides so as to keep them straight (see Fig. 8(a)). The thickness ratio of the plate is $h/a=1/160$, $\nu=0.316$ and $E=30.10^{6}$ 16/in^{2} This problem was solved by O'Donoghue and Atluri [19] using a 4x4 mesh per quadrant and linear interpolation functions for both line and area elements. Their results are compared with the series solution of Levy [33] in Fig. 8(b) that plots the average in-plane compressive stress $\bar{p}$ versus the transverse deflection at the center of the plate w_c normalized by the thickness h. The postbuckling behavior of the plate, which commences past the critical load $\bar{p}=4.0$ kips/in^{2}, is in very good agreement with the analytic solution.

Conclusions

This chapter presented the direct BEM as applied to the buckling analysis of thin plates and shallow shells. In the former case, both individual plates as well as plate structures were discussed, along with information on orthotropic plates, thermal buckling of plates, plates supported on a subgrade, etc. In the latter case, the classical stability analysis is not adequate and reference needs to be made to geometric nonlinearities through the retention of appropriate terms in the shell's strain-displacement relations. Also, the manner in which the stability formulation for plates can be expanded to include material and geometric nonlinearities was also presented. As evidenced by the numerical examples, the BEM is capable of producing excellent results and is a viable alternative to FEM approaches. As far as future research is concerned, it is the opinion of the author that the BEM stability formulations offer a good starting point for introducing both material and geometric nonlinearities, since the Euler load for complicated structures consisting of plates and/or shells is just an upper bound solution. Although this has already been done, there is still scope for new formulations and new computation schemes, as well as comparisons among the various approaches in an effort to identify optimal methodologies.

Acknowledgement

The author would like to thank Prof. D. E. Beskos for bringing to his attention certain references.

References

1. Sekiya, T.; Katayama, T.: Analysis of buckling using the influence function. Theor. Appl. Mech. 29 (1981) 25-31.

2. Tai, H.; Katayama, T.; Sekiya, T.: Buckling analysis by influence function. Mech. Res. Commun. 9 (1982) 139-144.

3. Bézine, G.; Cimetiere, A.; Gelbert, J.P.: Unilateral buckling of thin elastic plates by the boundary integral equation method. Int. J. Num. Meth. Engng. 21 (1985) 2189-2199.

4. Costa, J.A.; Brebbia, C.A.: Elastic buckling of plates using the boundary element method. In Brebbia, C.A.; Maier, G. (eds.) Boundary Elements VII, 4.29-4.42. Berlin: Springer-Verlag 1985.

5. Manolis, G.D.; Beskos, D.E.; Pineros, M.F.: Beam and plate stability by boundary elements. Comput. Struct. 22 (1986) 917-923.

6. Syngellakis, S.; Kang, M.: A boundary element solution of the plate buckling problem. Engng. Analysis 4 (1987) 75-81.

7. Gospodinov, G.; Ljutskanov, D.: The boundary element method applied to plates. Appl. Math. Modelling 6 (1982) 237-244.

8. Kawabe, H: Plate buckling analysis by the boundary element method. In Tanaka, M.; Du, Q. (eds) Theory and Applications of Boundary Element Methods, 367-374. Oxford: Pergamon Press 1987.

9. Manolis, G.D.: Stability analysis of beams and plates. In Beskos, D.E. (ed.) Boundary Element Analysis in Structural Analysis, 119-137. New York: Amer. Soc. Civil Engrs. 1988.

10. Liu, Y.: Elastic stability analysis of thin plates by the boundary element method-a new formulation. Engng. Analysis 4 (1987) 160-164.

11. Jin, M.: A mixed boundary integral-finite difference approach to plate buckling problems. In Brebbia, C.A. (ed) Boundary Elements X, vol. 3, 457-464. Berlin: Springer-Verlag 1988.

12. Tanaka, M.; Miyazaki, K.: Elastic buckling analysis of assembled plate structures by boundary element method. In Tanaka, M.; Brebbia, C.A. (eds.) Boundary Elements VIII, 547-559. Berlin: Springer-Verlag 1986.

13. Tanaka, M.; Miyazaki, K.: A boundary element method for elastic buckling analysis of assembled plate structures. Computational Mech. 3 (1988) 49-57.

14. Shi, G.; Bézine, G.: Buckling analysis of orthotropic plates by boundary element method. Mech. Res. Commun. 17, (1990) 1-8.

15. Kamiya, N.; Sawaki, Y.; Nakamura, Y.: Finite and post-buckling deformations of heated plates and shallow shells. In Brebbia, C.A.; Futagami, T.; Tanaka, M. (eds.) Boundary Elements, 507-516. Berlin: Springer-Verlag 1983.

16. Kamiya, N.; Sawaki, Y.; Nakamura, Y.: Post-buckling analysis by the boundary element method. Engng. Analysis 1 (1984) 40-44.

17. Okada, H.; Fujimoto, M.; Abe, H.: Elastoplastic instability analysis of thin plates. In Brebbia, C.A.; Futagami, T.; Tanaka, M. (eds.) Boundary Elements, 589-597. Berlin: Springer-Verlag 1983.

18. Song, G.S.; Mukherjee, S.: Boundary element analysis of bending of inelastic plates with general boundary conditions. Computational Mech. 5 (1989) 104-112.

19. O'Donoghue, P.E.; Atluri, S.N.: Field/boundary element approach to the large deflection of thin flat plates. Comput. Struct. 27 (1987) 427-435.

20. Zhang, J.D.; Atluri, S.N.: Nonlinear quasi-static and transient response analysis of shallow shells: formulations and interior/boundary element algorithms. In Du, Q. (ed.), Boundary Elements, 87-110. Oxford: Pergamon Press 1986.

21. Zhang, J.D.; Atluri, S.N.: Post-buckling analysis of shallow shells by the field-boundary element method. Int. J. Num. Meth. Engng. 26 (1988) 571-587.

22. Tosaka, N.; Miyake, S.: Integral equation analysis for geometrically nonlinear problems of elastic bodies. In Tanaka, M.; Du, Q. (eds.) Theory and Applications of Boundary Element Methods, 251-260. Oxford: Pergamon Press 1987.

23. Timoshenko, S.P.; Gere, J.M.: Theory of Elastic Stability. New York: McGraw-Hill 1961.

24. Lachat, J.P.; Watson, J.O.: Effective numerical treatment of boundary integral equations: A formulation for three-dimensional elastostatics. Int. J. Num. Meth. Engng. 10 (1976) 991-1005.

25. Tabarrok, B.; Simpson, A.: An equilibrium finite element model for buckling analysis of plates. Int. J. Num. Meth. Engng. 11 (1977) 1733-1751.

26. Kapur, K.K.; Hartz, B.J.: Stability of plates using the finite element method. J. Engng. Mech. Div., Proc. ASCE 92 (1966) 177-195.

27. Lekhnitskii, S.G.: Anisotropic Plates. New York: Gordon and Breach 1968.

28. Rizzo, F.J.: An integral equation approach to boundary-value problems of classical elastostatics. Quart. App. Math. 25 (1967) 83-95.

29. Brush, D.O.; Almroth, B.O.: Buckling of Bars, Plates and Shells. New York: McGraw-Hill 1975.

30. Budiansky, B.: Buckling of clamped shallow spherical shells. In Koiter, W.T. (ed.), Proc. Symp. on Theory of Thin Elastic Shells, 64-94. Amsterdam: North Holland 1960.

31. Weinitschke, H.J.: On the stability problem for shallow shells. J. Math. Phys. 38, No. 4 (1960) 209-231.

32. Leicester, R.H.: Finite deformations of shallow shells. J. Engng. Mech. Div., Proc. ASCE 94, No. EM6 (1968) 1409-1423.

33. Levy, S.: Bending of rectangular plates with large deflections. NACA Tech. Report 737, 139-157. Washington, D.C. 1942.

Special Methods for Plate Analysis

J.T.KATSIKADELIS

Department of Civil Engineering
National Technical University, GR-157 73 Athens, Greece.

Summary

Special boundary element methods for the solution of plate bending problems are presented in this chapter. Some of these methods have been developed during the first efforts to apply the boundary integral equation method to the plate bending problem and before the appearance of general direct BEM formulations in the literature. Other special BEM's have been developed later in order to overcome certain shortcomings and computational difficulties in the general direct BEM formulations or in order to solve problems for which the fundamental solution can not be established or is difficult to treat numerically. On the basis of common characteristics the special methods are classified in five groups: (a) Methods based on the biharmonic analysis, (b) Indirect boundary element methods (IBEM´s) (c) Boundary differential - integral equation methods (BDIEM´s) (d) Green´s function methods (GFM´s), (e) Other methods which lack common characteristics. For each group of special methods a separate section is devoted. The special methods are described by the most representative methods of each group. The description of each special method is supplemented by several numerical results which are compared with those obtained by analytical or other numerical methods in order to illustrate the versatility, the effectiveness and the accuracy of the special BEM´s. Concluding remarks are presented in the last section.

Introduction

The formulation of the elastic plate bending problems via boundary integral equations furnishes the basis for an alternative to the domain type approaches (such as finite difference and finite element methods) to the solution of plate bending problems. General direct BEM formulations have been developed by Bezine [1], Stern [2], Katsikadelis [3] and further developed by many other authors, e.g. [4,5]. In these formulations the reciprocity theorem for the biharmonic equation is used to establish a pair of integral equations involving quantities which have direct physical significance, that is the displacement, the normal slope, the normal bending moment and the equivalent shear force on the boundary. These integral equations can be used to treat directly plate problems with any type of boundary conditions (essential, natural or mixed). In these BEM formulations the second boundary integral equation is established from the first one by taking its derivative in the direction normal to the boundary. This procedure yields hypersingular kernels which need special care in the numerical solution of the boundary integral equations.

In addition to the aforementioned general direct BEM formulations, certain other BEM's, which we call special BEM's, have been developed. Some of these methods have been developed before the general direct BEM formulations during the first efforts to apply the boundary integral equation method to the plate bending problem. Others have been developed later in order to overcome certain shortcomings and computational difficulties in the general direct formulations or in order to solve problems for which the fundamental solution is not possible to establish or is difficult to treat numerically. Most of these special BEM's are very effective when applied to plates with specific geometry, boundary conditions and loading. With few exceptions [6], efforts to extend some of these special BEM's to general BEM formulations did not produce useful and easy to handle methods. The special BEM's can be classified in five groups: (a) Methods based on the biharmonic analysis (b) Indirect boundary element methods (IBEM's) (c) Boundary differential - integral equation methods (BDIEM's) (d) Green's function methods (GFM's) (e) Other methods.

In the first group we distinguish four different methods which can be considered as an extension of the harmonic analysis to solve the biharmonic equation. The first method was developed by Jaswon et al. [7-9]. In this method the solution of the nonhomogeneous biharmonic equation, which governs the plate bending problem, is sought as a sum of a particular solution satisfying the nonhomogeneous plate equation and the solution of the homogeneous (biharmonic) equation subjected to nonhomogeneous boundary conditions. The solution of the homogeneous equation is obtained by expressing the biharmonic function in terms of two harmonic functions using the Almansi representation. Each of these two harmonic functions is represented by a single layer potential generated by an unknown boundary distribution. These two boundary distributions are determined from the solution of two coupled singular boundary integral equations derived from the prescribed boundary conditions. The method is convenient to analyze plates with clamped and simply supported edges. Moreover, the use of intrinsic coordinates permits the treatment of plates with curvilinear boundaries. The second method is a variation of the first and was developed by Maiti and Chakrabarty [10]. The solution of the homogeneous equation is obtained by representing the biharmonic function as the sum of two potentials, one harmonic and one biharmonic, which depend on two unknown boundary distributions that are established from the solution of two coupled singular boundary integral equations. They called this representation bipotential. This method was applied to polygonal plates with simply supported edges and has the advantage that it is not necessary to round-off the corners at the boundary. In the third method the Green's reciprocal identities for the harmonic equation (Green's third identity) and for the biharmonic equation (Rayleigh-Green identity) are employed to obtain two integral representations which, when applied to the boundary points, produce two compatibility relations between the boundary quantities w, $\partial w/\partial n$, $\nabla^2 w$ and $\partial\nabla^2 w/\partial n$. These relations are treated as singular boundary integral equations and are used to establish the two unknown boundary quantities. The other two are prescribed by the boundary conditions. This method has been developed by Segedin and Brickel [11] for simply supported corner plates, by Katsikadelis et al. [12,14] for plates on elastic foundation and by Camp and Gibson [13] for rectilinear plates. The last method in this group was developed by Paris and Leon [15-18]. They used the Marcus' decomposition method to replace the fourth order equation of the plate by two second order differential equations each of which represents the deflection of a membrane (Poisson's equation). The one of these equations involves an intermediate variable. The solution of the harmonic equations was obtained using a BEM approach based on Green's third identity. Although this method has been developed by the authors to treat plates subjected to all types of boundary conditions, it seems to be effective and easy to handle only for plates with simply supported edges for which the two integral equations are uncoupled.

In the second group of the special methods (the IBEM's) the integral representation of the deflection is expressed in terms of two unknown boundary distributions which have no specific physical significance. However, once these distributions have been established from the numerical solution of two boundary integral equations the values of the deflection and stress resultants anywhere within the plate can be calculated from them by simple integration processes. Such methods have been developed by many investigators including Niwa et al.[19], Tottenham [20], Altiero and Sikarskie [21,22], Zhu [23]. Variations of the second group of methods are those presented by Wu and Altiero [24], Muhajerin and Burgess [25] and Karageorghis and Fairweather [26].

In the third group of special BEM's (the BDIEM's) we include methods based on the work of Katsikadelis et al.[6,27]. In these methods the deflection of the plate is expressed by an integral representation involving four unknown boundary quantities; the deflection w, its Laplacian $\nabla^2 w$ and their normal derivatives $\partial w/\partial n$ and $\partial \nabla^2 w/\partial n$. The integral representation is derived using the Raleigh-Green identity and the fundamental solution of the biharmonic equation. The unknown four boundary quantities are established by solving on the boundary four coupled equations, two ordinary differential and two singular integral. The differential equations are derived from the boundary conditions while the integral equations are derived from the integral representation for the deflection. One of the main advantages of these boundary equation methods is that only four different kernels instead of eight [1-3] appear in the integral equations, which are simple in form. What is more important, those kernels which are singular have either logarithmic or Cauchy-type singularity i.e. the singular integrals are single layer or double layer potentials which are readily integrated. Moreover, the use of intrinsic coordinates facilitates the modelling of plates with curvilinear boundaries. The BDIEM's in conjunction with domain integration have been effectively employed as domain/boundary element methods (D/BEM's) to solve complicated plate problems, static or dynamic, linear or nonlinear, concerning plates having constant or variable thickness as well as plates resting on elastic foundation with bilateral or unilateral contact [28-33]. A BDIEM developed by Katsikadelis and Sapountzakis to solve vibration problems of membranes [34] has also been extended to solve vibration problems of thick plates governed by Mindlin's equations of motion [35].

In the fourth group of methods (the GFM's) we include those using the Green's function approach. From the theory of linear differential equations it is known that the solution of a boundary value problem is obtained by a simple direct evaluation of an integral over the domain, if the Green's function of the problem and the source distribution are given. The Green's function for the plate problem represents the deflection at a point of the plate due to a unit load at another point. The Green's function can be obtained analytically, as in the case of plates with simple geometry and boundary conditions (circular or rectangular plates), or numerically using the BEM. The GFM's have been developed by Katsikadelis and Sapountzakis [36] and have been used in conjunction with Gauss domain integration as D/BEM's to solve several static or dynamic, linear or nonlinear plate problems [37-40]. In this group of methods a BEM developed by Irschik, Ziegler et al. [41-47] could be included. These authors utilized existing Green's functions for basic finite domains to generate the kernel functions for given domains by embedding them properly into the basic domains with partially coinciding boundaries. On the non coinciding part of the boundary two boundary integral equations are derived employing the IBEM developed by Altiero and Sikarskie [22] and Wu and Altiero [48]. This method is an extension of the Melnikov's technique to solve torsion and elasticity problems involving rectangular domains with cut-offs or holes [49]. The method has been used to analyze polygonal plates embedded in rectangular domains. Although this method is called by the authors "Green's function method" it would be rather classified in the IBEM's.

In the last (fifth) group we include mainly methods whose formulation is based on considerations other that the conventional BEM. Some of these methods aim at overcoming certain shortcomings of the typical BEM formulations, such as inaccuracy of the results near the boundary or treatment of free edges or stress resultant distributions around holes. All these methods use integral representations at a certain stage. Without making reference to all these methods we mention here the variations of the superposition method [50,51], the methods which focus their interest in treating plates with holes [52,53] as well as a method in which the plate bending problem is converted into an analogous elastostatic problem described by the Navier equations by introducing intermediate potentials corresponding to displacement components [54]. These methods will not be presented in this chapter because they lack common characteristics.

In the sequel a section giving the governing equations for the plate bending problem is presented. It is followed by sections describing the special methods according to the aforegoing classification.

Governing Equations for the Plate Bending Problem

Consider a thin elastic plate consisting of homogeneous, linear elastic material, having thickness h and occupying a two-dimensional domain R in the x-y plane, bounded by a curve C_o. The domain may be multiply connected, i.e., it may have M holes, bounded by the curves $C_1, C_2, \ldots, C_M$ (see Fig.1).

Moreover, the curves C_i $(i=0,1,2,...M)$ may be piecewise smooth, i.e., the boundary of the plate may have a finite number of corners. When the plate is subjected to a transverse loading $f(P)$, its deflection $w(P)$ must satisfy the following differential equation

$$\nabla^4 w = f/D \tag{1}$$

where $D=Eh^3/12(1-\nu^2)$ is the flexural rigidity of the plate having modulus of elasticity E and Poisson's ratio ν; ∇^4 is the biharmonic operator defined as

$$\nabla^4 = \left(\frac{\partial^2}{\partial x^2} + \frac{\partial^2}{\partial y^2}\right)^2 = \frac{\partial^4}{\partial x^4} + 2\frac{\partial^4}{\partial x^2 \partial y^2} + \frac{\partial^4}{\partial y^4} \tag{2}$$

Moreover, the deflection of the plate must satisfy prescribed boundary conditions on the boundary $C=\cup_{i=0}^{M} C_i$ of the form [6]

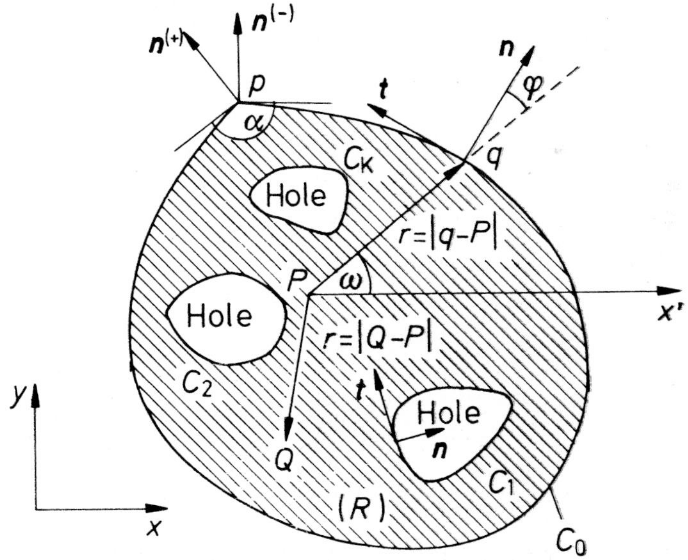

Fig.1. Two-dimensional domain R occupied by the plate.

$$\begin{aligned} \alpha_1 w + \alpha_2 V_n &= \alpha_3 \\ \beta_1 \frac{\partial w}{\partial n} + \beta_2 M_n &= \beta_3 \end{aligned} \tag{3}$$

For a free or elastically supported edge the boundary conditions (3) are supplemented by the corner condition

$$c_{1k}w + c_{2k}[\![M_{nt}]\!]_k = c_{3k} \quad \text{at the corner } k \tag{4}$$

In Eqs (3) and (4) $\alpha_i = \alpha_i(q)$, $\beta_i = \beta_i(q)$, $q \in C$ $(i=1,2,3)$ denote functions specified on the boundary C and c_{ik} $(i=1,2,3)$ are constants specified at the corner k. Moreover, w, $\frac{\partial w}{\partial n}$, M_n, V_n and M_{nt} are the deflection, its normal derivative, the bending moment, the equivalent (Kirchhoff's) shear force and the twisting moment on the boundary with outer normal vector $\underline{n}$, respectively; $[\![M_{nt}]\!]_k$ denotes the jump of discontinuity of the twisting moment at the corner k.

The boundary quantities M_n, V_n, M_{nt} at a regular (smooth) point are expressed in terms of the deflection w by the relations

$$M_n = Mw = -D\left(\frac{\partial^2 w}{\partial n^2} + \nu\frac{\partial^2 w}{\partial t^2}\right) = -D\left[\nabla^2 w + (\nu-1)\frac{\partial^2 w}{\partial t^2}\right] \tag{5}$$

$$V_n = Vw = -D\left[\frac{\partial}{\partial n}\nabla^2 w - (\nu-1)\frac{\partial}{\partial s}\left(\frac{\partial^2 w}{\partial n \partial t}\right)\right] \tag{6}$$

$$M_{nt} = Tw = D(1-\nu)\frac{\partial^2 w}{\partial n \partial t} \tag{7}$$

Note that the bending moment M_t at the boundary along the tangential direction is given as

$$M_t = -D\left(\frac{\partial^2 w}{\partial t^2} + \nu\frac{\partial^2 w}{\partial n^2}\right) = -D\left[\nu\nabla^2 w - (\nu-1)\frac{\partial^2 w}{\partial t^2}\right] \tag{8}$$

In the aforementioned relations $\partial/\partial n$ and $\partial/\partial t$ denote differentiation along the outward normal and the tangential directions, respectively, while $\partial/\partial s$ denotes differentiation with respect to the arc length of the boundary.

Eqs (3) express the most general case of linear boundary conditions for the plate problem. The conventional boundary conditions are obtained from Eqs (3) by specifying appropriately the functions α_i and β_i. Thus, the boundary C is

a. clamped ($w = 0$, $\partial w/\partial n = 0$) if
$\alpha_1=1$, $\alpha_2=0$, $\alpha_3=0$, $\beta_1=1$, $\beta_2=0$, $\beta_3=0$

b. simply supported ($w = 0$, $M_n = 0$) if
$\alpha_1=1$, $\alpha_2=0$, $\alpha_3=0$, $\beta_1=0$, $\beta_2=1$, $\beta_3=0$

c. free ($M_n = 0$, $V_n = 0$) if
$\alpha_1=0$, $\alpha_2=1$, $\alpha_3=0$, $\beta_1=0$, $\beta_2=1$, $\beta_3=0$

d. guided ($\partial w/\partial n = 0$, $V_n = 0$) if
$\alpha_1=0$, $\alpha_2=1$, $\alpha_3=0$, $\beta_1=1$, $\beta_2=0$, $\beta_3=0$

Notice that at points where the boundary conditions change, the functions α_i, β_i are discontinuous.

If intrinsic coordinates s, n, i.e. the arc length s and the coordinate n along the outward normal to the boundary are used, the following relations are valid

$$\frac{\partial w}{\partial t} = \frac{\partial w}{\partial s}$$

$$\frac{\partial^2 w}{\partial t^2} = \frac{\partial^2 w}{\partial s^2} + \kappa\frac{\partial w}{\partial n} \qquad (9)$$

$$\frac{\partial^2 w}{\partial n \partial t} = \frac{\partial^2 w}{\partial s \partial n} - \kappa\frac{\partial w}{\partial s}$$

where $\kappa=\kappa(s)$ is the curvature of the boundary at point s. For a rectilinear edge it is $\kappa=0$ and the variable t is identical to s.

Using relations (9), Eqs (5) to (8) can be written as

$$M_n = -D[\nabla^2 w + (\nu-1)(\frac{\partial^2 w}{\partial s^2} + \kappa\frac{\partial w}{\partial n})]$$

$$V_n = -D[\frac{\partial}{\partial n}\nabla^2 w - (\nu-1)\frac{\partial}{\partial s}(\frac{\partial^2 w}{\partial s \partial n} - \kappa\frac{\partial w}{\partial s})] \qquad (10)$$

$$M_{nt} = D(1-\nu)(\frac{\partial^2 w}{\partial s \partial n} - \kappa\frac{\partial w}{\partial s})$$

$$M_t = -D[\nu\nabla^2 w - (\nu-1)(\frac{\partial^2 w}{\partial s^2} + \kappa\frac{\partial w}{\partial s})]$$

The bending moments M_x, M_y, the twisting moments M_{xy}, M_{yx} and the shear forces Q_x, Q_y at any point in the interior of the plate are given by the relations [55]

$$M_x = -D(\frac{\partial^2 w}{\partial x^2} + \nu\frac{\partial^2 w}{\partial y^2})$$

$$M_y = -D(\frac{\partial^2 w}{\partial y^2} + \nu\frac{\partial^2 w}{\partial x^2}) \tag{11}$$

$$M_{xy} = -M_{yx} = D(1-\nu)\frac{\partial^2 w}{\partial x \partial y}$$

$$Q_x = -D\frac{\partial}{\partial x}\nabla^2 w$$

$$Q_y = -D\frac{\partial}{\partial y}\nabla^2 w$$

a) Methods Based on the Biharmonic Analysis

Since Eq. (1) is linear its solution can be obtained as a sum of two functions w_1 and W

$$w = w_1 + W \tag{12}$$

where w_1 is a particular solution of Eq. (1), i.e., it satisfies the nonhomogeneous differential equation

$$\nabla^4 w_1 = f/D \tag{13}$$

and W is a biharmonic function, i.e., it is the solution of the homogeneous differential equation

$$\nabla^4 W = 0 \tag{14}$$

satisfying nonhomogeneous boundary conditions.

In simple loading cases (e.g. $f=f_o$=constant) the particular solution w_1 of Eq. (13) can be obtained by inspection. For more general loading cases the procedure presented by Katsikadelis et al. [6,56] can be employed. In this method complex variables

$$z = x+iy \quad , \quad \bar{z} = x-iy \quad , \quad i = \sqrt{-1} \tag{15}$$

are used and Eq. (13) is transformed to

$$16\frac{\partial^4 w_1}{\partial z^2 \partial \bar{z}^2} = \frac{f(z,\bar{z})}{D} \tag{16}$$

A particular solution $w_1=w_1(z,\bar{z})$ is obtained by integrating Eq. (16) consecutively four times and omitting the unnecessary constants of integration. Subsequently, the solution is transformed into the real domain using Eqs (15).

As it was already mentioned in the introduction, the solution of Eq. (14) can be obtained by the following methods based on biharmonic analysis :

i. **By expressing the biharmonic function in terms of two harmonic ones.** The developments in this section are based on the work of Jaswon et al. [7-9]. According to this method the biharmonic function can be constructed by employing the Almansi representation

$$W = \varrho^2 \varphi + \psi \tag{17}$$

where

$$\varrho^2 = x^2+y^2 \tag{18}$$

and $\varphi = \varphi(x,y)$, $\psi = \psi(x,y)$ are two harmonic functions, i.e.

$$\nabla^2 \varphi = 0 \quad , \quad \nabla^2 \psi = 0 \tag{19}$$

The origin of the coordinates, $\varrho=0$, lies inside the domain R, if it is simply connected. Moreover, in a multiply connected domain R, bounded externally by C_o and internally by $C_1, C_2, \ldots, C_M$, the representation (17) can be also used if the origin lies within one of the inner boundaries C_j; $1 \le j \le M$.

The first derivatives of representation (17) with respect to x and y are

$$\frac{\partial W}{\partial x} = \varrho^2 \frac{\partial \varphi}{\partial x} + 2x\varphi + \frac{\partial \psi}{\partial x}$$
$$\frac{\partial W}{\partial y} = \varrho^2 \frac{\partial \varphi}{\partial y} + 2y\varphi + \frac{\partial \psi}{\partial y} \qquad (20)$$

and the second derivatives are

$$\frac{\partial^2 W}{\partial x^2} = \varrho^2 \frac{\partial^2 \varphi}{\partial x^2} + 4x\frac{\partial \varphi}{\partial x} + 2\varphi + \frac{\partial^2 \psi}{\partial x^2}$$
$$\frac{\partial^2 W}{\partial y^2} = \varrho^2 \frac{\partial^2 \varphi}{\partial y^2} + 4y\frac{\partial \varphi}{\partial y} + 2\varphi + \frac{\partial^2 \psi}{\partial y^2} \qquad (21)$$
$$\frac{\partial^2 W}{\partial x \partial y} = \varrho^2 \frac{\partial^2 \varphi}{\partial x \partial y} + 2\left(y\frac{\partial \varphi}{\partial x} + x\frac{\partial \varphi}{\partial y}\right) + \frac{\partial^2 \psi}{\partial x \partial y}$$

Using relations (20) and (21) the normal derivative of W and its Laplacian at a point on the boundary are given as

$$\frac{\partial W}{\partial n} = 2\varrho\frac{\partial \varrho}{\partial n}\varphi + \varrho^2\frac{\partial \varphi}{\partial n} + \frac{\partial \psi}{\partial n} \qquad (22)$$

$$\nabla^2 W = 4\left(x\frac{\partial \varphi}{\partial x} + y\frac{\partial \varphi}{\partial y} + \varphi\right) \qquad (23)$$

To be consistent with Ref. [7], in this analysis the normal is taken inward to the boundary C (see Fig.2). The harmonic function φ can be represented by a single layer potential generated by an unknown boundary source distribution $\sigma(q)$, $q \in C$. Thus, we write

$$\varphi(P) = \int_C \ell n r \sigma(q) d\sigma_q. \qquad (24)$$

$r = |P-q|$ is the distance between the points $P:\{x,y\} \in R$ and $q:\{\xi,\eta\} \in C$. This potential remains continuous as $P \rightarrow p \in C$, i.e., $\varphi(P) \rightarrow \varphi(p)$ as $P \rightarrow p$, while the normal derivative of the potential

(24) at point $p \in C$ is discontinuous. Thus, we have

$$\varphi(p) = \int_C \ell n r \sigma(q) d\sigma_q$$
$$\frac{\partial \varphi(p)}{\partial n} = \int_C \frac{\partial}{\partial n_p} \ell n r \sigma(q) ds_q + \pi \sigma(p) \tag{25}$$

The additional term in the second of Eqs (25) is due to the fact that the normal derivative of the single layer potential behaves like a double layer potential and, thus, it exhibits a discontinuity jump as $P \to p \in C$. Note that throughout this chapter points inside the domain R are denoted by capital letters, while points on the boundary C are denoted by lower case letters. The subscripts p or q indicate the point which varies during differentiation or integration.

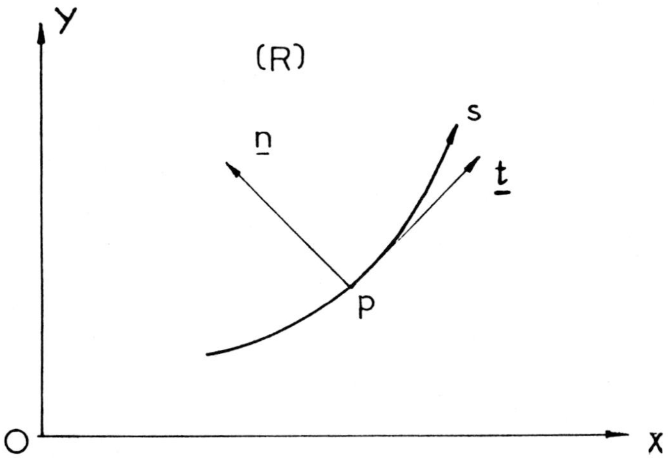

Fig.2. Orientation of tangent and normal at point of the boundary C enclosing domain R.

Similarly, we have

$$\psi(P) = \int_C \ell n r \mu(q) d\sigma_q \tag{26}$$

and

$$\psi(p) = \int_C \ell n r \mu(q) d\sigma_q$$

$$\frac{\partial\psi(p)}{\partial n} = \int_C \frac{\partial}{\partial n_p} \ell n r \mu(q) d\sigma_q + \pi\mu(p) \tag{27}$$

The derivatives of φ at any interior point $P:\{x,y\}$ may be generated by the formulae

$$\frac{\partial\varphi}{\partial x} = \int_C \frac{\partial}{\partial x} \ell n r \sigma(q) ds_q \quad , \quad r=|P-q| \tag{28}$$

etc., where

$$\frac{\partial}{\partial x}\ell n r \mp \frac{x-\xi}{r^2}$$

$$\frac{\partial^2}{\partial x \partial y}\ell n r = - \frac{2(x-\xi)(y-\eta)}{r^4} \tag{29}$$

$$\frac{\partial^2}{\partial x^2}\ell n r = \frac{1}{r^2} - \frac{2(x-\xi)^2}{r^4} \quad , \quad \text{etc.}$$

However, difficulties arise on C owing to the discontinuities exemplified by Eqs (25) and (27). By contrast to the normal derivative the tangential derivative of a simple layer potential remains continuous on C, i.e.

$$\frac{\partial\varphi(p)}{\partial t} = \frac{\partial}{\partial t_p}\int_C \ell n r \sigma(q) ds_q = \int_C \frac{\partial}{\partial t_p} \ell n r \sigma(q) ds_q \quad , \quad r=|p-q| \tag{30}$$

Accordingly, since

$$\frac{\partial}{\partial x} = \frac{\partial}{\partial n}\frac{dn}{dx} + \frac{\partial}{\partial t}\frac{dt}{dx} \tag{31}$$

it follows that

$$\frac{\partial}{\partial x}\int_C \ell n r \sigma(q) d\sigma_q = \int_C \frac{\partial}{\partial x} \ell n r \sigma(q) ds_q + \pi\sigma(p)\frac{dn}{dx} \tag{32}$$

and similarly

$$\frac{\partial}{\partial y}\int_C \ell n r \sigma(q) d\sigma_q = \int_C \frac{\partial}{\partial y} \ell n r \sigma(q) ds_q + \pi\sigma(p)\frac{dn}{dy} \tag{33}$$

where

$$\frac{dn}{dx} = \cos(n,x) \quad , \qquad \frac{dn}{dy} = \cos(n,y)$$

Similar expressions are obtained for the potential ψ.

For a clamped plate the boundary conditions are

$$W(p) = -w_1(p)$$
$$\frac{\partial W(p)}{\partial n} = -\frac{\partial w_1(p)}{\partial n} \tag{34}$$

or using Eqs (17) and (22)

$$\varrho^2\varphi(p) + \psi(p) = -w_1(p)$$
$$2\varrho\frac{\partial\varrho}{\partial n}\varphi + \varrho^2\frac{\partial\varphi(p)}{\partial n} + \frac{\partial\psi(p)}{\partial n} = -\frac{\partial w_1(p)}{\partial n} \qquad p\in C \tag{35}$$

For a simply supported plate the boundary conditions are

$$W(p) = -w_1(p)$$
$$\nabla^2 W(p) + \varkappa(1-\nu)\frac{\partial W(p)}{\partial n} = -\nabla^2 w_1(p) - \varkappa(1-\nu)\frac{\partial w_1(p)}{\partial n} \tag{36}$$

or using Eqs (17) and (23)

$$\varrho^2\varphi(p) + \psi(p) = -w_1(p)$$
$$4[x\frac{\partial\varphi(p)}{\partial x}+y\frac{\partial\varphi(p)}{\partial y}+\varphi(p)] + \varkappa(1-\nu)[2\varrho\frac{\partial\varrho}{\partial n}+\varrho^2\frac{\partial\varphi(p)}{\partial n}+\frac{\partial\psi(p)}{\partial n}] =$$
$$= -\nabla^2 w_1(p) - \varkappa(1-\nu)\frac{\partial}{\partial n}w_1(p) \tag{37}$$

For plates with rectilinear edges the curvature vanishes, $\varkappa=0$, and the boundary conditions are drastically simplified. Substitution of Eqs (25) and (27) into the boundary conditions (35) yields two coupled linear boundary integral equations for the unknown boundary distributions σ and μ. Similarly, substitution of Eqs (25) and (27) as well as (32) and (33) into the boundary conditions (37) yields again two coupled linear boundary integral equations for σ and μ.

An analytic solution of the boundary integral equations is out of question. However, they can be solved numerically by employing the boundary element technique. When constant boundary elements are considered the boundary C is divided into N smooth segments (elements) on each of which the unknown function is taken constant (see Fig.3). Thus, an integral of the form

$$\varphi(p) = \int_C K(p,q)u(q)ds_q$$

is approximated by

$$\varphi(p) \simeq \sum_{j=1}^{N} u_j \int_j K(p,q)ds_q \tag{38}$$

where u_j is the value of the function u at the nodal point of the j-element and $\int_j K(p,q)ds_q$ is the integral of the kernel K(p,q) on the j-element. This integral can be evaluated analytically. However, an approximation of the geometry of the element by a straight line, two-straight lines or by a parabolic arc (see Fig.4) simplifies the computational work. The constant boundary element approximation is adequate for a large variety of problems.

This approximation of the boundary integral equations yields a system of 2N linear algebraic equations with respect to the nodal values σ_j and μ_j. The equations are solved and the computed nodal values of the functions σ and μ are used to evaluate the potentials $\varphi(P)$ and $\psi(P)$ at any point P inside the domain R from the discretized form of Eqs (24) and (26). Thus

$$\begin{aligned} \varphi(P) &= \sum_{j=1}^{N} \sigma_j \int_j \ell n r_{Pq} ds_q \\ \psi(P) &= \sum_{j=1}^{N} \mu_j \int_j \ell n r_{Pq} ds_q \end{aligned} \tag{39}$$

where

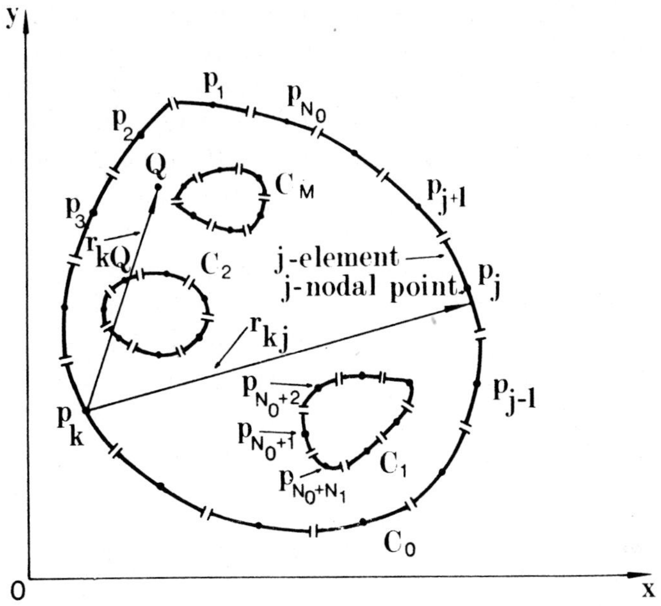

Fig.3. Discretization of the boundary into N constant elements

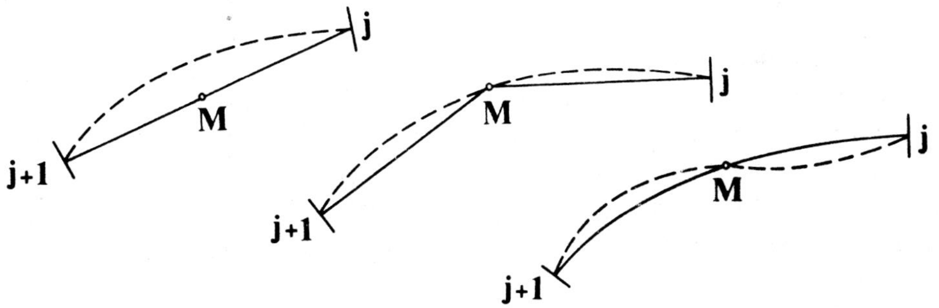

Fig.4. Types of constant elements

$$r_{Pq} = |P-q| \qquad P \in R, \quad q \in j\text{-element}$$

Using Eqs (39) the function W is evaluated from Eq. (17) and subsequently the deflection w from Eq. (12). The moments M_x, M_y, M_{xy} and the shear forces Q_x, Q_y are evaluated from Eqs (11) by directed differentiation of the deflection.

For the case of a plate with clamped boundary the resulting integral equations are rather simple. However, for a plate with simply supported boundary the second integral equation is more complicated but it still involves no higher than the first derivatives of φ and ψ. Plates with other boundary conditions (free or guided) have not been analyzed by this

Table 1. Central deflection $\bar{w}=w/(qb^4/D)$ and some important bending moments $\bar{M}=M/qb^2$ of a clamped rectangular plate subjected to uniform load for various side ratios ($\nu=0.3$). Upper numbers: computed [8], lower numbers: analytic [55].

a/b	$\bar{w}(0,0)$	$\bar{M}_x(0,0)$	$\bar{M}_x(a,0)$	$\bar{M}_y(0,0)$	$\bar{M}_y(0,b)$
1.0	0.0202	0.0916	-0.2042	0.0916	-0.2042
	0.0202	0.0924	-0.2052	0.0924	-0.2052
1.5	0.0351	0.0811	-0.2268	0.1471	-0.3020
	0.0352	0.0812	-0.2280	0.1473	-0.3028
2.0	0.0405	0.0631	-0.2270	0.1646	-0.3312
	0.0406	0.0632	-0.2284	0.1648	-0.3316

Table 2. Central deflection $\bar{w}=w/(qa^4/D)$ and some important bending moments $\bar{M}=M/qa^2$ of a uniformly loaded square plate having two opposite edges clamped and the other two simply supported ($\nu=0.3$). Upper numbers: computed [8], lower numbers: analytic [55].

$\bar{w}(0,0)$	$\bar{M}_x(0,0)$	$\bar{M}_y(0,0)$	$\bar{M}_y(0,\frac{a}{2})$
0.0019	0.0244	0.0333	-0.0699
0.0019	0.0244	0.0332	-0.0697

method. Such an effort would yield too complicated integral equations, which would be difficult to handle numerically. A defect of the method is that the corners have to be rounded off when dealing with polygonal plates and hence the procedure cannot take adequate account of the irregular behaviour (if any) of a physical quantity at the corners. Some numerical results illustrating the accuracy of the method are given in Tables 1 and 2.

ii. **By the method of bipotential.** The method was developed by Maiti and Chakrabarty [10]. In this method the biharmonic function is expressed in terms of two potentials one of which is biharmonic and the other logarithmic (single layer potential). The biharmonic function, thus expressed and termed as bipotential, depends on two unknown boundary source distributions σ and μ. Adopting the aforegoing notation we write

$$W(P) = \int_C r^2(\ell nr-1)\sigma(q)ds_q + \int_C \ell nr\mu(q)ds_q \tag{40}$$

where $r=|P-q|$, $P\in R$, $q\in C$ and $\sigma(q)$, $\mu(q)$ are the source distributions at point q.

Eq. (40) yields

$$\nabla^2 W(P) = 4\int_C \ell nr\sigma(q)ds_q \tag{41}$$

$W(P)$ and $\nabla^2 W(P)$ remain continuous as $P\to p\in C$. Hence, the following two boundary integral equations are derived for the determination of σ and μ

$$\begin{aligned} W(p) &= \int_C r^2(\ell nr-1)\sigma(q)ds_q + \int_C \ell nr\mu(q)ds_q \\ \nabla^2 W(p) &= 4\int_C \ell nr\sigma(q)ds_q \end{aligned} \tag{42}$$

where $r=|p-q|$, $p,q\in C$.

Eqs (42) are convenient to analyze plates with simply

supported polygonal boundary. In this case the boundary quantities W(p) and $\nabla^2 W(p)$ are obtained from Eqs (36) for $\kappa=0$. Eqs (42) are solved numerically by employing the boundary element technique with constant elements. Thus, discretizing the boundary, as previously, into N elements a system a 2N linear algebraic equations is obtained, which in matrix form may be written as

$$\begin{aligned} &[A]\{\sigma\} + [B]\{\mu\} = \{c\} \\ &[B]\{\sigma\} = \{d\} \end{aligned} \tag{43}$$

where

$\{\sigma\},\{\mu\}$: are Nx1 column matrices including the nodal values of the unknown functions σ and μ.

$\{c\},\{d\}$: are Nx1 column matrices including the known nodal values of W and $\nabla^2 W/4$.

$[A],[B]$: are NxN coefficient matrices the elements of which are computed from the relations

$$A_{ij} = \int_j r_{iq}^2 (\ell n r_{iq} - 1) ds_q$$

$$B_{ij} = \int_j \ell n r_{iq} ds_q$$

$$r_{iq} = |p_i - q|, \quad q \in j\text{-element}$$

Eq. (43) has a unique solution except for certain boundaries, referred to as Γ-boundaries [57]. Maiti and Chakrabarty [10] used this method to analyze simply supported polygonal plates with various shapes (rectangular, triangular, rhombic, hexagonal). In their examples they treated and discussed the problem of unbounded bending stress in the neighborhood of the junction of two edges including an obtuse angle. Some numerical results which illustrate the accuracy of the method are presented in Tables 3 and 4.

iii. By the Green's identity methods. There are certain formulations for the solution of the homogeneous as well as the nonhomogeneous biharmonic equation which are based on two integral representations, one holding for the harmonic function, the harmonic formula, and the other for the biharmonic function, the biharmonic formula [11-14]. In the development presented herein, which is based on the work of Katsikadelis et al. [6,12,14], the biharmonic formula is first established and thereafter the harmonic one is obtained by direct differentiation.

The Green's reciprocal identity for the biharmonic operator known as the Rayleigh-Green identity is written as [58]

$$\iint_R (v\nabla^4 w - w\nabla^4 v)d\sigma = \int_C (v\frac{\partial}{\partial n}\nabla^2 w - w\frac{\partial}{\partial n}\nabla^2 v - \frac{\partial v}{\partial n}\nabla^2 w + \frac{\partial w}{\partial n}\nabla^2 v)ds \quad (44)$$

The functions w and v have continuous fourth order derivatives inside the domain R and third order derivatives on its boundary C.

Table 3. Deflections $\bar{w}=w/(qa^4/D)$ and bending moments $\bar{M}=M/qa^2$ at the center of a simply - supported, uniformly - loaded equilateral triangular plate (ν=0.3) obtained using N boundary elements.

N	$\bar{w}\times10^3$	$\bar{M}_x\times10^2$	$\bar{M}_y\times10^2$
12	1.108	2.587	2.384
18	1.047	2.445	2.409
24	1.034	2.422	2.410
Exact	1.029	2.407	2.407

Table 4. Deflections $\bar{w}=w/(qa^4/D)$ and bending moments $\bar{M}=M/qa^2$ at the center of a simply - supported, uniformly - loaded hexagonal plate (ν=0.3) obtained using N boundary elements.

N	$\bar{w}$	$\bar{M}_x$	$\bar{M}_y$
12	0.0550	0.1760	0.1760
18	0.0548	0.1758	0.1758
24	0.0547	0.1757	0.1756
Exact	0.0548	0.1760	0.1760

Consider the nonhomogeneous biharmonic equation

$$\nabla^4 v = \delta(P-Q)/D \tag{45}$$

where $\delta(P-Q)$ is the two-dimensional (Dirac's) delta-function. Eq. (45) admits a particular solution

$$v = v(P,Q) = \frac{1}{8\pi D} r^2 \ell n r \quad , \qquad r = |P-Q| \tag{46}$$

which is the fundamental solution of the biharmonic equation. It is a two-point function, which is symmetric with respect to points P and Q and, thus, the roles of the source and field points can be interchanged.

Application of the identity (44) to the functions w and v satisfying Eqs (1) and (45) yields the following integral representation

$$w(P) = \iint_R v f d\sigma - D\int_C \left(v\frac{\partial}{\partial n}\nabla^2 w - w\frac{\partial}{\partial n}\nabla^2 v - \frac{\partial v}{\partial n}\nabla^2 w + \frac{\partial w}{\partial n}\nabla^2 v\right) ds \tag{47}$$

The harmonic formula can be readily obtained by applying the operator ∇^2 to Eq. (47). Thus, we have

$$\nabla^2 w(P) = \iint_R \nabla^2 v f d\sigma - D\int_C \left(\nabla^2 v\frac{\partial}{\partial n}\nabla^2 w - \nabla^2 w\frac{\partial}{\partial n}\nabla^2 v\right) ds \tag{48}$$

Note that the integral representation (48) can be established directly from the Green's identity for the harmonic operator, if it is applied to the functions $\nabla^2 w$ and $\nabla^2 v$ satisfying Eqs (1) and (45), respectively [11,13].

By letting point P in Eqs (47) and (48) approach a point p on the boundary C and by noting that the kernel $\partial\nabla^2 v/\partial n$ behaves like a double layer potential, two boundary integral equations are derived

$$\alpha\Omega = \frac{1}{D}\iint_R \Lambda_4(r) f d\sigma - \int_C [\Lambda_1(r)\Omega + \Lambda_2(r)X + \Lambda_3(r)\Phi + \Lambda_4(r)\Psi] ds$$

$$\alpha\Phi = \frac{1}{D}\iint_R \Lambda_2(r)f\,d\sigma - \int_C [\Lambda_1(r)\Phi+\Lambda_2(r)\Psi]ds \tag{49}$$

where the following notation has been used

$$w = \Omega \qquad \frac{\partial w}{\partial n} = X \qquad \nabla^2 w = \Phi \qquad \frac{\partial}{\partial n}\nabla^2 w = \Psi \tag{50}$$

and the kernels $\Lambda_i(r)$ $(i=1,2,3,4)$ are defined as

$$\Lambda_1(r) = -\frac{\cos\varphi}{r} \qquad \Lambda_2(r) = \ell nr+1$$
$$\Lambda_3(r) = -\frac{1}{4}(2r\ell nr+r)\cos\varphi \qquad \Lambda_4(r) = \frac{1}{4}r^2\ell nr \tag{51}$$

Notice that for the line integrals it is $r=|p-q|$ while for the domain integrals it is $r=|p-Q|$; φ is the angle between the direction of $\underline{r}$ and the normal $\underline{n}$ to the boundary; α is the angle between the tangents at point p; $\alpha=\pi$ at points where the boundary is smooth.

Eqs (49) constitute two compatibility relations between the boundary quantities Ω, X, Φ, Ψ. They can be considered as two coupled boundary integral equations from which any two unknown boundary quantities can be determined if the rest are prescribed. In plate bending problems these boundary quantities are also related to the boundary conditions. For plates with clamped or simply supported edges these relations are simple. Thus, we have: (a) for a clamped plate $\Omega=0$, $X=0$ and (b) for a simply supported plate $\Omega=0$, $\Phi+\kappa(\nu-1)X=0$. However, for plates with a free edge ($M_n=0$, $V_n=0$) or a guided edge ($\frac{\partial w}{\partial n}=0$, $V_n=0$) the corresponding relations are complicated since they involve derivatives of the boundary quantities with respect to the boundary arc length s (see Eqs 10). Therefore, this approach can be readily employed to analyze plates with clamped or simply supported edges.

This method has been applied either directly to the nonhomogeneous plate equation [12,13] or to the biharmonic (homogeneous) equation by setting the solution in the form of Eq. (12) [11,56,59]. Although the first approach is more direct, the second one seems to be a pure boundary integral formulation. In the first case the effort to maintain the strictly boundary oriented formulation by transforming the domain integral due to loading into boundary ones increases the analytical as well as the computational task.

The set of integral equations (49) can be solved numerically using the boundary element technique. Thus, discretizing the boundary of the plate into N constant elements (see Figs 3,4) we obtain a system of 2N linear algebraic equations.

For a clamped plate ($\Omega=0$, $X=0$) this system is written as

$$\begin{bmatrix} [A] & [B] \\ [C] & [D] \end{bmatrix} \begin{bmatrix} \{\Phi\} \\ \{\Psi\} \end{bmatrix} = \begin{bmatrix} \{F\} \\ \{G\} \end{bmatrix} \tag{52}$$

where [A],[B],[C],[D] are NxN coefficient matrices and {F},{G} are Nx1 column matrices of the known terms. $\{\Phi\}$,$\{\Psi\}$ are Nx1 column matrices including the nodal values of the unknown boundary quantities Φ and Ψ. The elements of the above known matrices are computed from the relations

$$\begin{aligned} A_{ij} &= \int_j \Lambda_3(r_{iq})ds_q \\ B_{ij} &= \int_j \Lambda_4(r_{iq})ds_q \\ C_{ij} &= \pi\delta_{ij} + \int_j \Lambda_1(r_{iq})ds_q \\ D_{ij} &= \int_j \Lambda_2(r_{iq})ds_q \\ F_i &= \frac{1}{D}\iint_R \Lambda_4(r_{iQ})f d\sigma_Q \\ G_i &= \frac{1}{D}\iint_R \Lambda_2(r_{iQ})f d\sigma_Q \end{aligned} \tag{53}$$

where δ_{ij} is the Kronecker delta; $r_{iq}=|p_i-q|$; $r_{iQ}=|p_i-Q|$ $q\in j$-element, $Q\in R$.

For a simply supported plate ($\Omega=0$, $\Phi+\kappa(\nu-1)X=0$) the aforementioned system is written as

$$\begin{bmatrix} [A'] & [B] \\ [C'] & [D] \end{bmatrix} \begin{bmatrix} \{X\} \\ \{\Psi\} \end{bmatrix} = \begin{bmatrix} \{F\} \\ \{G\} \end{bmatrix} \tag{54}$$

The matrices $[A']$, $[C']$ are given in terms of $[A]$ and $[C]$ as

$$\begin{aligned} [A'] &= [D]-\kappa(\nu-1)[A] \\ [C'] &= -\kappa(\nu-1)[C] \end{aligned} \tag{55}$$

Eqs (52) or (54) are solved and the nodal values of the boundary quantities are obtained. These values are used in Eq. (47) to evaluate the deflection at any interior point P of the plate, which using the same boundary discretization is written as

$$\begin{aligned} w(P) = & \frac{1}{2\pi D}\iint_R \Lambda_4(r) f d\sigma \\ & - \frac{1}{2\pi}\sum_{j=1}^{N} [\Omega_j \int_j \Lambda_1(r)ds + X_j \int_j \Lambda_2(r)ds + \Phi_j \int_j \Lambda_3(r)ds \\ & + \Psi_j \int_j \Lambda_4(r)ds] \end{aligned} \tag{56}$$

The bending moments M_x, M_y, the twisting moment M_{xy} and the shear forces Q_x and Q_y at any point P are obtained from Eqs (11). The derivatives involved in these equations are obtained by direct differentiation of relation (56) [6]. Thus

$$\begin{aligned} d_i W = & \frac{1}{2\pi D}\iint_R B_i(r) f d\sigma - \frac{1}{2\pi}\sum_{j=1}^{N} [\Omega_j \int_j C_i(r)ds + X_j \int_j D_i(r)ds \\ & + \Phi_j \int_j E_i(r)ds + \Psi_j \int_j B_i(r)ds] \end{aligned} \tag{57}$$

where the operators d_i $(i=1,2,3,4,5)$ are defined as

$$d_1 = \frac{\partial^2}{\partial x^2} + \frac{\partial^2}{\partial y^2} , \quad d_2 = \frac{\partial^2}{\partial x^2} - \frac{\partial^2}{\partial y^2} , \quad d_3 = \frac{\partial^2}{\partial x \partial y}$$

$$d_4 = \frac{\partial}{\partial x}\nabla^2 , \quad d_5 = \frac{\partial}{\partial y}\nabla^2 \tag{58}$$

and the kernels B_i, C_i, D_i, E_i are given as

$$B_1(r) = \ln r + 1 , \quad B_2(r) = \frac{1}{2}\cos 2\omega , \quad B_3(r) = \frac{1}{4}\sin 2\omega$$

$$B_4(r) = -\frac{\cos\omega}{r} , \quad B_5(r) = -\frac{\sin\omega}{r}$$

$$C_1(r) \doteq 0 , \quad C_2(r) = \frac{4\cos(2\omega-\varphi)}{r^3} , \quad C_3(r) = \frac{2\sin(2\omega-\varphi)}{r^3}$$

$$C_4(r) = 0 , \quad C_5(r) = 0 \tag{59}$$

$$D_1(r) = 0 , \quad D_2(r) = \frac{2\cos 2\omega}{r^2} , \quad D_3(r) = \frac{\sin 2\omega}{r^2}$$

$$D_4(r) = 0, \quad D_5(r) = 0$$

$$E_1(r) = \frac{\cos\varphi}{r} , \quad E_2(r) = \frac{\sin 2\omega \sin\varphi}{r} , \quad E_3(r) = -\frac{2\cos 2\omega \sin\varphi}{r}$$

$$E_4(r) = \frac{\cos(\omega-\varphi)}{r^2} , \quad E_5(r) = \frac{\sin(\omega-\varphi)}{r^2}$$

ω is the angle between the x-axis and the direction of $\underline{r}$. Note that in Eqs (56) and (57) it is $r=|P-Q|$, $P,Q \in R$ for the domain integrals, while $r=|P-q|$, $P \in R$ and $q \in$ j-element for the line integrals.

In Eqs (49), (56) and (57), owing to the transverse loading, there appear domain integrals of the form

$$I = \iint_R K(r_{PQ}) f(Q) d\sigma_Q \tag{60}$$

where the kernel $K(r_{PQ})$, $r_{PQ}=|P-Q|$, may be singular. Thus, their numerical evaluation needs special care. We distinguish four loading cases.

1. Concentrated load. The plate is loaded by a concentrated load F applied to a certain point Q_o. In this case the loading

function f(Q) can be represented as

$$f(Q) = F\delta(Q-Q_o) \tag{61}$$

and the value of the integral (60) is

$$I = FK(r_{PQ_o}) \tag{62}$$

2. Line load. The plate is loaded by a line load p(s) distributed along a curve L^* in R. In this case, the domain integral can be computed by the line integral

$$I = \int_{L^*} K(r_{PQ})p(Q)ds_Q \quad , \qquad Q\in L^* \tag{63}$$

3. Linearly varying load. The plate is subjected to a uniform or linearly varying load distributed over an area $R^*\subseteq R$ of the plate bounded by a curve C^*. In this case, which is very usual in engineering practice, it is $\partial^2 f/\partial x^2=\partial^2 f/\partial y^2=0$ and the domain integral can be readily converted into a line integral on the boundary. Consequently, the method maintains its strictly boundary equation formulation. Many investigators have developed techniques for converting the domain integrals into boundary line integrals [13]. We present here the technique developed by Katsikadelis and Armenakas [6]. We distinguish two cases.

Case i. $K(r)=\Lambda_2(r)$ or $K(r)=\Lambda_4(r)$. Employing Green's reciprocal identity for the harmonic operator we obtain

$$\iint_{R^*} K(r)f d\sigma = \int_{C^*}(f\frac{\partial u}{\partial n} - u\frac{\partial f}{\partial n})ds \tag{64}$$

where u is a particular solution of the equation

$$\nabla^2 u = \frac{1}{r}\frac{d}{dr}(r\frac{du}{dr}) = K(r)$$

and is obtained by direct integration of this equation. Thus, we have

$$u = \frac{1}{128}r^4(2\ell nr-1) \qquad \text{if} \qquad K(r) = \Lambda_4(r)$$
$$u = \frac{1}{4}r^2\ell nr \qquad \text{if} \qquad K(r) = \Lambda_2(r) \qquad (65)$$

Case ii. $K(r)=d[\Lambda_4(r)]$ where $d[\ ]$ is one of the operators defined by Eqs (58). In this case the following relations derived from Gauss divergence theorem and valid for two functions u and v are employed

$$\iint_{R^*} u\frac{\partial v}{\partial x}dxdy = -\iint_{R^*} v\frac{\partial u}{\partial x}dxdy + \int_{C^*} uv\cos\alpha ds$$
$$\iint_{R^*} u\frac{\partial v}{\partial y}dxdy = -\iint_{R^*} v\frac{\partial u}{\partial y}dxdy + \int_{C^*} uv\sin\alpha ds \qquad (66)$$

$$\alpha = \hat{x,\tilde{n}}$$

Noting that the second derivatives with respect to the points $P:\{x,y\}$ and $Q:\{\xi,\eta\}$ can be interchanged and that $\nabla^2\Lambda_4(r)=\Lambda_2(r)$, we have

$$\iint_{R^*} f\left(\frac{\partial^2}{\partial x^2} - \frac{\partial^2}{\partial y^2}\right)\Lambda_4(r)d\xi d\eta = -\int_{C^*}\Lambda_4(r)\left(\frac{\partial f}{\partial \xi}\cos\alpha - \frac{\partial f}{\partial \eta}\sin\alpha\right)ds + \int_{C^*} f\left(\frac{\partial}{\partial \xi}\cos\alpha - \frac{\partial}{\partial \eta}\sin\alpha\right)\Lambda_4(r)ds$$

$$\iint_{R^*} f\frac{\partial^2}{\partial x\partial y}\Lambda_4(r)d\xi d\eta = \int_{C^*}\left[f\frac{\partial\Lambda_4(r)}{\partial \eta}\cos\alpha - \frac{\partial f}{\partial \xi}\ \Lambda_4(r)\sin\alpha\right]ds$$

$$\iint_{R^*} f\frac{\partial}{\partial x}\nabla^2\Lambda_4(r)d\xi d\eta = -\int_{C^*} f\Lambda_2(r)\cos\alpha ds + \int_{C^*}\frac{\partial f}{\partial \xi}\frac{\partial\Lambda_4(r)}{\partial n}ds \qquad (67)$$

$$\iint_{R^*} f\frac{\partial}{\partial y}\nabla^2\Lambda_4(r)d\xi d\eta = -\int_{C^*} f\Lambda_2(r)\sin\alpha ds + \int_{C^*}\frac{\partial f}{\partial \eta}\frac{\partial\Lambda_4(r)}{\partial n}ds$$

4. Arbitrary load. In the general case where the loading is given by an arbitrary function f(Q) over R^*, the conversion of the domain integrals into boundary line integrals is also feasible using the Rayleigh-Green identity [6,13]. Although, this approach is conceptually sound and it works, however,

from the computational point of view, it should be avoided since the required transformations and computations are highly increased. Thus, an efficient domain integration technique such that developed by Katsikadelis [60], according to the opinion of this author, might be more effective.

From the preceding analysis we can make the following comment. The solution of the plate equation can be accomplished either by using the superposition given by Eq. (12) and, thus,

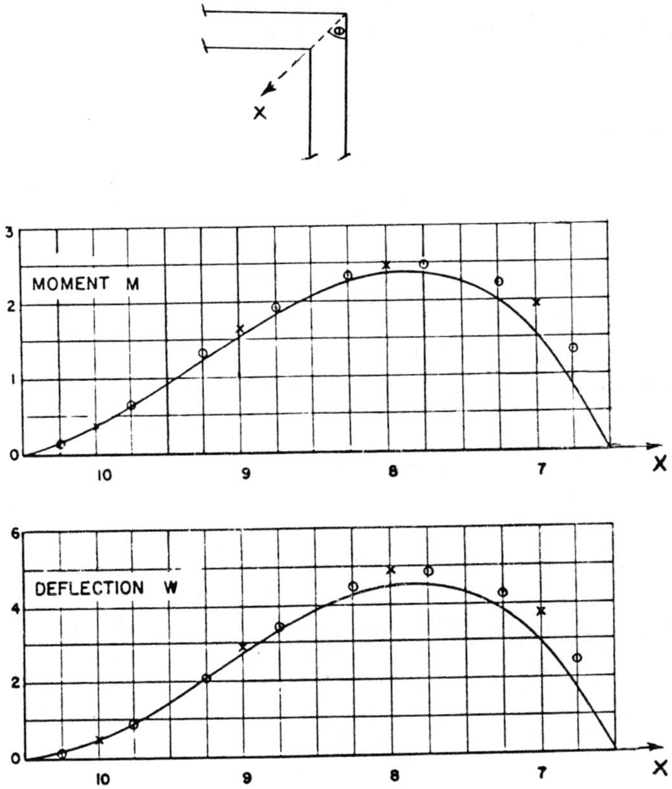

Figure 5. Distributions of the bending moment and the deflection along the diagonal of a uniformly - loaded, simply-supported corner plate ($\theta=45^{\circ}$) obtained by BEM [11] as compared with the FDM solution [61] o : BEM 38 nodal points, x : BEM 19 nodal points, — : FDM

solving the homogeneous biharmonic equation or by treating directly the nonhomogeneous equation. The first approach establishes a pure boundary formulation since there appear no domain integrals in the equations. However, its applicability is restricted only to cases in which the particular solution can be easily established. Obviously, this happens when the function f is continuous and is extended over the whole region R of the plate. In all other loading cases the direct treatment of the nonhomogeneous equation is recommended although conversion of domain integrals into line ones is necessary.

In Figs 5 and 6 results for a corner plate [11] and a plate

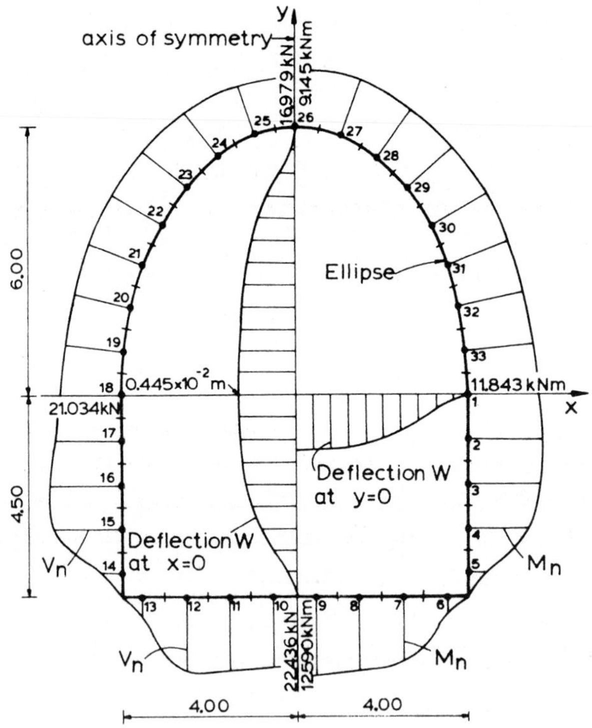

Figure 6. Reaction and deflection distribution in a uniformly loaded clamped plate of composite geometry resting on an elastic formulation [12] ($k=4905kN/m^3$, $h=0.10m$, $E=20.601x10^3$ MPa, $\nu=0.30$, $q_o=19.62kN/m^2$).

with composite shape resting on an elastic foundation [12] obtained by this method are shown.

iv. By decomposing the biharmonic equation in two harmonic. This method is based on Marcus method who replaced the plate equation by two Poisson's equations by means of an intermediate variable. For this purpose we write Eq. (1) as

$$\nabla^2\nabla^2 w = f/D \tag{68}$$

Adding together the first two of Eqs (11) for the bending moments we observe that

$$M_x+M_y = -D(1+\nu)\nabla^2 w \tag{69}$$

Introducing the new variable

$$M = \frac{M_x+M_y}{1+\nu} = -D\nabla^2 w \tag{70}$$

Eqs (68) and (69) can be represented in the following form

$$\begin{aligned} \nabla^2 M &= -f \\ \nabla^2 w &= -M/D \end{aligned} \tag{71}$$

The developments in this section are based on the work of Paris and Leon [15-18]. These authors used Eqs (71) to develop a boundary element solution for the plate problem. These equations can be written in an integral form through the second Green's formula

$$\varepsilon(P)M(P) = \iint_R vf d\sigma_Q + \int_C \left(v\frac{\partial M}{\partial n} - M\frac{\partial v}{\partial n}\right) ds_q \tag{72}$$

$$\varepsilon(P)w(P) = \frac{1}{D}\iint_R vM d\sigma_Q + \int_C \left(v\frac{\partial w}{\partial n} - w\frac{\partial v}{\partial n}\right) ds_q \tag{73}$$

where $v=-1/2\pi\ell nr$ is the fundamental solution of the harmonic equation, that is a particular solution of the equation

$$\nabla^2 v + \delta(P-Q) = 0 \tag{74}$$

The coefficient $\varepsilon(P)$ is given as

$$\begin{aligned} \varepsilon(P) &= 1 && \text{if P is inside R} \\ \varepsilon(P) &= \alpha/2\pi && \text{if P is on the boundary C} \end{aligned} \tag{75}$$

in which α is the angle between the tangents at point $P \equiv p \in C$ (see Fig.1). For points where the boundary is smooth it is $\alpha=\pi$, hence $\varepsilon(P)=1/2$.

Eqs (72) and (73) for points $P \equiv p \in C$ constitute a set of two generally coupled integral equations which can be solved together with the boundary conditions to give the unknown boundary quantities M, $\frac{\partial M}{\partial n}$, w, $\frac{\partial w}{\partial n}$. These equations are solved numerically using the BEM technique. Discetization of the boundary into N linear elements leads to the following 2N linear algebraic equations

$$[H]\{M\} - [G]\{q^M\} = \{D\} \tag{76}$$

$$[H]\{w\} - [G]\{q^w\} = \{E\} \tag{77}$$

where $\{w\},\{q^w\},\{M\},\{q^M\}$ represent the vectors of the unknown values of the variables w, $\frac{\partial w}{\partial n}$, M, $\frac{\partial M}{\partial n}$, respectively, at the N boundary nodal points. [H] and [G] are NxN coefficient matrices resulting from the integrations along the boundary elements. Finally {D} and {E} represent the domain integration vectors.

In the case of simply supported plates with rectilinear edges, Eqs (76) and (77) are uncoupled and can be solved successively with intermediate use of Eq. (72) inside the domain in order to evaluate the domain integral of Eq. (73). However, for nonrectilinear boundaries or other boundary conditions Eqs (76) and (77) are coupled and domain discretization for the evaluation of the domain integral is required. In order to maintain the strictly boundary element character of the method the domain integrals are approximated by boundary integrals. This approximation is performed by the so called dual reciprocity principle as it was used by Brebbia and Nardini [62] in the "static" approach of the elastodynamic problem. The domain integrals that appear in Eqs (72) and (73) have the general form

$$I = \iint_R v(P,Q)g(Q)d\sigma_Q \qquad P,Q \quad \text{in } R \text{ or on } C \tag{78}$$

Assuming that g(Q) admits a representation in the form

$$g(Q) = \alpha_j g_j(J,Q) \qquad j=1,2,\ldots L \tag{79}$$

where the functions g_j are L functions associated to L points J and α_j are constants to be determined. If the function ξ_j is a particular solution of equation

$$\nabla^2 \xi_j = g_j \tag{80}$$

then, applying again the Green's second formula to Eq. (80), we obtain a boundary integral representation of the integral (78)

$$\iint_R g(Q)v(P,Q)d\sigma_Q = -\alpha_j [\varepsilon(P)\xi_j(J,P) + \int_C \xi_j(J,q)\frac{\partial}{\partial n}v(P,q)ds_q$$

$$- \int_C \frac{\partial}{\partial n}\xi_j(J,q)v(P,q)ds_q] \tag{81}$$

Applying Eq. (81) for the loading function f, that is g=f, and noting that the integrations are similar to those appearing in Eqs (72) and (73) the vector {D} in Eq. (76) can be expressed as

$$\{D\} = -([H][\xi]-[G][q^{\xi}])\{\alpha\} \tag{82}$$

where [H], [G] are NxN matrices having the same meaning as in Eqs (76) and (77), [ξ], $[q^{\xi}]$ are NxL matrices and {α} is the vector of the coefficients in Eq. (79).

A linear expression has been adopted for the functions $g_j(J,Q)$

$$g_j(J,Q) = 1-r(J,Q) \qquad r=|J-Q| \tag{83}$$

Substitution of Eq. (83) in Eq. (80) and integration yields

$$\xi_j(J,Q) = \frac{1}{4}r^2-\frac{1}{9}r^3 \tag{84}$$

The vector $\{\alpha\}$ is computed from the following relation

$$\{f\} = [g]\{\alpha\} \tag{85}$$

where $\{f\}$ is an Lx1 column matrix and $[g]$ is an LxL matrix including the values of the functions f and g at the L points, respectively. Substituting Eqs (82) into Eq. (76) and using similar reasoning for $\{E\}$ we obtain

$$[H]\{M\}-[G]\{q^M\} = -([H][\xi]-[G][q^\xi])\{\alpha\} \tag{86}$$

$$[H]\{W\}-[G]\{q^W\} = -([H][\xi]-[G][q^\xi])\{\beta\} \tag{87}$$

where the vector $\{\beta\}$ is evaluated from the relation

$$\{M^*\} = [g]\{\beta\} \tag{88}$$

In the above equation the vector $\{M^*\}$ includes the values of the function M at the L points.

In order to simplify the computations the same L points have been used in both cases. However, whereas $\{\alpha\}$ can be directly determined as the load is known, it is not possible to evaluate $\{\beta\}$ because M is an intermediate and unknown variable. Moreover, a better approximation of the M requires that some of the L collocation points, say LI, are placed inside the domain R. These LI points represent LI extra unknowns. The LB (=L-LI) boundary points do not supply new unknowns. However, the LI extra unknown values $\{M^I\}$ inside the domain can be expressed in terms of the boundary values $\{M\}$ using the integral rerpesentation (72) for $\varepsilon(P)=1$. Making the corresponding integration we obtain the following set of equations

$$[H^I]\{M\}-[G^I]\{q^M\}+\{M^I\} = -([H^I][\xi]-[G][q^\xi])\{\alpha\} \tag{89}$$

where similarly to Eqs (76) and (77), $[H^I]$ and $[G^I]$ are LIxN matrices including integration coefficients resulting from Eq. (72) when it is applied to the LI internal points. Therefore, the vector $\{\beta\}$ adopts the form

$$\{\beta\} = [g]^{-1}\begin{Bmatrix} \{M\} \\ - - - - - \\ \{M^I(M,q^M)\} \end{Bmatrix} \tag{90}$$

In this way $\{\beta\}$ is related to the boundary vectors $\{M\}$ and $\{q^M\}$. Therefore, substituting Eqs (85) and (88) into Eqs (86) and (87) and taking into consideration Eqs (89) and (90) a final set of 2N linear algebraic equations including the 4N boundary quantities $\{M\}$, $\{q^M\}$, $\{w\}$ and $\{q^w\}$ is obtained. The number of the unknowns is reduced to 2N by employing the boundary conditions as following.

Taking into account Eq. (70) the first two of Eqs (10) can be written as

$$M = M_n - D(1-\nu)\left(\frac{\partial^2 w}{\partial s^2}+\kappa\frac{\partial w}{\partial n}\right) \tag{91}$$

$$\frac{\partial M}{\partial n} = V_n + D(1-\nu)\frac{\partial}{\partial s}\left(\frac{\partial^2 w}{\partial s\partial n}-\kappa\frac{\partial w}{\partial s}\right) \tag{92}$$

a. For a simply supported edge, it is $w=\bar{w}$, $M_n=\bar{M}_n$. Thus, using Eq. (91), we have

$$w = \bar{w}, \quad M = \bar{M}_n - D(1-\nu)\left(\frac{\partial^2 w}{\partial s^2}+\kappa q^w\right) \tag{93}$$

For homogeneous boundary conditions and a rectilinear edge it is $\kappa=0$, $\partial^2 w/\partial s^2=0$ and relations (93) are drastically simplified as

$$w = 0 \quad , \quad M = 0$$

b. For a clamped edge it is $w=\bar{w}$, $q^{w}=\bar{q}^{w}$.

c. For a free edge it is $M_n = \bar{M}_n$, $V_n = \bar{V}_n$. Then, using Eqs (91) and (92), we obtain the following relations among the boundary quantities

$$\begin{aligned} M &= \bar{M}_n - D(1-\nu)\left(\frac{\partial^2 w}{\partial s^2}+\kappa q^{w}\right) \\ q^{M} &= \bar{V}_n + D(1-\nu)\left[\frac{\partial^2 q^{w}}{\partial s^2}-\frac{\partial \kappa}{\partial s}\frac{\partial w}{\partial s}-\kappa\frac{\partial^2 w}{\partial s^2}\right] \end{aligned} \tag{94}$$

In this case the relations involve derivatives of w and q^{w}. They can be simplified if the derivatives are approximated by finite differences using the nodal points as pivotal points. For instance, if equal distances Δs between the nodal points are taken, the derivatives at point p are approximated as

$$\frac{\partial w}{\partial s} = \frac{w(p+1)-w(p-1)}{\Delta s} \tag{95}$$

$$\frac{\partial^2 w}{\partial s^2} = \frac{w(p+1)-2w(p)+w(p-1)}{\Delta s^2} \tag{95}$$

Similar expressions are valid for $\partial^2 q^{w}/\partial s^2$. It is apparent from Eqs (94) and (95) that the values of M and q^{M} at a point p are expressed through the values of w and q^{w} associated to the adjacent points p-1 and p+1.

d. For a guided edge it is $q^{w}=0$, $V_n=\bar{V}_n$. Hence the additional relations for the boundary quantities are

$$\begin{aligned} q^{w} &= 0 \\ q^{M} &= \bar{V}_n+D(1-\nu)\left[\frac{\partial^2 q^{w}}{\partial s^2}-\frac{\partial \kappa}{\partial s}\frac{\partial w}{\partial s}-\kappa\frac{\partial^2 w}{\partial s^2}\right] \end{aligned} \tag{96}$$

It is apparent that in this special BEM no divergent integrals appear and the discretization of the domain in the sense of using FEM cells has been avoided. However, the use of some internal points to evaluate the domain integral is necessary, which means a reduction of the effectiveness of the method.

Table 5. Deflections $\bar{w} = w/(qa^4/D)$ at the center of a uniformly-loaded, simply-supported square plate.

	Discretization	$\bar{w}\times 10^2$
BEM [16]	16/5	0.3632
	16/9	0.4024
	32/49	0.4072
FDM [16]	5x5	0.4021
	9x9	0.4023
FEM [63]	8x8	0.4033
	16x16	0.4056
Analytical [55]	-	0.4062

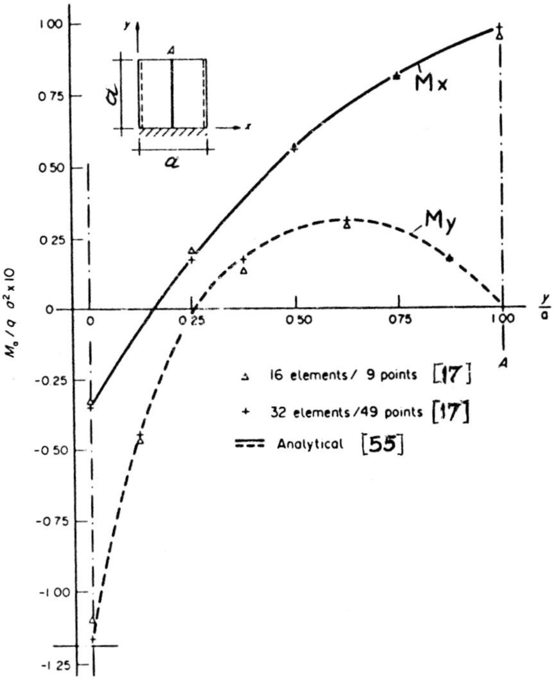

Fig. 7. Bending moments along the symmetry axis of a uniformly loaded square plate having two opplosite simply supported edges, one clamped edge and one free (ν=0.3).

Some numerical results obtained by this method as compared with analytical ones are presented in Table 5 and Fig. 7.

b) The Indirect Boundary Element Methods (IBEM's)

The indirect BEM formulation presented below follows the spirit of Tottenham's paper [20] as presented in Ref. [64]. The fundamental solution $w^{\circ}(P,Q)$ expresses the deflection at any point P in an infinite extended plate produced by a unit load acting at a point Q and is given as

$$w^{\circ}(P,Q) = \frac{1}{8\pi D} r^2 \ell n \frac{r}{r_o} = G^{\circ}(P,Q) \qquad P:(x,y),\ Q:(\xi,\eta) \qquad (97)$$

The radius r_o locates an arbitrary circle on which the deflection is zero (i.e. the deflections are relative to a datum at $r=r_o$) and therefore we shall have to introduce auxiliary terms in the IBEM to eliminate "reactions" from the infinite boundary. For the development of the method we shall also require the fundamental solution due to a unit moment at a point Q, that is the deflection at a point P due to a unit moment at point Q acting in the direction normal to a vector $\underline{n}$. The deflection can be conveniently obtained from $w^{\circ}(P,Q)$ by considering two equal and opposite loads f, -f (see Fig.8) at points Q and Q+dQ, dQ being co-linear with the unit vector $\underline{n}$. The applied forces define a couple

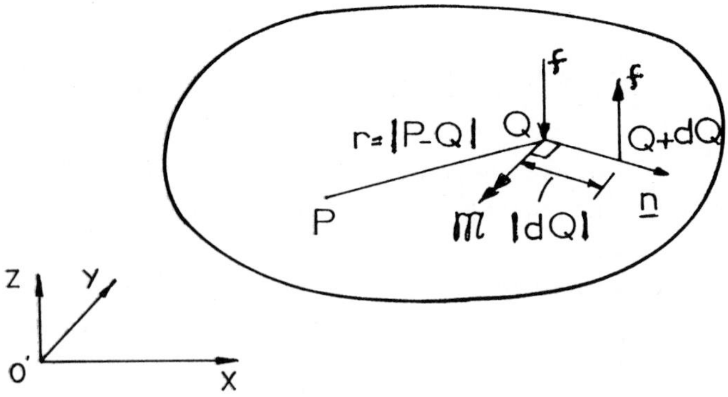

Fig.8.

$$\mathfrak{M} = f dQ \qquad (98)$$

and if we use the superfix 1, $w^1(P,Q)$, to denote the displacements due to the "first-order" moment, we have

$$w^1(P,Q) = fG^\circ(P,Q) - fG^\circ(P,Q+dQ) = -(fdQ)\frac{\partial G^\circ(P,Q)}{\partial n_Q} \qquad (99)$$

or by interchanging points P and Q and noting that $\partial/\partial n_Q = -\partial/\partial n_P$

$$w^1(P,Q) = \mathfrak{M}\,\frac{\partial G^\circ(P,Q)}{\partial n_P} \qquad (100)$$

if, in particular, $\mathfrak{M}$ is a unit moment and $\underline{n}$ is directed along the normal to the boundary C then the solution for a unit normal boundary moment becomes

$$w^1(P,Q) = \frac{\partial G^\circ}{\partial n_P} = G^1(P,Q) \qquad (101)$$

The result given by Eq. (101) can be also obtained by using Betti's reciprocal theorem.

By distributing "fictitious" edge loads $\varphi^\circ(q)$ and normal boundary moments $\varphi^1(q)$, where q is now on the boundary C, we arrive at

$$w(P) = \int_C [\varphi^\circ(q)G^\circ(P,q)+\varphi^1(q)G^1(P,q)]ds_q \; +$$

$$+ \iint_R f(Q)G^\circ(P,Q)d\sigma_Q + c^\circ \qquad (102)$$

Application of the operators $\Theta=\partial/\partial n_P$ as well as M and V defined by Eqs (5) and (6) to Eq. (102) yields

$$\Theta w(P) = \int_C (\varphi^\circ F^\circ + \varphi^1 F^1)ds + \iint_R fF^\circ d\sigma + c_x^1\cos\alpha + c_y^1\sin\alpha$$

$$Mw(P) = \int_C (\varphi^\circ E^\circ + \varphi^1 E^1)ds + \iint_R fE^\circ d\sigma \qquad (103)$$

$$Vw(P) = \int_C (\varphi^\circ D^\circ + \varphi^1 D^1)ds + \iint_R fD^\circ d\sigma$$

where α is the angle between the vector $\underline{n}_P$ and the x axis ; F^o, F^1, E^o, E^1, D^o, D^1 are two-point kernels which are obtained by applying the operators Θ, M and V to $G^o(P,Q)$ and $G^1(P,Q)$. They express displacements due to unit generalized forces (first-order, second-order and higher-order moments) which are combinations of dipoles, quadrapoles and octapoles of mathematical physics. The constants c^o, c^1_x and c^1_y match three conditions, which φ^o and φ^1 have to satisfy to ensure that the system is in equilibrium without support at any infinitely distant boundary, that is

$$\begin{aligned} &\int_C \varphi^o ds + \iint_R f d\sigma = 0 \\ &\int_C \varphi^1 \cos\alpha ds = 0 \qquad\qquad (104) \\ &\int_C \varphi^1 \sin\alpha ds = 0 \end{aligned}$$

The boundary C on which the integral equations are defined may be either the real boundary of the plate [20,23] or a fictitious boundary surrounding the real one [19,21,22]. If the real plate boundary has corners additional corner force components φ^o_c, one per corner, should be included in the discretized φ^o vector. The normal direction for φ^1_c at such a corner is ambiguous but it seems reasonable to use the bisector of the corner angle to define the direction there.

By letting point P, taking the direction n to coincide with the normal to the boundary at that point and noting that strong singularities arise in both the equivalent shear force boundary integral (due to φ^o) and the moment one (due to φ^1) Eqs (102) and (103) yield the following boundary integral equations

$$\begin{aligned} w(p) = &\int_C [\varphi^o(q)G^o(p,q)+\varphi^1(q)G^1(p,q)]ds_q + \\ &+ \iint_R f(Q)G^o(p,Q)d\sigma_Q + c^o \end{aligned}$$

$$\Theta w(p) = \int_C [\varphi^o F^o + \varphi^1 F^1] ds_q + \iint_R f F^o d\sigma_Q + c_x^1 \cos\alpha + c_y^1 \sin\alpha \tag{105}$$

$$Mw(p) = \frac{1}{2}\varphi^1(p) + \int_C (\varphi^o E^o + \varphi^1 E^1) ds_q + \iint_R f E^o d\sigma_Q$$

$$Vw(p) = \frac{1}{2}\varphi^o(p) + \int_C (\varphi^o D^o + \varphi^1 D^1) ds_q + \iint_R f D^o d\sigma_Q$$

The above equations hold for points p where the boundary is smooth. For corner points at the boundary the angle between the tangents should be considered.

In a well-posed plate problem two of the quantities w, Θw, Mw, Vw are prescribed to enable two boundary integral equations to be selected from Eqs (105), which together with Eqs (104) can be solved to establish the boundary distributions φ^o and φ^1 on C and the three constants c^o, c_x^1, c_y^1. The deflection at internal points P is evaluated from Eq. (102).

Although the aforegoing formulation is straight in concept, however, the differentiations involved in the operators Θ, M

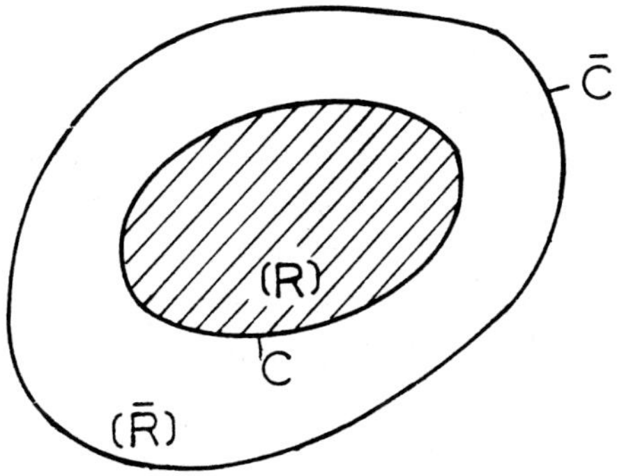

Fig. 9. Plate occupying the domain R bounded by the boundary C embedded in an auxiliary (fictitious) domain R̄ bounded by the boundary C̄.

and V result in kernels with two major disadvantages: a) they are complicated in form and b) they are hypersingular, that is, they include nonintegrable singularities and the theory of finite part integration must be employed for their evaluation. Thus, great computational difficulties must be overcome. A technique to avoid integration of hypersingular kernels is to consider the unknown boundary quantities φ^{o}, φ^{1} distributed on a fictitious boundary $\bar{C}$ including the real one of the plate (see Fig. 9). Inasmuch as the fictitious boundary is arbitrary, it can be chosen to have simple form to facilitate the integration (e.g. polygonal shape). Several example problems have been treated by the IBEM. In the following we present some of them which are given in the most representative papers for the IBEM.

a) A uniformly loaded square plate with a central square opening (Fig. 10) has been analyzed by Tottenham [64]. The outer edges of the plate are simply supported and the inner

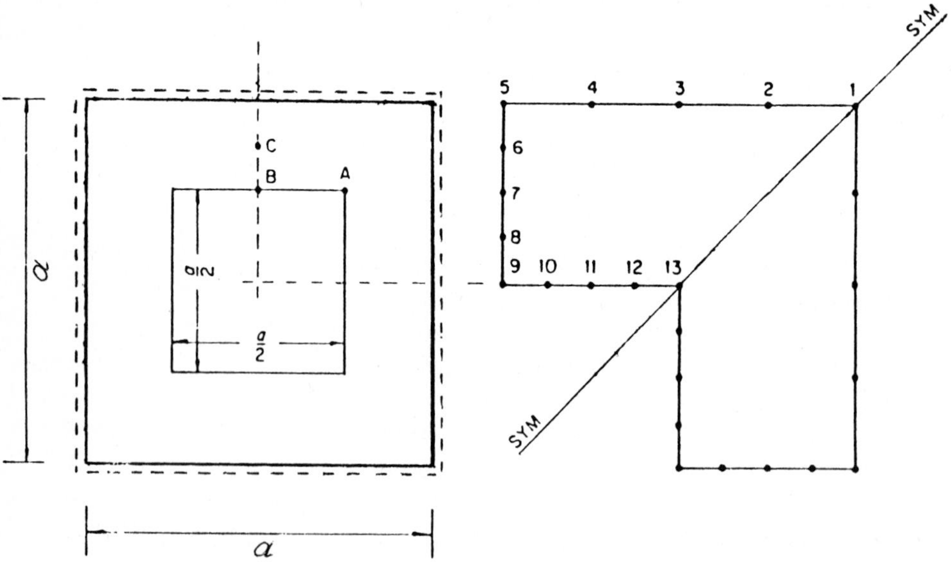

Fig. 10. Uniformly-loaded simply-supported square plate with a central square opening [64].

Table 6. Deflections at points A, B and C of the uniformly loaded square plate of Fig. 10 (ν=0.25) [64].

	$w \times qa^4/100D$		
Point	BEM	FEM	FDM
A	0.2188	0.2185	0.2174
B	0.3107	0.3156	0.3006
C	0.1558	-	0.1541

edges free. In analyzing this problem, the corner forces are ignored. The number of nodal unknowns are reduced by using the symmetry of the plate. Some numerical results are presented in Table 6 as compared with those obtained by the FEM and the FDM.

b) Clamped plates have been analyzed by Altiero and Sikarskie [21,22]. The IBEM developed by these authors involves embedding of the real plate in a fictitious plate for which the Green's function is known. In their examples they employed the known solution of a clamped circular plate due to a unit load to generate the kernels of the integral equations.

Table 7. Deflections and bending moments of clamped plates compared with the exact ones.

Plate geometry	Deflections moments	BEM [22]	Exact [55]	Per cent error
Rectangular (point load)	w(0,0)	0.00179	0.00180	-0.56
Rectangular (uniform)	w(0,0)	0.000311	0.000317	-1.89
Rectangular (uniform)	$M_x(0,0)$	0.0197	0.0206	-4.37
Rectangular (uniform)	$M_y(0,0)$	0.0073	0.0079	-7.59
Triangular	$M_x(0,0)$	0.0179	0.0196	-8.67
Triangular	$M_y(0,0)$	0.0180	0.0191	-5.76
Semi-circular	w(0,0.406)	0.00128	0.00129	-0.78
Semi-circular	$M_x(0,0.525)$	0.01219	0.01235	-1.30
Semi-circular	$M_y(0,0.483)$	0.0222	0.0226	-1.77

Although this interesting formulation gives accurate numerical results, it is algebraically very cumbersome, particularly if other than clamped boundary conditions are considered. For this reason only clamped boundary conditions have been treated numerically. In Table 7 some numerical results are presented and compared with the exact ones.

c) Circular and rectangular clamped or simply supported plates have been analyzed by Niwa et al. [19] who employed an IBEM with an auxiliary boundary surrounding the real one. In this method the integral representations of the normal derivative, the normal bending moment and the equivalent shear force, which are expressed in terms of the two unknown boundary distributions on the fictitious auxiliary boundary, are established by introducing fundamental solutions owing to higher order singularities (dipoles, quadrapoles or octapoles). Results for the displacements, radial and tangential moment for a circular clamped plated obtained by this method are presented in Table 8. The integration is carried out on a fictitious boundary of polygonal shape with N sides. The authors investigated the dependence of the accuracy on the parameter δ/a (a is the radius of the plate and δ is the distance of the auxiliary boundary from the real clamped boundary) and on the number N of the straight boundary elements.

d) Some numerical results have also been obtained by Zhu [23] by employing an IBEM based on the Rayleigh - Green identity which the author obtains as a special case of the Betti's reciprocal identity applied to the plate bending problem. The integral equations are taken on the real boundary by application of the appropriate differential operators to the integral representation of the deflection. The kernels of the integral equations include nonintegrable singularities. The great difficulties for the evaluation of the line integrals are circumvented by converting the integral equations into an equivalent variational problem and, subsequently, by employing a finite element approximation for the numerical evaluation.

Table 8. Deflections, radial and tangential bending moments of a circular clamped plate subjected to uniform load [19].

		$w(\times qa^4/64D)$					
N	r/a δ/a	0.02	0.2	0.4	0.6	0.8	1.0
24	0.1	1.003	0.924	0.709	0.412	0.131	0.0
	0.2	1.000	0.923	0.707	0.410	0.130	0.0
40	0.1	1.000	0.922	0.706	0.410	0.130	0.0
	0.2	0.999	0.922	0.706	0.410	0.130	0.0
Exact		0.999	0.922	0.705	0.410	0.130	0.0

		$M_r(\times qa^2/16)$					
N	r/a δ/a	0.02	0.2	0.4	0.6	0.8	1.0
24	0.1	1.302	1.171	0.725	0.115	-0.810	-1.992
	0.2	1.300	1.169	0.723	0.113	-0.811	-2.005
48	0.1	1.300	1.168	0.722	0.112	-0.812	-2.004
	0.2	1.299	1.168	0.722	0.112	-0.812	-2.000
Exact		1.299	1.168	0.722	0.112	-0.812	-2.000

		$M_\theta(\times qa^2/16)$					
N	r/a δ/a	0.02	0.2	0.4	0.6	0.8	1.0
24	0.1	1.302	1.227	0.999	0.619	0.088	-0.580
	0.2	1.300	1.225	0.997	0.617	0.085	-0.582
48	0.1	1.300	1.224	0.996	0.616	0.084	-0.586
	0.2	1.299	1.224	0.996	0.616	0.084	-0.600
Exact		1.299	1.224	0.996	0.616	0.084	-0.600

Table 9. Deflections along the radius $\theta=0$ of a unit circular plate with $w=\cos 2\theta$ and $\partial w/\partial n=0$ on the boundary [23].

	w	
r	BEM	Analytical
0.25	0.1211	0.1211
0.50	0.4376	0.4375
0.75	0.8086	0.8086
1.00	0.9997	1.0000

In Table 9 numerical results are presented for a circular plate of unit radius with prescribed displacement and normal derivative on the boundary.

c) <u>The Boundary Differential - Integral Equation Methods (BDIEM's)</u>

The developments in this section are based on the work of Katsikadelis et al. [6,27]. The basic ingredients of these methods are shown by presenting the BDIEM developed by Katsikadelis and Armenakas [6] for the plate bending problem governed by Eqs (1), (3) and (4). The deflection of the plate is expressed by Eq. (47) in terms of the four unknown boundary quantities w, $\frac{\partial w}{\partial n}$, $\nabla^2 w$, $\frac{\partial}{\partial n}\nabla^2 w$. These quantities are established by solving four simultaneous boundary equations. Two of them are differential and the rest are integral.

The boundary integral equations employed in this method are Eqs (49) which were derived in the section dealing with the Green's identity methods. The boundary differential equations are obtained from the boundary conditions (3) if M_n and V_n are replaced by their expressions given in Eqs (10) and if notation (50) is used. Thus, we have the following set of four boundary equations

$$\begin{aligned}
\alpha\Omega &= \frac{1}{D}\iint_R \Lambda_4 f d\sigma - \int_C (\Lambda_1\Omega+\Lambda_2 X+\Lambda_3\Phi+\Lambda_4\Psi)ds \\
\alpha\Phi &= \frac{1}{D}\iint_R \Lambda_2 f d\sigma - \int_C (\Lambda_1\Phi+\Lambda_2\Psi)ds \\
\alpha_1\Omega &- D\alpha_2[\Psi-(\nu-1)\frac{\partial}{\partial s}(\frac{\partial X}{\partial s}-\kappa\frac{\partial\Omega}{\partial s})] = \alpha_3 \\
\beta_1 X &- D\beta_2[\Phi+(\nu-1)(\frac{\partial^2\Omega}{\partial s^2}+\kappa X) = \beta_3
\end{aligned} \tag{106}$$

where $\Lambda_i=\Lambda_i(r)$ (i=1,2,3,4) are the kernels given by Eqs (51). Eqs (106) constitute a set of four coupled boundary equations from which the boundary quantities Ω, X, Φ, Ψ can be established. Thereafter, the deflection at any interior point is evaluated from its integral representation (Eq. 47). The boundary equations are solved numerically. Discretizing the boundary into N constants elements and using the boundary element technique to approximate the line integrals and the finite difference method, with pivotal points the nodal boundary points, to approximate the differential equations, a system of 4N algebraic equations is obtained involving the nodal values of Ω, X, Φ and Ψ, which in matrix form is written as

$$\begin{bmatrix} [A_{11}] & [A_{12}] & [0] & [A_{14}] \\ [A_{21}] & [A_{22}] & [A_{23}] & [0] \\ [A_{31}] & [A_{32}] & [A_{33}] & [A_{34}] \\ [0] & [0] & [A_{43}] & [A_{44}] \end{bmatrix} \begin{bmatrix} \{\Omega\} \\ \{X\} \\ \{\Phi\} \\ \{\Psi\} \end{bmatrix} = \begin{bmatrix} \{B_1\} \\ \{B_2\} \\ \{B_3\} \\ \{B_4\} \end{bmatrix} \tag{107}$$

where

$$\begin{aligned} \{\Omega\} &= [\Omega_1\ \Omega_2\ \dots\ \Omega_N]^T \\ \{X\} &= [X_1\ X_2\ \dots\ X_N]^T \\ \{\Phi\} &= [\Phi_1\ \Phi_2\ \dots\ \Phi_N]^T \\ \{\Psi\} &= [\Psi_1\ \Psi_2\ \dots\ \Psi_N]^T \\ \{B_k\} &= [(B_k)_1 (B_k)_2\ \dots\ (B_k)_N]^T \quad , \qquad k=1,2,3,4. \end{aligned} \tag{108}$$

The matrix coefficients $(A_{kl})_{ij}$, and the constant terms $(B_k)_i$ ($k,l=1,2,3,4$ and $i,j=1,2,\dots N$) are evaluated by the following relations

$$\begin{aligned} (A_{11})_{i,i-1} &= -(\alpha_2)_i s_i (-\frac{\partial\kappa_i}{\partial s} s_i + 2\kappa_i) \\ (A_{11})_{ii} &= (\alpha_1)_i / [(\nu-1)De_i] \\ &\quad + (\alpha_2)_i (s_{i-1} + s_i)[(s_{i-1} - s_i)\frac{\partial\kappa_i}{\partial s} + 2\kappa_i] \\ (A_{11})_{i,i+1} &= -(\alpha_2)_i s_{i-1} (\frac{\partial\kappa_i}{\partial s} s_{i-1} + 2\kappa_i) \\ (A_{12})_{i,i-1} &= 2(\alpha_2)_i s_i \end{aligned} \tag{109}$$

$$(A_{12})_{ii} = -2(\alpha_2)_i(s_{i-1}+s_i)$$

$$(A_{12})_{i,i+1} = 2(\alpha_2)_i s_{i-1}$$

$$(A_{14})_{ii} = -(\alpha_2)_i/[(\nu-1)e_i]$$

$$(A_{21})_{i,i-1} = -2(\beta_2)_i s_i$$

$$(A_{21})_{ii} = 2(\beta_2)_i(s_{i-1}+s_i)$$

$$(A_{21})_{i,i+1} = -2(\beta_2)_i s_{i-1}$$

$$(A_{22})_{ii} = (\beta_1)_i/[(\nu-1)De_i]-(\beta_2)_i\varkappa_i/e_i$$

$$(A_{23})_{ii} = -(\beta_2)_i/[(\nu-1)e_i]$$

$$(A_{31})_{ij} = -\int_j d\omega_{iq}+\alpha\delta_{ij}$$

$$(A_{32})_{ij} = \int_j (\ln r_{iq}+1)ds_q$$

$$(A_{33})_{ij} = -\frac{1}{4}\int_j r_{iq}^2(2\ln r_{iq}+1)d\omega_{iq}$$

$$(A_{34})_{ij} = \frac{1}{4}\int_j r_{iq}^2\ln r_{iq}ds_q$$

$$(A_{43})_{ij} = (A_{31})_{ij}$$

$$(A_{44})_{ij} = (A_{32})_{ij} \tag{109}$$

$$(B_1)_i = (\alpha_3)_i/[De_i(\nu-1)]$$

$$(B_2)_i = (\beta_3)_i/[De_i(\nu-1)]$$

$$(B_3)_i = \frac{1}{4D}\iint_R r_{iQ}\ln r_{iQ}f(Q)d\sigma_Q$$

$$(B_4)_i = \frac{1}{D}\iint_R (\ln r_{iQ}+1)f(Q)d\sigma_Q$$

where $e_i=1/[s_{i-1}s_i(s_{i-1}+s_i)]$; $r_{iQ}=|p_i-Q|$, $Q\in R$; $r_{iq}=|p_i-q|$,

$q\in j$-element; ω_{iq}=is the angle between the x-axis and the line r_{iq}; $(\alpha_k)_i$ and $(\beta_k)_i$ are values of the functions $\alpha_k(s)$ and $\beta_k(s)$, respectively, at point p_i; the symbol $\int_j$ indicates integration over the j-element. The integrals in the expressions for the coefficients $(A_{31})_{ij}$ and $(A_{33})_{ij}$ have been obtained using the relation $\cos\varphi ds = r d\omega$.

In deriving Eqs (107) the derivatives at the nodal points have been approximated by unevenly spaced central differences. However, the function $X=\partial w/\partial n$ is discontinuous at corner points and, thus, the derivatives at the nodal points before (after) the corner are approximated by backward (forward) differences.

Special care must be taken at the corner points of the boundary when the deflections are not prevented (free corner). In this case the replacement of the twisting moments along the boundary by a distribution of equivalent couples of vertical forces gives rise to fictitious concentrated corner forces which affect greatly the deflections and the stress resultants. This shortcoming of Kirchhoff's plate theory is overcome by imposing the additional corner condition

$$[\![Tw]\!] = (Tw)^{+} - (Tw)^{-} = 0 \tag{110}$$

where Tw is the twisting moment along the boundary, which using intrinsic coordinates and notation (50), can be expressed as

$$Tw = D(1-\nu)\left(\frac{\partial^2 w}{\partial s \partial n} - \kappa\frac{\partial w}{\partial s}\right) = D(1-\nu)\left(\frac{\partial X}{\partial s} - \kappa\frac{\partial \Omega}{\partial s}\right) \tag{111}$$

Substituting relation (111) into (110), the corner condition may be written as

$$\left(\frac{\partial X}{\partial s}\right)^{+} - \left(\frac{\partial X}{\partial s}\right)^{-} = (\kappa^{+} - \kappa^{-})\frac{\partial \Omega}{\partial s} \tag{112}$$

Denoting by p_i and p_{i+1} the nodal points adjacent to the corner, and approximating the derivatives of X by forward and backward differences and the derivatives of Ω by central differences, condition (112) is expressed as

$$\sum_{j=i-1}^{j=i+2} c_j \Omega_j + \sum_{j=i-2}^{j=i+3} d_j X_j = 0 \tag{113}$$

where

$$
\begin{aligned}
c_{i-1} &= \kappa_i s_i/[s_{i-1}(s_{i-1}+s_i)] \\
c_i &= -\kappa_i(s_i-s_{i-1})/(s_{i-1}s_i) - \kappa_{i+1}/[s_i(s_i+s_{i+1})] \\
c_{i+1} &= -\kappa_i s_{i-1}/[s_i(s_{i-1}+s_i)] + \kappa_{i+1}(s_{i+1}-s_i)/(s_i s_{i+1}) \\
c_{i+2} &= \kappa_{i+1}s_i/[s_{i+1}(s_i+s_{i+1})] \\
d_{i-2} &= -s_{i-1}/[s_{i-2}(s_{i-2}+s_{i-1})] \\
d_{i-1} &= (s_{i-1}+s_{i-2})/(s_{i-2}s_{i-1}) \\
d_i &= -(s_{i-2}+2s_{i-1})/[s_{i-1}(s_{i-2}+s_{i-1})] \\
d_{i+1} &= -(2s_{i+1}+s_{i+2})/[s_{i+1}(s_{i+1}+s_{i+2})] \\
d_{i+2} &= (s_{i+1}+s_{i+2})/s_{i+1}s_{i+2}) \\
d_{i+3} &= -s_{i+1}/[s_{i+2}(s_{i+1}+s_{i+2})]
\end{aligned}
\tag{114}
$$

Condition (113) represents an additional equation which must be satisfied simultaneously with Eqs (107). Thus, the number of equations which must be solved exceeds the number of unknowns. To overcome this difficulty, it is assumed that an unknown concentrated force acts at each free corner of the plate. These forces are evaluated by requiring that the results satisfy the additional Eq. (113) at each corner.

For plates with clamped or simply supported boundary Eqs (107) are simplified to Eqs (52) and (54). Once the nodal values of the boundary quantities are established from Eqs (107), the deflection and the stress resultants are computed from Eqs

Table 10. Deflections and stress resultants of a simply supported square plate with side length a and Poisson s ratio $\nu=0.2$ subjected to a uniform load q. Upper numbers: computed [6]; lower numbers: exact [55].

y=x	$w/(qa^4/D)$	M_x/qa^2	M_{xy}/qa^2	Q_x/qa	V_x/qa x=a/2
0.	.4063E-02 .4063E-02	.4421E-01 .4420E-01	0 0	0 0	-.2162E+01 -.2160E+01
0.1a	.3704E-02 .3704E-02	.4125E-01 .4125E-01	.2728E-02 .2728E-02	-.4854E-01 -.4854E-01	-.2102E+01 -.2107E+01
0.2a	.2744E-02 .2744E-02	.3291E-01 .3290E-01	.1025E-01 .1025E-01	-.8827E-01 -.8827E-01	-.1955E+01 -.1950E+01
0.3a	.1503E-02 .1503E-02	.2079E-01 .2079E-01	.2069E-01 .2069E-01	-.1097E+00 -.1097E+00	-.1647E+01 -.1651E+01
0.4a	.4349E-03 .4346E-03	.7852E-02 .7843E-02	.3119E-01 .3119E-01	-.9881E-01 -.9888E-01	-.1260E+01 -.1129E+01

(56) and (57), respectively. Moreover, to maintain the stricktly boundary character of the method, the domain integrals are evaluated using the procedure described by Eqs (64) to (67). The method also treats the case of internal point or line supports which may yield elastically. Several example problems have been worked out by this method and numerical results have been obtained which are in excellent agreement with existing from analytical or other numerical methods. Some results are presented in Tables 10 to 13 and in Figs 11 to 14, which illustrate the accuracy and efficiency of the method.

The BDIEM has been also employed to solve the bending problem of plates resting on biparametric elastic foundation [27] and in conjuction with domain integration as D/BEM (domain/boundary element method) to solve several other plate problems such as vibrations of plates [28], plates with variable thickness under static and dynamic loading [31,32], unilaterally supported plates on elastic foundation [33], large deflections of plates [29,30] as well as vibrations of thick plates [35].

In the following we present the D/BEM as it was developed by

Table 11. Deflections $\bar{w}=w/(qa^4/Eh^3)$ at the inner free edge (r=a) and bending stress $\bar{\sigma}_r=6M_r/qa^2$ at the outer clamped edge (r=b) of an annular plate (ν =0.30) subjected to a uniform load.

b/a		BEM [6]	BEM [65]	Exact [55]
1.25	$\bar{w}$	0.00199	0.00201	0.00199
	$\bar{\sigma}_r$	0.1050	0.1050	0.1050
1.5	$\bar{w}$	0.01390	0.01391	0.01390
	$\bar{\sigma}_r$	0.2592	0.2587	0.2590
2.0	$\bar{w}$	0.05753	0.05758	0.05750
	$\bar{\sigma}_r$	0.4800	0.4795	0.4800
3.0	$\bar{w}$	0.1296	0.1301	0.1300
	$\bar{\sigma}_r$	0.6567	0.6560	0.6570
4.0	$\bar{w}$	0.1621	0.1629	0.1620
	$\bar{\sigma}_r$	0.7099	0.7099	0.7100

Katsikadelis [28] to solve the vibration problem of plates.

When a homogeneous, isotropic, thin elastic plate is subjected to a transverse loading $f(P,\tau)$, under the assumption of small deflections, its flexural vibrations are governed by the differential equation

$$D\nabla^4 W + \varrho\ddot{W} = f \quad \text{in} \quad R \tag{115}$$

where R is the two-dimensional plane region occupied by the plate bounded by the boundary $C=\bigcup_{i=0}^{i=M} C_i$; $W=W(P,\tau)$, $P:\{x,y\}\in R$; $\tau\geq 0$ is the time and ϱ is the surface mass density of the plate.

The deflection W must satisfy boundary conditions of the same form with (3) and (4), which for the dynamic problem become

$$\begin{aligned} &\alpha_1(p)W + \alpha_2(p)V_n = \alpha_3(p,\tau) \\ &\beta_1(p)\frac{\partial W}{\partial n} + \beta_2(p)M_n = \beta_3(p,\tau), \qquad p\in C, \quad \tau \geq 0 \end{aligned} \tag{116}$$

$$c_{1k}W + c_{2k}[\![M_{nt}]\!]_k = c_{3k}(\tau) \quad \text{on the corner } k \tag{117}$$

Table 12. Corner reaction $R=[\![Tw]\!]/qa^3$ in a uniformly-loaded, simply-supported square plate (ν =0.30) compared with the exact and other BEM solutions.

	Number of Nodes	R
BEM [6]	32	0.068
	60	0.067
BEM [2]	32	0.0651
	64	0.0648
BEM [4]	36	0.0648
Exact [55]		0.065

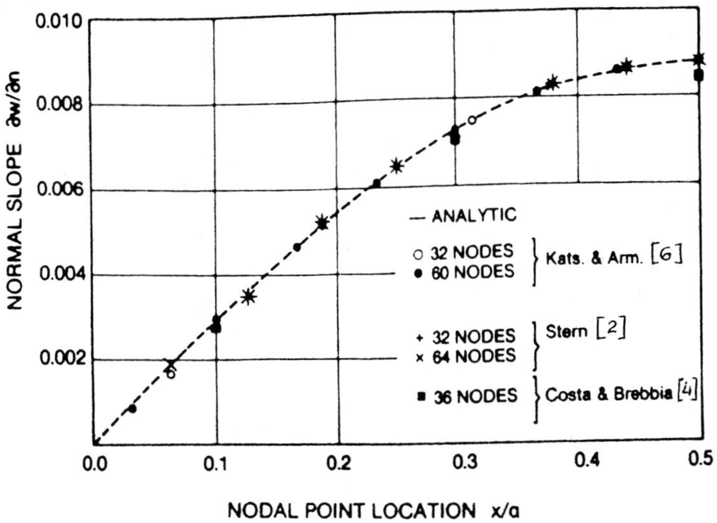

Fig.11. Normal slope on an edge of a uniformly-loaded, simply-supported square plate.

Table 13. Deflections and bending moments at the center of a uniformly-loaded, simply-supported equilateral triangular plate with side length a and ν=0.30.

	$w/(qa^4/D)$ $\times 10^3$	M_x/qa^2 $\times 10^2$	M_y/qa^2 $\times 10^2$
Kats. & Arm. [6] 24 const. bound. elem.	0.580	1.807	1.807
Maiti and Chakr.[10] 24 const. bound. elem.	0.582	1.816	1.807
Costa and Brebbia [4] 27 const. bound. elem.	0.568	1.830	1.830
Exact [55]	0.579	1.805	1.805

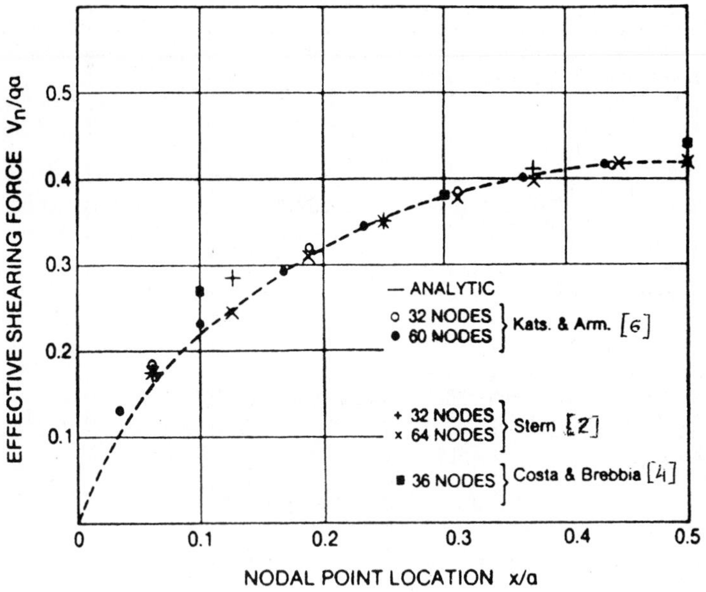

Fig. 12. Equivalent shear force on an edge of a uniformly - loaded, simply-supported square plate

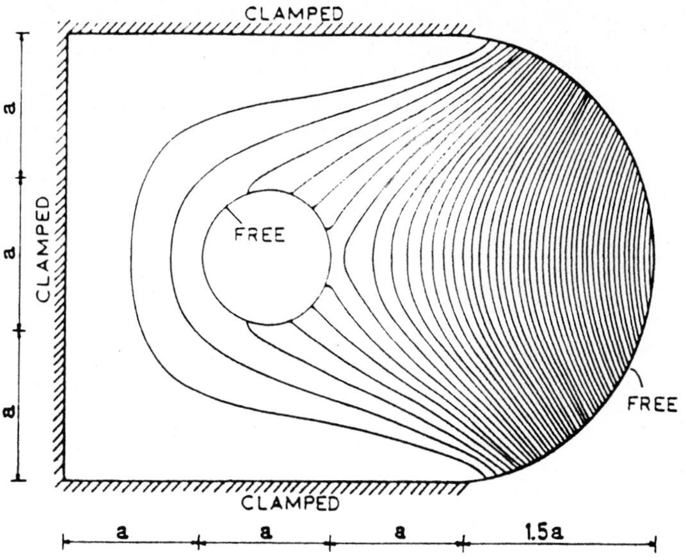

Fig. 13. Deflections $\bar{w}=w/(qa^4/D)$ of a plate with composite shape ($\nu=0.30$) subjected to a uniform load q. The contour lines are drawn $\bar{w}=0.035$ apart[6]

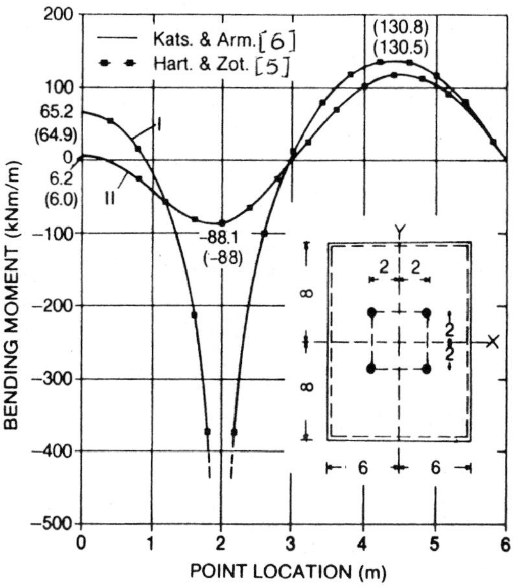

Fig. 14. Distribution of the bending moment Mx at y=2 (curve I) and at y=0 (curve II) in a rectangular simply supported plate with four internal supports ($\nu=0.3$, D=2700kNm, q=100kN/m^2). The values in the parentheses are taken from Hartmann and Zotemantel [5].

The boundary conditions (116),(117) include also support excitations ($\alpha_3, \beta_3, c_3 \neq 0$).

Moreover, the deflection $W(P,\tau)$ must also satisfy the initial boundary conditions

$$\left.\begin{aligned} W(P,0) &= \bar{w}(P) \\ \dot{W}(P,0) &= \dot{\bar{w}}(P) \end{aligned}\right\} \quad \text{in } R \tag{118}$$

where $\bar{w}(P)$ and $\dot{\bar{w}}(P)$ are prescribed functions of the spatial coordinate P.

Replacing f by $f-\varrho\ddot{W}$ in Eqs (47) and (49) we obtain an integral representation for the deflection W and two domain/boundary integral equations, i.e.

$$W(P,\tau) = \frac{1}{2\pi D}\iint_R \Lambda_4 f d\sigma - \frac{1}{2\pi D}\iint_R \varrho\Lambda_4 \ddot{W} d\sigma - \\ - \frac{1}{2\pi}\int_C (\Lambda_1\Omega+\Lambda_2 X+\Lambda_3\Phi+\Lambda_4\Psi)ds \tag{119}$$

$$\alpha\Omega = \frac{1}{D}\iint_R \Lambda_4 f d\sigma - \frac{1}{D}\iint_R \varrho\Lambda_4 \ddot{W} d\sigma - \int_C (\Lambda_1\Omega+\Lambda_2 X+\Lambda_3\Phi+\Lambda_4\Psi)ds \tag{120}$$

$$\alpha\Phi = \frac{1}{D}\iint_R \Lambda_2 f d\sigma - \frac{1}{D}\iint_R \varrho\Lambda_2 \ddot{W} d\sigma - \int_C (\Lambda_1\Phi+\Lambda_2\Psi)ds \tag{121}$$

The kernels $\Lambda_i = \Lambda_i(r)$ are given by Eqs (51) and the boundary quantities Ω, X, Φ, Ψ are defined by Eqs (50). Note that in this case the boundary quantities depend also on time.

Eqs (119) to (121) are supplemented by the boundary differential equations (see Eqs 106)

$$\alpha_1\Omega - D\alpha_2[\Psi-(\nu-1)\frac{\partial}{\partial s}(\frac{\partial X}{\partial s}-\kappa\frac{\partial\Omega}{\partial s})] = \alpha_3 \tag{122}$$

$$\beta_1 X - D\beta_2[\Phi+(\nu-1)(\frac{\partial^2\Omega}{\partial s^2}+\kappa X)] = \beta_3 \tag{123}$$

Eqs (119) through (123) constitute a system of five equations involving five unknown quantities, i.e. the deflection $W(P,\tau)$ inside the domain R and the boundary quantities $\Omega(s,\tau)$, $X(s,\tau)$, $\Phi(s,\tau)$, $\Psi(s,\tau)$ on the boundary. These equations are solved numerically. The differential equations are treated by the finite difference method and the integral equations by the boundary element method.

The domain integrals are evaluated using Gauss integration over domains of arbitrary shape, by developing a technique which is to be referred to here as the finite sector method (FSM). The major advantage of this technique is that it alleviates the D/BEM from the domain discretization in the sense of finite elements and, thus, its efficiency is increased.

According to the FSM the two-dimensional domain R is divided into a finite number of sectors by straight lines emanating from a point inside the region (common vertex of sectors) and reaching the boundary (see Fig.15). For domains with complex geometry more than one vertex may be used. Subsequently, each sector is mapped onto a triangle on which a ready-to-use Gauss-Radau integration scheme is employed. Thus, an integral over the domain R may be approximated as

$$\iint_R g(Q)d\sigma_Q = \sum_{k=1}^{S} \iint_{R_k^*} g(Q)|J_k(Q)|d\sigma_Q \simeq$$

$$\simeq \sum_{k=1}^{S} \sum_{j=1}^{m} C_j^k g(Q_j^k)|J_k(Q_j^k)| \qquad (124)$$

where S is the number of sectors, m is the number of Gauss-Radau points in the k-th sector, C_j^k and Q_j^k $(j=1,2,\ldots,m)$ are the weight factors and the Gauss-Radau points in the k-th sector, and $J(Q_j^k)$ are the values of the Jacobian of the transformation, which transforms the k-th sector onto the triangle R_k^*.

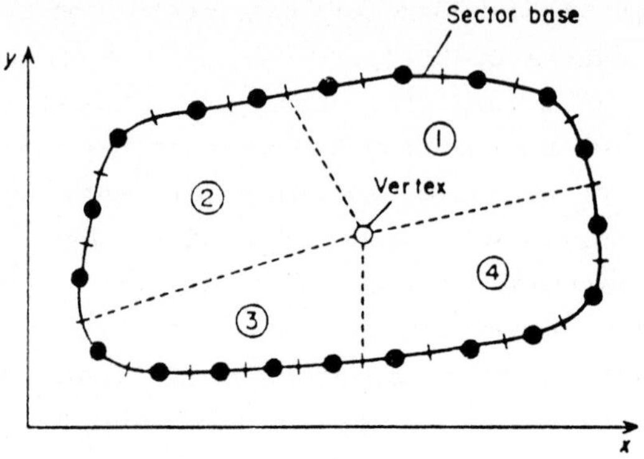

Fig. 15. Two-dimensional domain divided into four sectors.

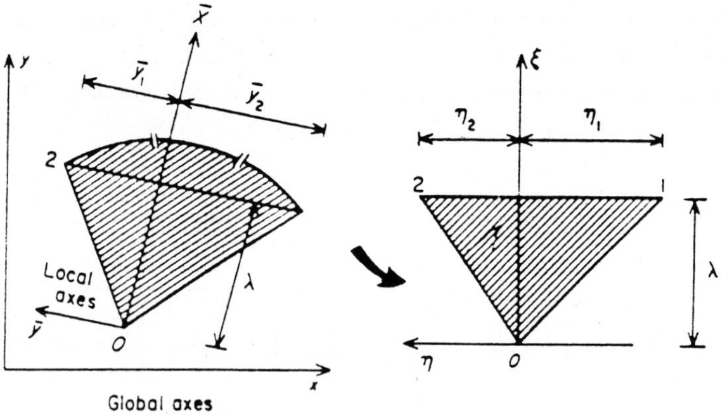

Fig. 16. Mapping of a sector onto a triangle.

The transformation that maps the sector onto a triangle has been given by Katsikadelis [60] as

$$\bar{x} = f(\lambda\frac{\eta}{\xi})\xi/\lambda \quad , \quad \bar{y} = \eta \tag{125}$$

where $\bar{x}=f(\bar{y})$ is the equation of the sector base in local coordinates (see Fig. 16).

When this technique is used with BEM, the sector base consists of a group of consecutive boundary elements and it is convenient to approximate the function $\bar{x}=f(\bar{y})$ by an interpolating polynomial rather than to use the analytic expression for the curve. Thus, if a polynomial approximation is used, the sector base is chosen so that it can be represented as

$$\bar{x} = f(\bar{y}) = \alpha_o+\alpha_1\bar{y}+\alpha_2\bar{y}^2+ \dots +\alpha_n\bar{y}^n \tag{126}$$

The coefficients α_i $(i=1,2,\dots,n)$ are computed from the coordinates of the nodal and/or the extreme points of the boundary elements. Thus, by using constant boundary elements to approximate the unknown boundary quantities, unevenly spaced finite difference schemes to approximate the derivatives and a collocation technique at the Gauss points in the interior of the plate the following system of simultaneous differential equations is established

$$\begin{bmatrix} [A_{11}] & [A_{12}] & [0] & [A_{14}] \\ [A_{21}] & [A_{22}] & [A_{23}] & [0] \\ [A_{31}] & [A_{32}] & [A_{33}] & [A_{34}] \\ [0] & [0] & [A_{43}] & [A_{44}] \end{bmatrix} \begin{bmatrix} \{\Omega\} \\ \{X\} \\ \{\Phi\} \\ \{\Psi\} \end{bmatrix} = \begin{bmatrix} \{B_1\} \\ \{B_2\} \\ \{B_3\} \\ \{B_4\} \end{bmatrix} + \begin{bmatrix} [0] \\ [0] \\ [C_3] \\ [C_4] \end{bmatrix} \{\ddot{W}\} \tag{127a}$$

$$\{W\} = \{B_5\}+[C_5]\{\ddot{W}\}+\big[[A_{51}][A_{52}][A_{53}][A_{54}]\big]\left[\{\Omega\}\{X\}\{\Phi\}\{\Psi\}\right]^T \tag{127b}$$

where

$$\{\Omega\} = [\Omega_1 \quad \Omega_2 \quad \dots \quad \Omega_N]^T$$

$$\{X\} = [X_1 \quad X_2 \quad \dots \quad X_N]^T \tag{128}$$

$$\{\Phi\} = [\Phi_1 \quad \Phi_2 \quad \ldots \quad \Phi_N]^T$$

$$\{\Psi\} = [\Psi_1 \quad \Psi_2 \quad \ldots \quad \Psi_N]^T$$

are the values of the unknown boundary quantities at the nodal points of the N boundary elements and

$$\{W\} = [W_1 \quad W_2 \quad \ldots \quad W_M]^T \tag{129}$$

are the values of the deflection W at the M Gauss integration points inside R. Moreover, $[A_{ij}]$ (i=1,2,3,4,5; j=1,2,3,4) and $[C_i]$ (i=3,4,5) are constant matrices whereas all the vector matrices $\{B_i\}$ (i=1,2,3,4,5) depend on time.

Solving Eqs (127a) for the boundary quantities $\{\Omega\}$, $\{X\}$, $\{\Phi\}$ and $\{\Psi\}$ and substituting the results into Eqs (127b) gives the following system of ordinary differential equations

$$[M]\{\ddot{W}\} + \{W\} = \{F\} \tag{130}$$

Eq. (130) is the equation of motion of the plate with respect to the Gauss integration nodal points. [M] is an MxM generalized mass matrix and {F} is an Mx1 force vector. When forced vibrations are considered ($\{F\}\neq 0$) Eq. (130) can be solved numerically by using time step integration. For free vibrations the eigenfrequencies and mode shapes are established by solving the corresponding linear algebra eigenvalue problem.

In the following, numerical results from the analysis of certain example problems are presented to illustrate the efficiency and accuracy of the method.

a) A circular simply supported plate with radius a and a Poisson's ratio $\nu=0.30$ is considered. In Table 14 the first six eigenfrequencies are presented as obtained by the D/BEM method [28], by the IBEM [66] and by the BEM with the

Table 14. Eigenfrequency parameter $\lambda = a\sqrt[4]{\omega^2 \varrho / D}$ of a simply supported circular plate of radius a.

λ_n	BEM [28]	BEM [66]	BEM [67]	Exact
λ_1	2.221	2.2	2.22	2.222
λ_2	3.726	3.8	3.73	3.728
λ_3	5.050	5.1	5.06	5.061
λ_4	5.437	5.5	5.45	5.452
λ_5	6.284	6.4	6.32	6.321
λ_6	6.926	7.0	6.96	6.963

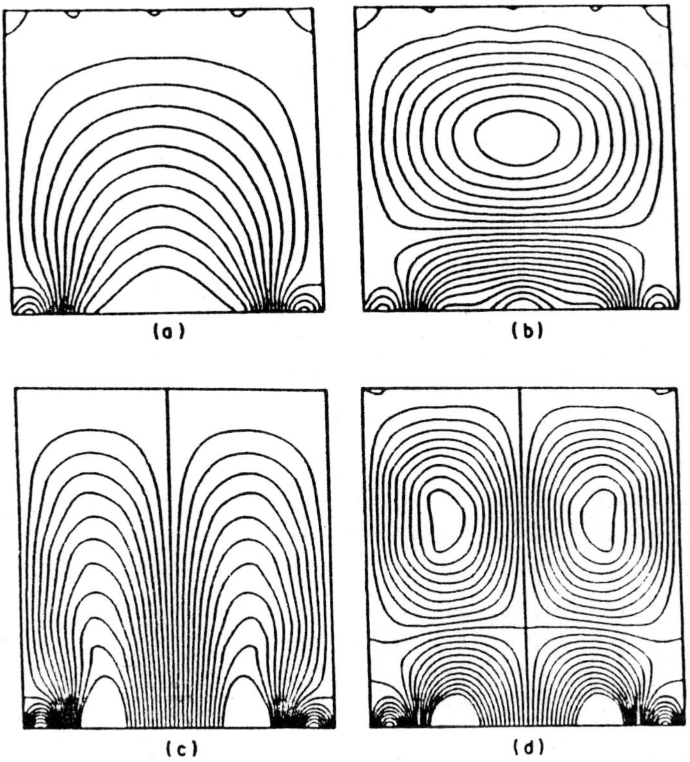

Fig. 17. Mode shapes and eigenfrequencies of a square plate subjected to mixed boundary conditions (SS-F-SS-C).The contour lines are drawn $\Delta w=0.02$ a part. (a) Mode 1, $\omega_1=12.79$ (12.69); (b) mode 2, $\omega_2=32.98$ (33.06); (c) mode 3, $\omega_3=43.04$ (41.70); (d) mode 4, $\omega_4=63.40$ (63.01). The values in the parentheses are taken from Ref. [68].

Table 15. Eigenfrequencies $\Omega = \omega a^2\sqrt{\varrho/D}$ of a rectangular simply supported plate with internal supports (a/b=0.75).

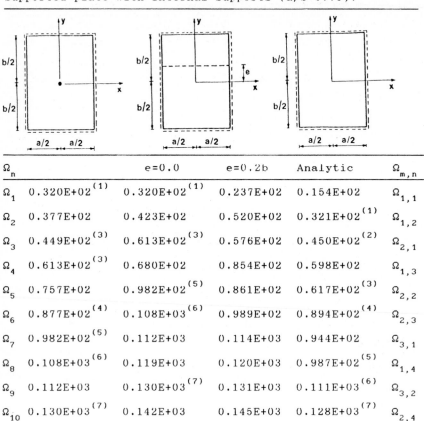

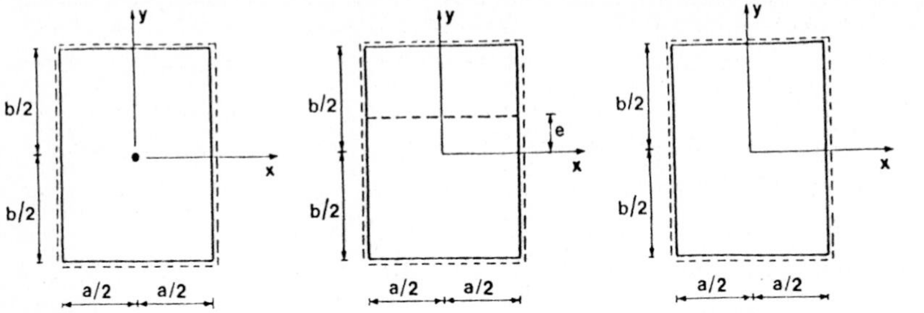

Ω_n		e=0.0	e=0.2b	Analytic	$\Omega_{m,n}$
Ω_1	0.320E+02 (1)	0.320E+02 (1)	0.237E+02	0.154E+02	$\Omega_{1,1}$
Ω_2	0.377E+02	0.423E+02	0.520E+02	0.321E+02 (1)	$\Omega_{1,2}$
Ω_3	0.449E+02 (3)	0.613E+02 (3)	0.576E+02	0.450E+02 (2)	$\Omega_{2,1}$
Ω_4	0.613E+02 (3)	0.680E+02	0.854E+02	0.598E+02	$\Omega_{1,3}$
Ω_5	0.757E+02	0.982E+02 (5)	0.861E+02	0.617E+02 (3)	$\Omega_{2,2}$
Ω_6	0.877E+02 (4)	0.108E+03 (6)	0.989E+02	0.894E+02 (4)	$\Omega_{2,3}$
Ω_7	0.982E+02 (5)	0.112E+03	0.114E+03	0.944E+02	$\Omega_{3,1}$
Ω_8	0.108E+03 (6)	0.119E+03	0.120E+03	0.987E+02 (5)	$\Omega_{1,4}$
Ω_9	0.112E+03	0.130E+03 (7)	0.131E+03	0.111E+03 (6)	$\Omega_{3,2}$
Ω_{10}	0.130E+03 (7)	0.142E+03	0.145E+03	0.128E+03 (7)	$\Omega_{2,4}$

frequency domain dynamic fundamental solution [67]. The results of these three methods are compared with the exact ones which were computed by numerical evaluation of the frequency equation

$$J_{n+1}(\lambda)/J_n(\lambda) + I_{n+1}(\lambda)/I_n(\lambda) = 2\lambda/(1-\nu) \qquad (131)$$

b) A square plate with side length a subjected to mixed boundary conditions has been studied. The computed eigenfrequencies and mode shapes are presented in Fig.17. The eigenfrequencies are in good agreement with those given by Leissa [68].

c) A rectangular plate with a point and a line support has been studied to demonstrate the capability of the presented method to treat problems having internal supports. The results are presented in Table 15. The comparison with analytic results is possible only for the cases in which the internal support is symmetric because for the antisymmetric modes the corresponding eigenfrequencies are identical with those of the plate without internal supports. In Table 15 the eigenfrequencies corresponding to the same mode shape are denoted by the same superscript.

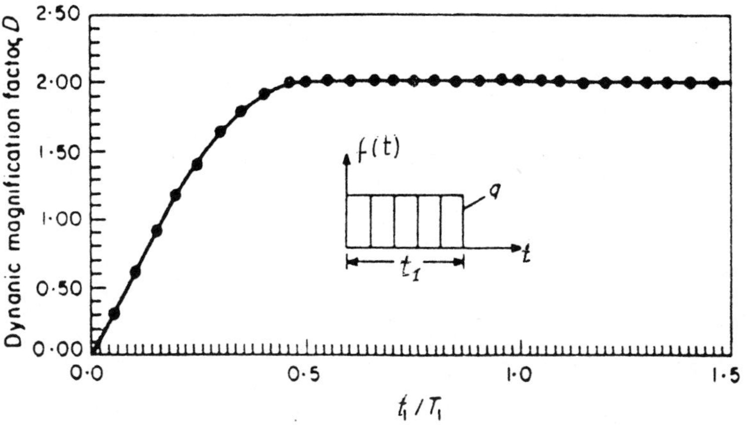

Fig. 18. Maximum response D=maxR(τ) of a square simply supported plate subjected to a rectangular impulse. T_1 is the fundamental period. ——, Exact; ••, BEM [28].

d) A simply supported square plate with side a subjected to a suddenly applied uniformly distributed load q of small duration (impulsive load) has been studied. The results are presented in Fig. 18.

We close this section by giving some additional results for plates that have been analyzed by D/BEM. Thus, numerical results for plates with variable thickness [31,32] are given in Tables 16,17 and Fig. 19, for large deflection analysis of plates [30] in Table 18 and Fig. 20, for the analysis of plates resting on an elastic foundation with unilateral

Table 16. Deflections and bending moments along line x=a/2 of a square simply supported plate with variable rigidity $D=D_0+D_1y$ subjected to a distributed load $q=q_0(1+yD_1/D_0)$. First row BEM [32]; second row: Analytic [55]; third row: FEM [32].

y/a	$\bar{w}=wa^5D_o/4q_o$	$\bar{M}_x=M_xa^3/4q_oa^2$	$\bar{M}_y=M_ya^3/4q_oa^2$
	0.023	0.04	0.10
0.063	0.022	0.04	0.11
	0.021	0.04	0.09
	0.208	0.58	0.85
0.175	0.207	0.59	0.87
	0.199	0.53	0.81
	0.309	1.15	1.22
0.335	0.310	1.21	1.27
	0.300	1.11	1.23
	0.327	1.67	1.42
0.494	0.327	1.66	1.48
	0.321	1.53	1.44
	0.277	1.78	1.48
0.653	0.279	1.76	1.51
	0.273	1.60	1.49
	0.171	1.30	1.20
0.812	0.183	1.40	1.23
	0.169	1.19	1.25
	0.027	0.21	0.21
0.972	0.031	0.28	0.28
	0.027	0.22	0.30
	0.0	-	-
1.0	0.0	-	-
	0.0	-	-

Table 17. Eigenfrequencies $\Omega = \omega a^2\sqrt{\varrho_0/D_0}$ for a linearly tapered clamped square plate ($h=h_0[1+\alpha x/a]$) with $\nu=0.3$.

Ω^2	$\alpha=0.2$		$\alpha=0.4$		$\alpha=0.6$	
	BEM [31]	Ref.[69]	BEM [31]	Ref.[69]	BEM [31]	Ref.[69]
Ω_1^2	0.155+4	0.156+4	0.183+4	0.184+4	0.211+4	0.213+4
Ω_2^2	0.618+4	0.644+4	0.725+4	0.761+4	0.871+4	0.877+4
Ω_3^2	0.621+4	0.647+4	0.738+4	0.763+4	0.835+4	0.884+4
Ω_4^2	0.139+5	0.141+5	0.164+5	-	0.190+5	-
Ω_5^2	0.199+5	-	0.229+5	-	0.256+5	-
Ω_6^2	0.203+5	-	0.237+5	-	0.271+5	-
Ω_7^2	0.298+5	-	0.352+5	-	0.408+5	-
Ω_8^2	0.299+5	-	0.353+5	-	0.411+5	-

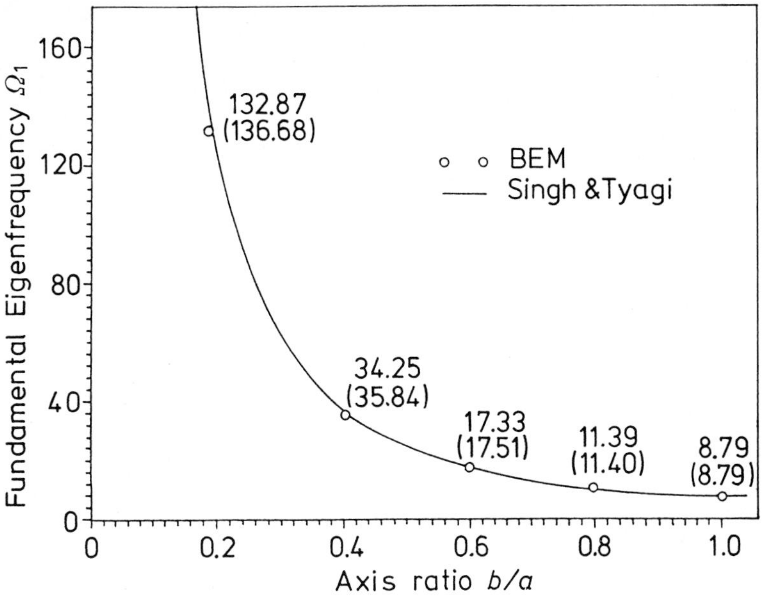

Fig. 19. Fundamental eigenfrequency $\Omega_1=\omega_1 a^2\sqrt{\varrho_0/D_0}$ versus axis ratio in a clamped elliptic plate of variable thickness $(h=h_o[1-0.2(x^2/a^2+y^2/b^2)])$ with $\nu=0.3$.

Table 18. Deflections, membrane and bending stresses along the radius of a uniformly loaded circular plate with clamped movable edge subjected to large deflections ($\nu=0.30$, $a/h=50$, $qa^4/Eh^4=10$).

r/a	w/h		$\sigma_r^m a^2/Eh^2$		$\sigma_t^m a^2/Eh^2$		$\sigma_r^b a^2/Eh^2$	
	BEM [30]	Anal. [55]	BEM [30]	Anal. [55]	BEM [30]	Anal. [55]	BEM [30]	Anal. [55]
0	1.308	1.310	0.780	0.782	0.780	0.782	3.253	3.250
0.098	1.286	1.290	0.768	0.770	0.743	0.744	3.208	3.214
0.305	1.101	1.105	0.664	0.666	0.445	0.442	2.812	2.821
0.562	0.658	0.660	0.415	0.420	-0.191	-0.202	1.218	1.214
0.802	0.188	0.190	0.171	0.159	-0.639	-0.632	-2.278	-2.285
0.960	0.009	0.010	0.026	0.026	-0.629	-0.629	-5.777	-5.750

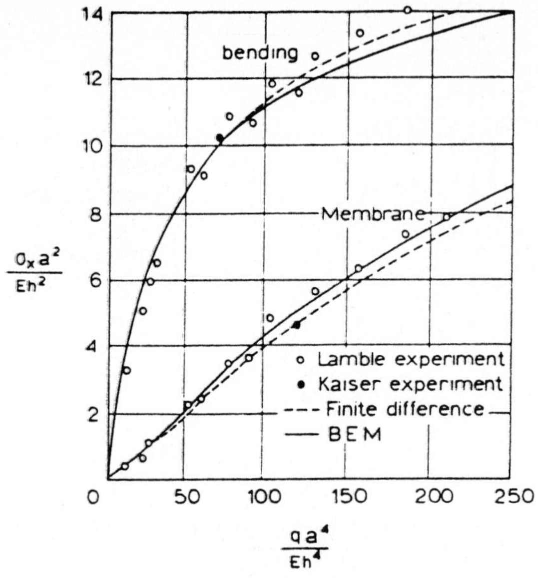

Fig. 20. Bending and membrane stresses at the center of a simply supported square plate with movable edges versus uniform lateral load (ν=0.30) obtained by BEM [30] as compared with those obtained by other methods [71]

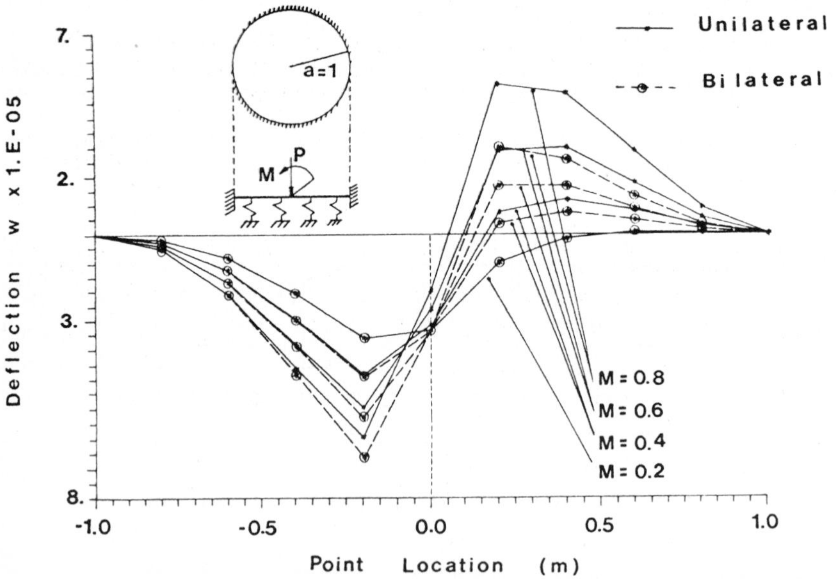

Fig. 21. Deflections along the diameter of a clamped circular plate (D=192.3077) subjected to a unit concentrated load and a concentrated moment at its center and resting on a unilateral (solid line) and a bilateral (dashed line) foundation with $\lambda = a/\sqrt[4]{D/k}$ =11.

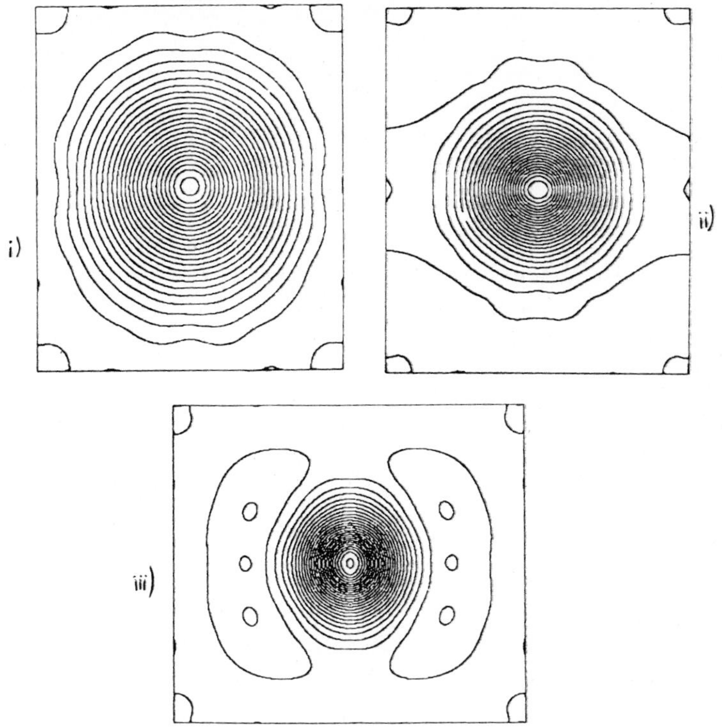

Fig. 22. Deflection contours of a clamped rectangular plate ($D=192.3077$) subjected to a unit concentrated load at its center and resting on a tensionless linear foundation for various values of the subgrade reaction parameter λ. The contours are drawn Δw apart. i) $\lambda=a/\sqrt[4]{D/k}=3$ ($\Delta w=0.33\times10^{-4}$), ii) $\lambda=a/\sqrt[4]{D/k}=5$ ($\Delta w=0.33\times10^{-4}$), iii) $\lambda=a/\sqrt[4]{D/k}=7$ ($\Delta w=0.27\times10^{-5}$).

Table 19. Fundamental eigenfrequencies $\Omega=\omega/\bar{\omega}$ ($\bar{\omega}=\pi\sqrt{G/\varrho h}$) of a simply supported square thick plate ($\nu=0.3$). Boundary conditions type I : $w=M_n=\psi_t=0$, boundary conditions type II : $w=M_n=M_{nt}=0$.

h/a	B.C.: Type I		B.C.: Type II
	Anal. [70]	BEM [35]	BEM [35]
0.05	0.007	0.007	0.007
0.10	0.028	0.029	0.027
0.20	0.108	0.108	0.103
0.40	0.342	0.342	0.312
0.60	0.609	0.610	0.557
0.80	0.883	0.884	0.850
1.00	1.157	1.159	1.085

contact [33] in Figs 21, 22 and for a thick simply supported square plate [35] in Table 19.

d) The Green's Function Methods (GFM's)

The Green's function K(P,Q) for a plate of given geometry and boundary conditions expresses, from the physical point of view, the deflection at a point P (field point) of the plate due to a unit concentrated transverse load at another point Q (source point). Both points, P and Q lie inside the region R occupied by the plate. The Green's function is sometimes called the finite domain Green's function to distinguish it from the free space Green's function, i.e. the fundamental solution. The Green's function is symmetric, i.e. K(P,Q)=K(Q,P), thus the roles of the field and source points can be interchanged. Green's functions which are due to higher order singularities, e.g. to a unit moment, can also be established. In this case the Green's function K(P,Q) expresses the deflection at a field point P due to unit moment at a source point Q. If the Green's function K(P,Q) for a plate problem is known, then the solution of Eq. (1) can be obtained by evaluating an integral over the domain of the plate. In the following we present the Green's function method as it was developed by Katsikadelis and Sapountzakis [36].

Consider the nonhomogeneous biharmonic equation

$$\nabla^4 w = g/D \tag{132}$$

subjected to the boundary conditions (3),(4). We can readily formulate the boundary value problem for the Green function of Eq. (132) and the integral representation of its solution using the Rayleigh-Green identity [2]

$$\iint_R (K\nabla^4 w - w\nabla^4 K)\,d\sigma = \int_C \left(-KVw+wVK+\frac{\partial K}{\partial n}Mw-\frac{\partial w}{\partial n}MK\right)ds - $$

$$- \sum_k (K[\![Tw]\!]_k - w[\![TK]\!]_k) \tag{133}$$

where the operator T is defined by Eq. (7).

Consider now a two-point function $K(P,Q)$, $P:\{x,y\}$, $Q:\{\xi,\eta\}$, $P,Q\in R$ which is the solution of the following boundary value problem

$$\nabla^4 K = \delta(P-Q)/D \quad \text{in} \quad R \tag{134}$$

$$\left.\begin{aligned} &\alpha_1 K+\alpha_2 VK = 0 \\ &\beta_1\frac{\partial K}{\partial n}+\beta_2 MK = 0 \end{aligned}\right\} \quad \text{on} \quad C \tag{135}$$

and

$$c_{1k}K+c_{2k}[\![TK]\!]_k = 0 \qquad \text{on the corner } k \tag{136}$$

where $\delta(P-Q)$ is the two-dimensional delta function. With the exception of the cases where the whole boundary C of the plate is either free (i.e. $MK=0$, $VK=0$) or guided (i.e. $\frac{\partial K}{\partial n}=0$, $VK=0$) the boundary value problem (134), (135) and (136) has a unique solution [72].

Employing the reciprocal identity (133) for the functions w and K satisfying Eqs (132), (3), (4) and (134), (135), (136), respectively, we obtain the following integral representation for the solution of Eq. (132)

$$\begin{aligned} w(P) = &\iint_R K(P,Q)g(Q)d\sigma_Q \\ &- D\int_{C_1}\left[-\frac{\beta_3(q)}{\beta_1(q)}MK(P,q)+\frac{\alpha_3(q)}{\alpha_1(q)}VK(P,q)\right]ds_q \\ &- D\int_{C_2}\left[+\frac{\beta_3(q)}{\beta_2(q)}\frac{\partial K(P,q)}{\partial n_q}+\frac{\alpha_3(q)}{\alpha_1(q)}VK(P,q)\right]ds_q \\ &- D\int_{C_3}\left[-\frac{\beta_3(q)}{\beta_1(q)}MK(P,q)-\frac{\alpha_3(q)}{\alpha_2(q)}K(P,q)\right]ds_q \\ &- D\int_{C_4}\left[+\frac{\beta_3(q)}{\beta_2(q)}\frac{\partial K(P,q)}{\partial n_q}-\frac{\alpha_3(q)}{\alpha_2(q)}K(P,q)\right]ds_q \end{aligned} \tag{137}$$

$$- D\sum_k [K(P,q)\frac{c_{3k}}{c_{2k}}]$$

where C_1, C_2, C_3, C_4 are the parts of the boundary on which the pairs (α_1,β_1), (α_1,β_2), (α_2,β_1), (α_2,β_2) do not vanish, respectively; $(C_1 \cup C_2 \cup C_3 \cup C_4 = C)$.

When the whole boundary is free or guided, special care must be taken in establishing the Green's function. For Dirichlet boundary conditions (clamped or simply supported) or mixed boundary conditions the plate is supported at least at a part of its boundary so that reactions (reacting forces and bending moments) are produced to keep the plate in equilibrium. However, in plates with free or guided boundary, the boundary condition VK=0 has no meaning since the plate, loaded by the unit load, is not in equilibrium. The problem in this case is analogous to that of establishing the Green's function for the Laplace equation subjected to Neumann boundary condition. Thus, the Green's function for free boundary can be established up to an arbitrary linear function while the Green's function for the guided boundary up to an arbitrary constant. In these cases the boundary conditions must be modified as follows

a) For a plate with free boundary

$$MK^*(P,q) = 0$$
$$VK^*(P,q) = \varepsilon_o(P)+\varepsilon_1(P)\xi+\varepsilon_2(P)\eta \tag{138}$$

$$[\![TK^*(P,q)]\!] = 0 \tag{139}$$

b) For a plate with guided boundary

$$\frac{\partial K^*(P,q)}{\partial n_q} = 0$$
$$VK^*(P,q) = \varepsilon_o(P) \tag{140}$$

where $q \in C$, $P \in R$

The constants $\varepsilon_i(P)$ $(i=0,1,2)$ depend on the point P and are established from the equilibrium conditions of the plate subjected to a unit concentrated force at point P using the procedure presented in Ref. [36]. Note that the Green's function $K^*(P,Q)$ is not symmetric.

Actually, the solution of the boundary value problem described by Eqs (134), (135) and (136) is much more difficult than the corresponding plate problem itself. Thus, very few analytical solutions have been obtained and they refer to plates with simple geometry and boundary conditions, e.g. circular and rectangular plates. Consequently, plate problems that could be solved using Eq. (137) are limited. Though an analytical solution for the Green's function for plates of arbitrary shape and boundary conditions is out of question, however a numerical solution is feasible. The BEM has been shown very convenient. In the following we present the BDIEM as it was applied by Katsikadelis and Sapountzakis [36] to establish numerically the Green's function for the plate bending problem.

On the basis of the boundary conditions (135) the boundary differential equations are written as (see also Eqs 106)

$$\alpha_1\Omega - \alpha_2[\Psi-(\nu-1)\frac{\partial}{\partial s}(\frac{\partial X}{\partial s}-\kappa\frac{\partial \Omega}{\partial s})] = 0 \tag{141}$$

$$\beta_1 X - \beta_2[\Phi+(\nu-1)(\frac{\partial^2\Omega}{\partial s^2} +\kappa X)] = 0 \tag{142}$$

where the following notation has been used

$$\Omega = K(P,q) \qquad X = \frac{\partial K(P,q)}{\partial n_q}$$

$$\Phi = \nabla^2 K(P,q) \qquad \Psi = \frac{\partial}{\partial n_q}\nabla^2 K(P,q) \tag{143}$$

Moreover, applying the Rayleigh - Green identity (44) to the functions $K(Z,Q)$ and $w=(1/8\pi D)r^2\ell nr$, $r=|P-Z|$, and using notation (143) we obtain the following integral representation for the Green's function

$$K(P,Q) = \frac{1}{8\pi D}r^2\ell nr - \frac{1}{2\pi}\int_C [\Lambda_1(r)\Omega+\Lambda_2(r)X+\Lambda_3(r)\Phi+\Lambda_4(r)\Psi]ds \tag{144}$$

where the kernels $\Lambda_i(r)$ $(i=1,2,3,4)$ are given by Eqs (51). Note that in the line integrals it is $r=|P-z|$, $P\in R$, $z\in C$ while in the free term it is $r=|P-Q|$. Thus, the Green function $K(P,Q)$ is established from Eq. (144) if the boundary quantities Ω, X, Φ and Ψ are known. These quantities are related by the differential Eqs (141) and (142). Consequently, two more equations are required. For this purpose the two boundary integral equations (49) are employed which for $f=\delta(P-Q)$ yield

$$\alpha\Omega = \frac{1}{4D}r^2\ell nr - \int_C [\Lambda_1(r)\Omega+\Lambda_2(r)X+\Lambda_3(r)\Phi+\Lambda_4(r)\Psi]ds \tag{145}$$

$$\alpha\Psi = \frac{1}{D}(\ell nr+1) - \int_C [\Lambda_1(r)\Phi+\Lambda_2(r)\Psi]ds \tag{146}$$

Note that in the line integrals it is $r=|P-z|$ while in the free terms it is $r=|P-q|$.

Eqs (141), (142), (145) and (146) constitute a set of four simultaneous equations for the unknown boundary quantities Ω, X, Φ, and Ψ. The equations are solved numerically. The differential equations are solved using the finite difference method, while the integral equations using the boundary element method. Thus, discretizing the boundary into N constant elements and using the nodes as pivotal points for the finite differences we obtain a system of 4N linear algebraic equations which in matrix form is written as

$$\begin{bmatrix} [A_{11}] & [A_{12}] & [0] & [A_{14}] \\ [A_{21}] & [A_{22}] & [A_{23}] & [0] \\ [A_{31}] & [A_{32}] & [A_{33}] & [A_{34}] \\ [0] & [0] & [A_{43}] & [A_{44}] \end{bmatrix} \begin{bmatrix} \{\Omega\} \\ \{X\} \\ \{\Phi\} \\ \{\Psi\} \end{bmatrix} = \begin{bmatrix} \{0\} \\ \{0\} \\ \{B_3\} \\ \{B_4\} \end{bmatrix} \tag{147}$$

where the elements of the constant matrices $[A_{kl}]$, $(k=1,2,3,4,$ $\ell=1,2,3,4)$ are given by Eqs (109), while the elements of the column matrices $[B_k]$ $(k=3,4)$ are given as

$$(B_3)_i = \frac{1}{4D} r_{Pi} \ell n r_{Pi}$$

$$(B_4)_i = \frac{1}{D}(\ell n r_{Pi}+1) \qquad (i=1,2,\ldots,N) \tag{148}$$

Finally, the column matrices $\{\Omega\}$, $\{X\}$, $\{\Phi\}$, $\{\Psi\}$ include the values of the boundary quantities Ω, X, Φ, Ψ at the nodal boundary points. The accuracy of the BDIEM used for the numerical evaluation of the Green's function is demonstrated in Table 20.

Table 20. Values of the Green function for a circular clamped plate with radius a. The unit concentrated load is at the source point r=0.56202a, θ=0

r/a	$K(\frac{r}{a}, 0; 0.56202, 0)$	
	BEM [38]	Analytic [55]
0	.63685E-2	.63685E-2
0.09853	.73922E-2	.73924E-2
0.30454	.92640E-2	.92642E-2
0.56202	.93113E-2	.93113E-2
0.80199	.29593E-2	.29590E-2
0.96019	.01468E-2	.01466E-2
1	0	0

The Green's function method presented previously has been employed to solve several plate problems governed by a differential equation of the general form

$$D\nabla^4 w + p(w, w_{xx}, w_{yy}, w_{xy}, x, y, \mu) = f(x,y) \tag{149}$$

subjected to the boundary conditions (3), (4); μ is a parameter. For the sake of conciseness and simplicity of the expressions only the solution for homogeneous boundary conditions $(\alpha_3=\beta_3=c_{3k}=0)$ will be considered in the presentation that follows.

Employing Eq. (137) for $g=f(x,y)-p(w,w_{xx},w_{yy}, w_{xy}, x,y,\mu)$ we obtain

$$w(P) = -\iint_R K(P,Q)p[w(Q),w_{xx}(Q),w_{yy}(Q),w_{xy}(Q),Q,\mu]d\sigma_Q$$

$$+\iint_R K(P,Q)f(Q)d\sigma_Q \qquad (150)$$

Differentiation of Eq. (150) twice with respect to x and y yields

$$w_{xx}(P) = -\iint_R K_{xx}(P,Q)p[w(Q),w_{xx}(Q),w_{yy}(Q),w_{xy}(Q),Q,\mu]d\sigma_Q$$

$$+\iint_R K_{xx}(P,Q)f(Q)d\sigma_Q \qquad (151)$$

$$w_{yy}(P) = -\iint_R K_{yy}(P,Q)p[w(Q),w_{xx}(Q),w_{yy}(Q),w_{xy}(Q),Q,\mu]d\sigma_Q$$

$$+\iint_R K_{yy}(P,Q)f(Q)d\sigma_Q \qquad (152)$$

$$w_{xy}(P) = -\iint_R K_{xy}(P,Q)p[w(Q),w_{xx}(Q),w_{yy}(Q),w_{xy}(Q),Q,\mu]d\sigma_Q$$

$$+\iint_R K_{xy}(P,Q)f(Q)d\sigma_Q \qquad (153)$$

Eqs (150) to (153) involve the unknown deflection and its second partial derivatives w_{xx}, w_{yy} and w_{xy} in the domain integrals. That is, they constitute a set of four coupled domain/ boundary integral equations with respect to these quantities which can be solved numerically as follows.

Application of two-dimensional Gauss integration for the domain integrals in Eqs (150) to (153) and collocation at the M Gauss points give 4M relations of the form

$$w_i = \sum_{j=1}^{M} A_{ij}p[w_j,(w_{xx})_j,(w_{yy})_j,(w_{xy})_j,Q_j,\mu] + C_{1i}$$

$$(w_{xx})_i = \sum_{j=1}^{M} B_{ij}p[w_j,(w_{xx})_j,(w_{yy})_j,(w_{xy})_j,Q_j,\mu] + C_{2i}$$

$$(w_{yy})_i = \sum_{j=1}^{M} C_{ij}p[w_j,(w_{xx})_j,(w_{yy})_j,(w_{xy})_j,Q_j,\mu] + C_{3i} \qquad (154)$$

$$(w_{xy})_i = \sum_{j=1}^{M} D_{ij}p[w_j,(w_{xx})_j,(w_{yy})_j,(w_{xy})_j,Q_j,\mu] + C_{4i}$$

in which C_{1i}, C_{2i}, C_{3i}, C_{4i} $(i=1,2,\ldots,M)$ are 4M constants due to the known terms of Eqs (150) to (153). Eqs (154) constitute a system of 4M simultaneous, in general nonlinear, algebraic equations for the values w_i, $(w_{xx})_i$, $(w_{yy})_i$, $(w_{xy})_i$ $(i=1,2,\ldots M)$. Eqs (154) can be solved iteratively and, subsequently, the deflections w(P) and its derivatives $w_{xx}(P)$, $w_{yy}(P)$, $w_{xy}(P)$ at any point P are evaluated from Eqs (150) to (153) using the same Gauss points for the evaluation of the domain integrals. From Eqs (144) and (151), it is apparent that the kernels $K_{xx}(P,Q)$, $K_{yy}(P,Q)$, $K_{xy}(P,Q)$ are singular and special care must be taken in performing the domain integrations. In this method the singular domain integrals are evaluated by extracting the singularity using the procedure presented in Ref. [36, 38].

From the examples presented below the efficiency and the versatility of the GFM is concluded.

a) Plates on elastic foundation. The problem of a plate resting on elastic foundation is governed by the equation

$$D\nabla^4 w + p(w,\nabla^2 w,x,y) = f$$

The function $p(w,\nabla^2 w,x,y)$, which expresses the reaction of the subgrade, is in general a nonlinear function in w and its Laplacian. For p=kw, where k is a constant, we take the conventional (one-parameter) Winkler foundation. For $p=-G\nabla^2 w+kw$, where G and k are constants, we take the two-parameter (Pasternak-type) foundation. Pure BEM solutions for plates on elastic foundations have been given by many authors [12,14,27,73,74]. Even in the cases where the fundamental solution is known (Kelvin or Hankel functions) the analytic and computational work is very tedious. The GFM presented here not only simplifies the computational effort, but also can give solution to much more difficult problems as it is the case of nonhomogeneous and/or nonlinear subgrade reaction. Numerical results for plates resting on Wilnkler type, nonhomogeneous and nonlinear elastic foundations as well as for plates resting on Pasternak type elastic foundations are presented in Tables 21, 22 and in Fig. 23.

Table 21. Deflections $\bar{w}=w/(Pa^2/D)$ of rectangular plates (2ax2b, b/a=1.2, a=2.5) resting on a Winkler elastic foundation with k=16D, i.e. $\lambda=a/\sqrt[4]{D/k}=5$, and subjected to a concentrated load P at their center.

y/b	x/a	Clamped		Simply Supported	
		GFM [36]	BEM [12]	GFM [36]	BEM [73]
	0.0	.499-2	.499-2	.500-2	.500-2
	0.2	.316-2	.315-2	.316-2	.315-2
0.0	0.4	.129-2	.129-2	.129-2	.129-2
	0.6	.339-3	.349-3	.332-3	.342-3
	0.8	.365-4	.398-4	.283-4	.318-4

b) Static and dynamic analysis of plates with internal supports. A GFM has been developed for the analysis of plates which in addition to the boundary supports are also supported inside the domain on isolated points (columns), lines (bearing walls), or regions (patches) (Fig. 24) [40]. The supports inside the domain may yield elastically. In Table 23 and in Fig. 27 numerical results obtained by this method are presented.

c) A flexibility matrix solution of the vibration problem of plates [39]. A Green's function method has been developed based on the capability to establish a flexibility matrix (discrete Green's function) with respect to a set of nodal mass points using the BEM solution for the static problem. The region of the plate is divided into a finite number of cells (see Fig. 28) and a lumped mass matrix is constructed from the

Table 22. Deflections $\bar{w}=w/(Pa^2/D)$ of a simply supported rectangular plate (2ax2b, b/a=1.2, a=2.5) subjected to a concentrated load at its center and resting (i) on a nonhomogeneous, (ii) on a nonlinear elastic foundation [36].

y/b	x/a	Nonhomogeneous $p=16Dw\exp[0.1(x^2+y^2)]$	Nonlinear $p=w^{1/3}$
	0.0	.4900-2	.1972-1
	0.2	.3066-2	.1670-1
0.0	0.4	.1205-2	.1188-1
	0.6	.2745-3	.7234-2
	0.8	.5091-5	.3318-2

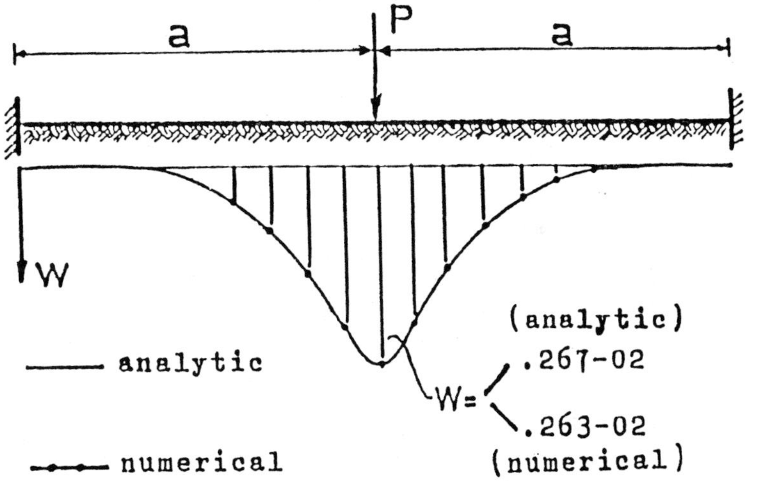

Fig. 23. Deflections $\bar{w}=w/(Pa^2/D)$ along the diameter of a clamped circular plate resting on a Pasternak-type elastic foundation ($\lambda=a/\sqrt[4]{D/k}=3$, $s=a/\sqrt{D/G}=3$) [36].

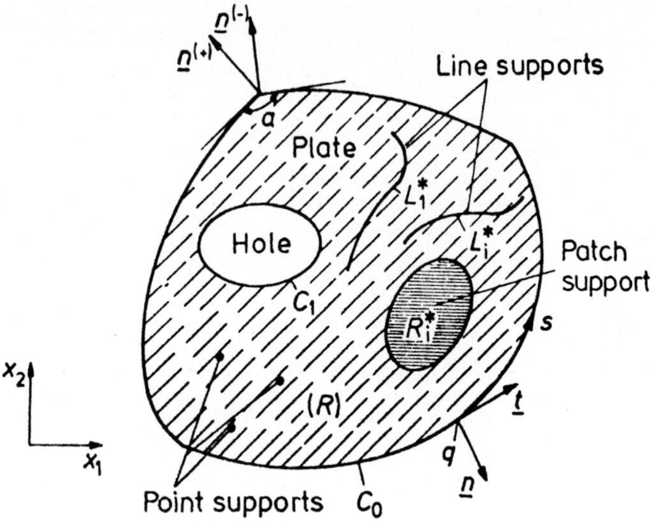

Fig. 24. Two-dimensional region R occupied by the plate

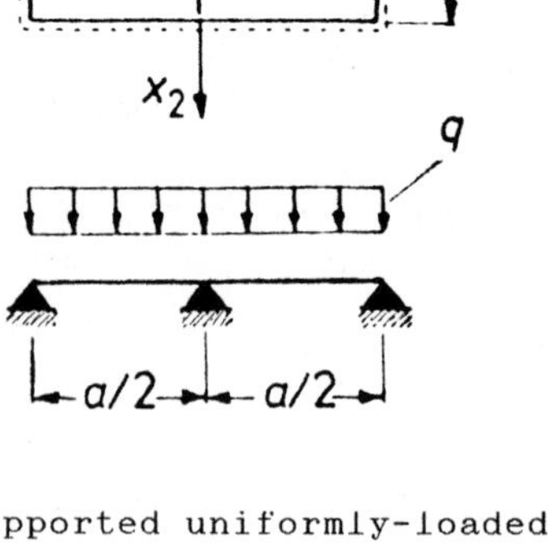

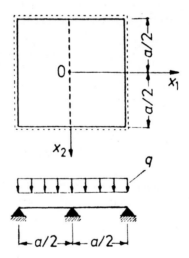

Fig. 25. Simply-supported uniformly-loaded two-span continuous plate.

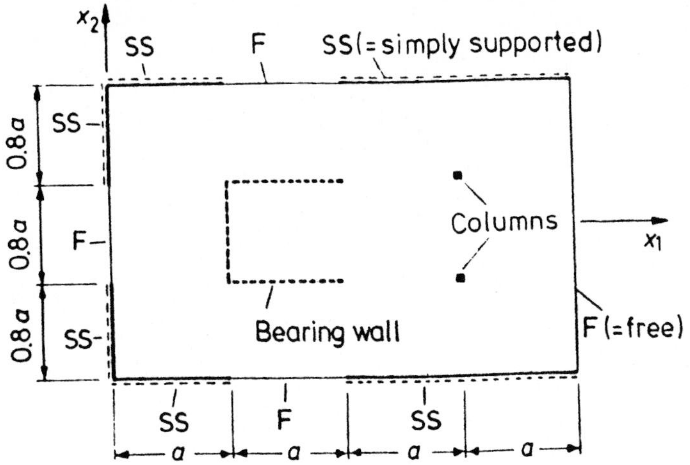

Fig.26. Uniformly loaded rectangular plate with mixed boundary conditions and internally supported (ν=0.3).

Table 23. Deflections and bending moments along the x_1 axis of the two-span rectangular continuous simply supported plate of Fig. 26 under uniform load [40].

x_1/a	$w/(qa^4/D)$		M_{x1}/qa^2	
	Computed	Analytic	Computed	Analytic
0	0.1025E-15	0.	-0.9090E-02	-0.9089E-02
0.10	0.1038E-03	0.1033E-03	-0.8626E-03	-0.8615E-03
0.20	0.2593E-03	0.2588E-03	0.4447E-02	0.4446E-02
0.30	0.3153E-03	0.3150E-03	0.6428E-02	0.6427E-02
0.40	0.2171E-03	0.2169E-03	0.4897E-02	0.4897E-02

tributary mass areas to the nodal mass points. Free and forced vibrations are considered. Numerical results obtained by this method are presented in Tables 24, 25 as compared with results obtained by other methods.

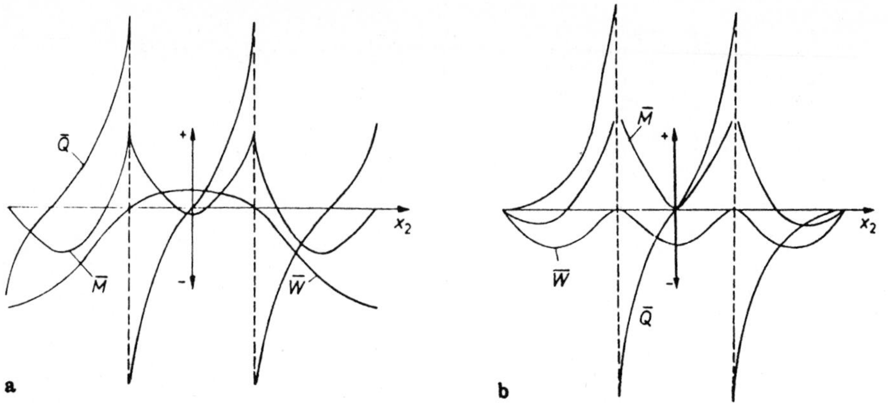

Fig. 27. Deflections $\bar{w}=w/(qa^4/D)$, bending moments $\bar{M}=M_{x2}/qa^2$ and shearing forces $\bar{Q}=Q_{x2}/qa$ along the lines a) $x_1=1.5a$, b) $x_1=3.0a$ of the plate of Fig. 27. For scale evaluation: at $\bar{x}_1=0.2$, a) $\bar{w}=0.7889E-02$, $\bar{M}=0.5531E-01$, $\bar{Q}=-0.1625E-01$ b) $\bar{w}=0.3981E-02$, $\bar{M}=0.36494E-01$, $\bar{Q}=0.2860E+00$

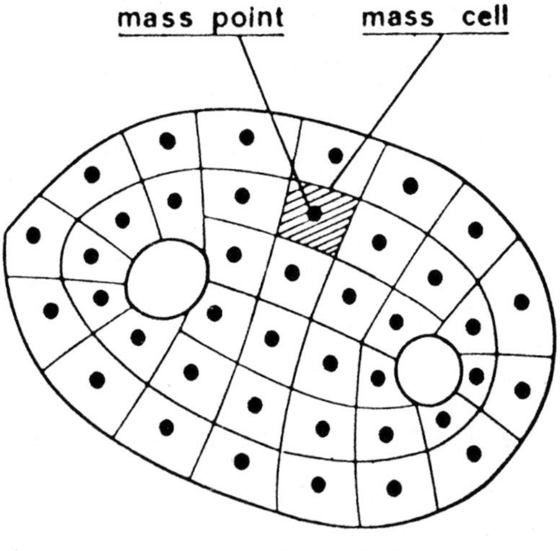

Fig. 28. Discretization of the plate.

Table 24. Eigenfrequencies $\Omega=\omega a^2\sqrt{\varrho/D}$ of a square plate with mixed boundary conditions, SS-C-SS-SS (SS=simply supported C=clamped).

Ω_{mn}	GFM [39]	FEM [39]	[68]
Ω_{11}	23.36	23.76	23.65
Ω_{21}	51.14	52.78	51.67
Ω_{12}	57.99	59.86	58.64
$\Omega_{2,2}$	84.98	88.88	86.12
$\Omega_{3,1}$	98.95	104.78	100.26
Ω_{13}	111.36	118.52	113.22
Ω_{32}	131.71	140.75	133.78
Ω_{33}	138.81	148.39	140.84

Table 25. Eigenfrequencies $\Omega=\omega a^2\sqrt{\varrho/D}$ of a simply supported square plate.

Ω_{mn}	BEM [39]	FEM [39]		Exact [68]
$\Omega_{1,1}$	19.54	19.85		19.74
$\Omega_{1,2}$	48.85*	50.45*		49.34*
$\Omega_{2,2}$	78.02	81.52		79.29
$\Omega_{1,3}$	97.46*	102.50	(104.21)	98.70*
$\Omega_{2,3}$	126.37*	135.28*		128.30*
$\Omega_{1,4}$	164.58*	182.14*		167.78*
$\Omega_{3,3}$	173.99	189.38		177.64
$\Omega_{2,4}$	192.79*	212.19	(218.11)	197.39*
$\Omega_{3,4}$	238.99*	270.22*		246.74*

* Double eigenfrequencies.

In closing this section we present a variation of the GFM which was developed by Irschik, Ziegler et al. [41-47]. In this method the authors utilized existing Green's functions for finite domains to generate the kernel functions and embedded properly the domain occupied by the given plate into a basic domain with partially coinciding boundaries on which the boundary conditions are satisfied. This method is an extension of the Melnikov's technique who applied it to solve torsion and plane elasticity problems on rectangular domains with cut-offs or holes [49].

To present the basic ingredients of the method we consider a plate occupying the plane domain $R=R_o \cup R_1 \cup R^*$, bounded by the curve $C \cup \bar{C}$ and subjected to prescribed boundary conditions (see Fig. 29). Suppose that the Green's function $K^o=K(P,Q)$, that is the solution of the boundary value problem described by Eqs (134), (135) and (136) for a plate problem, is known. Consider now a new plate occupying the plane domain R^* (shaded

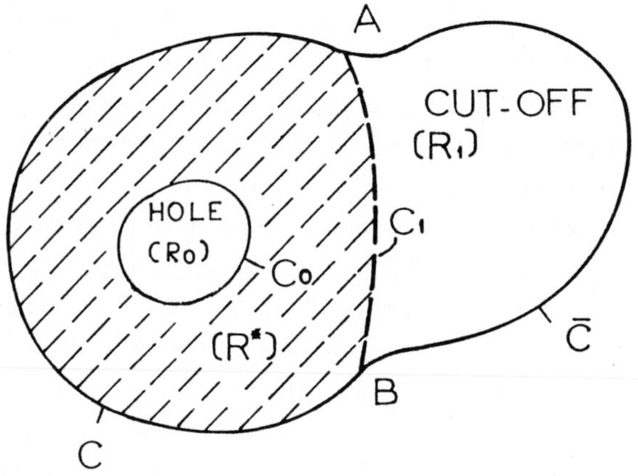

Fig.29. Plate occupying the region R^* (shaded area) embedded into a basic plate $R=R^* \cup R_1 \cup R_o$.

area in Fig.29) which results by making a cut-off R_1 and a hole R_o. The boundary of the new plate is $C^*=C \cup C_1 \cup C_o$. On the common portion C of the boundary the new plate has the same boundary conditions with the original plate whereas any type of boundary conditions may be specified on the portions C_o and C_1. The solution of the problem for the plate occupying the region R^* can be established by working as follows.

We assume the solution w as superposition of the homogeneous solution W and a particular solution w_1. The particular solution can be readily obtained using the known Green's function $K^o(P,Q)$ of the original plate. Thus

$$w_1(P) = \iint_R K^o(P,Q)f(Q)d\sigma_Q \tag{155}$$

For a convenient integration the loading f is extended from the domain R^* to the domain R. The deflection of the actual plate can be obtained using the IBEM as

$$w(P) = w_1(P) + \int_{C_o \cup C_1} [K^o(P,q)\varphi^o(q)+K^1(P,q)\varphi^1(q)]ds_q \tag{156}$$

where $K^1(P,q)$ is the deflection at point P due to a unit normal moment at point q and it is obtained by direct differentiation of $K^o(P,q)$ (see Eq.101). Moreover, $\varphi^o(q)$ and $\varphi^1(q)$ are unknown line local densities of fictitious transverse load and normal moment, respectively, distributed along the uncommon boundary portion $C_o \cup C_1$ and must be determined so that the boundary conditions are also satisfied on this part of the boundary of R^*. This is accomplished by working exactly as in the case of the IBEM with the exception that the integral equations are defined only on a part of the boundary, i.e. $C_o \cup C_1$. An advantage of this method over the classical BEM's, which make use of the free space Green's function to generate the kernels of the boundary integral equations, is that the boundary conditions are approximated only on a part of the boundary which decreases the boundary unknowns in the discretized equations and increases the accuracy. However, owing to the complexity of the expressions of the kernels of the integral equations and their strong singularities the solutions obtained by this method are limited only to plates with rectilinear boundaries (polygonal plates) embedded properly into a rectangular basic plate. The method has been extensively employed by Irschik et. al.

Table 26. Bending moment $(M_x/qa^2)\times 10^2$ at the center of a simply supported skew plate computed using the Green's function method [47] (ν=0.2).

k	γ	GFM [47]	Anal. [55]
2.02	$\pi/3$	9.68	9.68
2	$\pi/4$	9.01	8.98

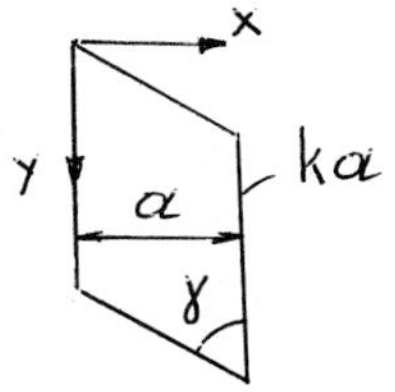

Table 27. Frequency ratios $\omega_1/\omega_{1,0}$ of simply supported rhombic Mindlin plates for various skew angles and thickness-to-span ratios obtained by GFM [46] as compared with results given in Ref. [75]. ω_1 is the lowest flexural eigenfrequency according to Mindlin's theory and $\omega_{1,0}$ is the lowest natural frequency of Kirchhoff's theory (ν=0.3).

Mode	h/a	$\gamma=0^\circ$		$\gamma=15^\circ$	
		GFM	[75]	GFM	[75]
1	0.05	0.9910	0.9910	0.9907	0.9905
	0.2	0.8830	0.8839	0.8807	0.8784
4	0.05	0.9655	0.9656	0.9654	0.9654
	0.2	0.6966	0.6971	0.6961	0.6961
Mode	**h/a**	**$\gamma=30^\circ$**		**$\gamma=45^\circ$**	
		GFM	[75]	GFM	[75]
1	0.05	0.9900	0.9884	0.9842	0.9821
	0.2	0.8603	0.8585	0.8199	0.8098
4	0.05	0.9634	0.9632	0.9533	0.9515
	0.2	0.6860	0.6848	0.6399	0.6337

[41-47] and numerical results have been obtained for several plate problems. Some results which illustrate the efficiency of the method are presented in Tables 26, 27.

Concluding Remarks

In the preceding discussion special BEM's, that is BEM's which are not based on the general direct formulations but on various integral representations, are presented. With regards to certain common characteristics the special BEM's are classified in five groups :

a) BEM's based on the biharmonic analysis, that is methods which are considered as an extension of the harmonic analysis to solve the biharmonic equation. Four variations of this approach have been presented.

b) Indirect boundary element methods (IBEM's) in which the deflection is expressed in terms of potentials produced by unknown boundary dstributions not having direct physical meaning. Once these potentials are established the deflections and stress resultants at any interior point are evaluated by simple integration.

c) Boundary differential-integral equation methods (BDIEM's). In these methods the solution of the problem is reduced to the solution of four boundary equations. Two of them, derived from the boundary conditions, are ordinary differential equations and hence can be readily integrated. The rest, derived from Green's reciprocity theorem, are boundary integral equations.

d) Green's function methods (GFM's). These methods employ the Green's function of the problem which is established numerically using BEM or they utilize existing Green's functions for certain basic domains to generate the kernels of the integral representations for other plates, which are properly embedded in the basic domains.

e) Methods with no common characteristics are referred to as "Other methods" and are not presented in this section making only reference to the literature.

The conclusions that can be drawn from the discussion of this chapter are :

a) Some special BEM's can be used effectively to solve certain plate problems with specific geometry and boundary conditions giving excellent results.

b) Some special BEM'S can overcome certain shortcomings of the general direct BEM formulations maintaining at the same time their generality concerning the geometry of the plate, the boundary conditions and the loading.

c) Special BEM's can be used as D/BEM's to solve plate problems for which the numerical treatment of the integral equations is tedious because the fundamental solutions are complicated (e.g. plates on elastic foundations, vibrations of plates) or it is impossible to establish the fundamental solutions (e.g. plates with variable thickness, large deflections of plates, plates on elastic foundation with unilateral contact).

Acknowledgements

The author wishes to express his appreciation and thanks to his student Dr. E.J. Sapountzakis for reading the manuscript of this chapter and making constructive comments. Moreover, the author would like to thank Professor D.E. Beskos for many helpful discussions and suggestions during the preparation of this chapter. Finally, the author wishes to thank Mrs Dia Troulinou-Yfanti, his secretary at the Institute of Structural Analysis and Aseismic Research of NTUA, for her able typing of the manuscript.

References

1. Bezine, G.: Boundary integral equations for plate flexure with arbitrary boundary conditions. Mech. Res. Comm. 5 (4) (1978) 197-206.

2. Stern M.: A general boundary integral formulation for the numerical solution of plate bending problems. Int. J. Solids Struct. 15 (1979) 769-782.

3. Katsikadelis J.T.: The Analysis of plates on elastic foundation by the boundary integral equation method. Thesis presented to the Polytechnic Institute of New York in partial fulfillment of the requirements for the degree of Doctor of Philosophy. New York 1982.

4. Costa, J.; Brebbia, C.A.: Plate bending problems using BEM. In: Proc. of the 6th Int. Conf. on Board the Liner the Queen Elizabeth II Southampton to New York Berlin: Springer-Verlag 3 1984 43-63.

5. Hartmann, F.; Zotemantel, R.: The direct boundary element method in plate bending. Int. J. Num. Meth. Engng 23 (1986) 2049-2069.

6. Katsikadelis, J.T.; Armenakas, A.E.: A new boundary equation solution to the plate problem. ASME J.Appl. Mech. 56 (1989) 364-374.

7. Jaswon, M.A.; Maiti, M.; Symm, G.T.: Numerical biharmonic analysis and some applications. Int. J. Solids Struct. 3 (1967) 309-332.

8. Jaswon, M.A.; Maiti, M.: An integral equation formulation of plate bending problems. J. Eng. Math. 2 (1968) 83-93.

9. Jaswon, M.A.; Symm, G.T.: Integral equation methods in potential theory and elastostatics. London: Acad. Press 1977.

10. Maiti, M.; Chakrabarty, S.K.: Integral equation solutions for simply supported polygonal plates. Int. J. Engng. Sci. 12 (1974) 793-806.

11. Segedin, C.M.; Brickell, D.G.A.: Integral equation method for a corner plate. ASCE J. Struct. Div. 94 (1968) 41-52.

12. Katsikadelis, J.T.; Armenakas, A.E.: Analysis of clamped plates on elastic foundation by the boundary integral equation method. ASME J. Appl. Mech. 51 (1984) 574-580.

13. Camp, C.V.; Gipson, G.S.: Biharmonic analysis of rectilinear plates by the boundary element method. Int. J. Num. Meth. Engng. 30 (1990) 517-539.

14. Katsikadelis, J.T.; Kallivokas, L.: Clamped plates on Pasternak-type elastic foundation by the boundary element method. ASME J. Appl. Mech. 53 (1986) 909-917.

15. Paris, F.; Leon, S.: An alternative analysis of thin elastic plates with any boundary conditions using BEM. In: Boundary Elements VII 4.17-4.28 C.A.Brebbia and G.Maier (eds.) Berlin: Springer-Verlag 1985.

16. Paris, F.; De Leon. S.: Simply supported plates by the boundary integral equation method. Int. J. Num. Meth. Engng., 25 (1987) 225-233.

17. Paris, F.; De Leon, S.: Boundary element method applied to the analysis of thin plates. Comp. & Struct. 25 (1987) 225-233.

18. Leon, S.; Paris, F.: Analysis of thin plates on elastic foundations with boundary element method. Engin. Anal. with Boundary Elements 6 (4) (1989) 192-196.

19. Niwa, Y.; Kobayashi, S.; Fukui, T.: An application of the integral equation method to plate - bending problems. Memoirs Faculty Engng. Kyoto Univ. 36 (1974) Pt.2 140-158.

20. Tottenham, H.: The boundary element method for plates and shells. In: Developments in Boundary Element Methods-1 Banerjee P.K. and Butterfield R. (eds.) Ch.8 London : Elsevier Applied Science Publishers 1979 173-205.

21. Altiero, N.J.; Sikarskie, D.L. (eds.): A boundary integral method applied to plates of arbitrary plan form. In: Proc. Int. Symp. Innovative Numerical Analysis in Applied Engineering Science 1.69-1.73 T.A. Cruse et al. (eds.) CETIM Cenlins France 1977.

22. Altiero, N.J.; Sikarskie, D.L.: A boundary integral method applied to plates of arbitrary plan form. Comput. & Struct. 9 (1978) 163-168.

23. Zhu, J.: Integral equation solutions for finite and infinite plate. In: Boundary Elements VII 4.103-4.112

C.A. Brebbia and G. Maier (eds.) Berlin: Springer-Verlag 1985.

24. Wu, B.C.; Altiero, N.J.: A new numerical method for the analysis of anisotropic thin-plate bending problems. Comp. Meth. Appl. Mech. Engng. 25 (1981) 343-353.

25. Mahajerin, E.; Burgess, G.: The numerical treatment of anisotropic plate bending problems. In: Computational Methods and Experimental Measurements 401-407 G.A. Keramidas and C.A.Brebbia (eds.) Berlin: Springer-Verlag 1986.

26. Karageorghis, A.; Fairweather, G.: The method of fundamental solutions for the numerical solution of the biharmonic equations. J. Comput. Phys. 69 (1987) 434-459.

27. Katsikadelis, J.T.; Kallivokas, L.: Plates on biparametric elastic foundation by BDIE method. ASCE J. Eng. Mech. 114 (5) (1988) 847-875.

28. Katsikadelis, J.T.: A boundary element solution to the the vibration problem of plates. J. Sound Vibr. 141 (2) (1990) 313-322.

29. Katsikadelis, J.T.: Large deflection analysis of plates on elastic foundation by the boundary element method. Int. J. Solids Struct. (1991)

30. Katsikadelis, J.T.; Nerantzaki, M.S. : Large deflections of thin plates by the boundary element method. In: Boundary Elements X 3 Stress Analysis C.A.Brebbia (ed.) Berlin: Springer Verlag 1988 435-456.

31. Katsikadelis, J.T.; Sapountzakis, E.J.: A BEM solution to dynamic analysis of plates with variable thickness. Comput. Mech. 7 (1991) 369-379.

32. Sapountzakis, E.J.; Katsikadelis, J.T.: "A Boundary element solution for plates with variable thickness", ASCE J. of Eng. Mech. (1991) 1241-1256.

33. Sapountzakis, E.J.; Katsikadelis, J.T.: Unilaterally supported plates on elastic foundation by the boundary element method. ASME J. Appl. Mech. (1991), in print.

34. Katsikadelis, J.T.; Sapountzakis, E.J.: An approach to the vibration problem of homogeneous, non-homogeneous and composite membranes based on the boundary element method. Int. J. Num. Meth. Engng. 26 (1988) 2439-2455.

35. Katsikadelis, J.T.; Yotis, A.J.; Sapountzakis, E.J.: An integral equation approach to the vibration problem of thick elastic plates. In: Structural Dynamics (Eurodyn '90) 2 W.B.Krätzig et al. (eds.) Rotterdam: Balkema 1990 869-875.

36. Katsikadelis, J.T.; Sapountzakis, E.J.: Numerical evaluation of the Green function for the biharmonic equation using BEM with applications to static and dynamic analysis of plates. In: Boundary Elements IX 2 Stress Analysis Applications Berlin: Springer-Verlag 1987 51-67.

37. Katsikadelis, J.T.; Sapountzakis, E.J.: A new method for the analysis of plates on elastic foundation. (in Greek) In : Proc. of First Hellenic Conference on Geotechnical Engineering, Athens: Technical Chamber of Greece (1986) 197-202 .

38. Nerantzaki, M.S.; Katsikadelis, J.T.: A Green's function method for nonlinear analysis of plates. Acta Mech., 75 (1988) 211-225.

39. Katsikadelis, J.T.; Kandilas, C.B.: A flexibility matrix solution of the vibration problem of plates based on the boundary element method. Acta Mech. 83 (1990) 51-60.

40. Katsikadelis, J.T.; Sapountzakis, E.J.; Zorba, E.G.: A BEM approach to static and dynamic analysis of plates with internal supports. Comput. Mech. 7 (1990) 31-40.

41. Irschik, H.: Ein Randintegralgleichungsverfahren zur Berechnung allseits frei drehbur gelagerter Trapezplatten mit rechten Winkeln. ZAMM 60 (1980) T125-T127.

42. Irschik, H.; Ziegler, F.: Application of the Green's function method to thin elastic polygonal plates. Acta Mech. 39 (1981) 155-169.

43. Irschik, H.: Erweiterung eines Randintegralgleichungs-verfahrens auf Platten mit elastisch gelagerten Randern. Zeits. Ang. Mat. Mech. No.63 (1983) T174 - T177.

44. Irschik, H.: Ein Randintegralgleichungsverfahren fur temperaturmomentbeanspruchte Platten. Ing. Archiv 53 (1983) 197-207.

45. Irschik, H.: A boundary-integral equation method for bending of orthotropic plates. Int. J. Solids Struct. 20 (1984) 245-255.

46. Heuer, R.; Irschik, H.: A boundary element method for eigenvalue problems of polygonal membranes and plates. Acta Mech. 66 (1987) 9-20.

47. Irschik, H.; Heuer, R.; Ziegler, F.: Free and forced vibrations of polygonal Mindlin-plates by an advanced BEM. In: Advanced Boundary Element Methods T.A.Cruse (ed.) Berlin: Springer-Verlag 1988 179-188

48. Wu, B.C.; Altiero, N.J.: A boundary integral method applied to plates of arbitrary plan form and arbitrary boundary conditions. Comput. & Struct. 10 (1979) 703-707.

49. Melnikov, Y.A.: Some applications of the Green's function method in mechanics. Int. J. Solids Struct. 13 (1977) 1045-1058.

50. Werner, H.; Protopsaltis, B.: A boundary superposition element method for the Kirchhoff plate bending problem. In: Boundary Elements VII C.A. Brebbia and G.Maier (eds.) Berlin: Springer-Verlag 1985 463-480.

51. Johnson, D.: Plate bending by a boundary point method. Comput. & Struct. 26 (1987) 673-680.

52. Hansen, E.B.: Numerical solution of integro-differential and singular integral equations for plate bending problems. J. Elasticity 6 (1976) 39-56.

53. Grover, R.L.; Chou, S.I.: Solution of plane stress and plate bending problems by boundary integral equations. In: Trans. 5th Int. Conf. on Struct. Mech. Reactor Technology M11/1 T.A. Jaeger and B.A. Boley (eds.) Amsterdam: North-Holland 1979.

54. Tai, H.; Katayama, T.; Sekiya, T.: Boundary element method for bending of plate with free edges. Mech. Res. Comm. 10 (1983) 121-126.

55. Timoshenko, S.; Woinowsky-Krieger, S.: Theory of Plates and Shells. 2nd Ed. New York: McGraw-Hill 1959.

56. Katsikadelis, J.T.; Massalas, C.V.; Tzivanidis, G.I.: A General Solution of the Clamped Plate with Arbitrary Shape. Techn. Rep. (83) Dept. of Mechanics, University of Ioannina: December 1976.

57. Jaswon, M.A.; Ponter, A.R.S.: An Integral Equation Solution of the Torsion Problem. Proc. Roy. Soc. of London, Ser.A 273 (1963) 237-246.

58. Duff, G.; Naylor, D.: Differential equations of applied mathematics. New York: John Wiley and Sons Inc. 1966.

59. Katsikadelis, J.T.; Massalas, C.V.; Tzivanidis, G.I.: An Integral Equation Solution of the Plane Problem of the Theory of Elasticity. Mech. Res. Comm. 4 (1977) 199-208.

60. Katsikadelis, J.T.: A Gaussian Quadrature Technique for Two - Dimensional Regions with Arbitrary Shape. Eng. Anal. (1991) to appear.

61. Salvadori, M.G.; Reggini, H.C.: Simply supported corner plate. ASCE J. Struct. Div. 86 (1960) 141-154.

62. Brebbia, C.A.; Nardini, D.: Dynamic analysis in solid mechanics by an alternative boundary element procedure. Soil Dyn. Earth. Engng. 3 (1983) 228-233.

63. Zienkiwicz, O.C.: The finite element method. London: McGraw Hill 1977.

64. Banerjee, P.K.; Butterfield, R.: Developments in boundary element methods - 1. London:Elsevier Applied Science Publishers 1979.

65. Guoshu, S.; Mukherjee, S.: Boundary element method of bending of elastic plates of arbitrary shape with general boundary conditions. Engng. Anal. 3 (1986) 36-44.

66. Niwa, Y.; Kobayashi, S.; Kitahara, M.: Eingenfrequency analysis of a plate by the integral equation method. Theor. Appl. Mech. 29 (1981) 287-307.

67. Providakis, C.P. ; Beskos, D.E.: Free and forced vibrations of plates by boundary elements. Comp. Meth. Appl. Mech. Engng. 74 (1989) 231-250.

68. Leissa, A.W.: Vibration of Plates (NASA SP-160). Washington D.C.: U.S. Government Printing Office 1969.

69. Kuttler, J.T.; Sigillito, V.G.: Vibrational frequencies of variable thickness. J.Sound Vibr. 86 2 (1983) 181-189.

70. Singh, B.; Tyagi, D.: Transverse vibrations of an elliptic plate with variable thickness. J. Sound Vibr. 99 3 (1985) 379-391.

71. Chia, C.Y.: Nonlinear analysis of plates New York: McGraw-Hill 1980.

72. Bergman, S.; Schiffer, M.: Kernel functions and elliptic differential equations in mathematical physics. New York: Academic Press 1953.

73. Katsikadelis, J.T.; Armenakas, A.E.: Plates on elastic foundation by the BIE method. ASCE J. Eng. Mech. 110 (1984) 1086-1105.

74. Costa Jr., J.A.; Brebbia, C.A.: The boundary element method applied to plates on elastic foundations. Eng. Anal. 2 (4) (1985) 174-183.

75. Kanaka Raju, K.; Hinton, E.: Natural frequencies and modes of rhombic Mindling plates. Earthquake Eng. Sruct. Dyn. 8 (1985) 55-62.

Static and Dynamic Analysis of Reissner-Mindlin Plates

H. ANTES

Institute of Applied Mechanics
Technische Universität Braunschweig, D-3300 Germany

Summary

The problem of bending under static loading as well as of free and forced flexural vibrations of Reissner-Mindlin plates is formulated by the direct and also by the indirect boundary element method. Fundamental solutions for both types of singularities, of single forces and moments and of deflection and rotation discontinuities are used for the static bending problem. For the vibration problem, however, not only the static fundamental solutions but the exact singular solutions of Reissner-Mindlin's frequency domain equations of motion are employed. While the use of the static fundamental solution for the dynamic analysis creates not only boundary but also domain integrals due to the inertia terms, the exact dynamic fundamental solution enables to avoid those domain integrals which affect the basic boundary character of the representation. Numerical solutions of some basic plate problems are presented to demonstrate the applicability of those boundary integral formulations.

Introduction

In classical linear thin plate theory, as introduced by Kirchhoff [1], it is assumed in the form of the hypothesis of non-deformable normals to the mid-surface that the in-plane deformation is linearly distributed across the thickness of the plate and the transverse shear deformation effects are negligible. Besides, the influence of normal stresses with respect to the mid-surface is not taken into account, and the deformation of the mid plane is assumed to cause no in-plane stresses. Based on these assumptions, the governing differential equation is of fourth-order in conjunction with only two boundary conditions. Since, as already demanded by Poisson (see [2], p. 27), "physical intuition" leads one to expect three edge conditions, a sixth-order rather than a fourth-order differential equation ought to be in charge of the problem.

Starting in 1945 with E. Reissner [3], several attempts have been made (for a survey see [4] or [5]) to resolve the Poisson-Kirchhoff boundary condition paradox and to improve Kirchhoff's theory by an approximate consideration of transverse shear deformation. Since their papers had the most impact upon this subject, the thick plate static theory is usually referred to as Reissner Plate Theory while the dynamic thick plate theory carries Mindlin's name [6]. Besides including the effect of rotary inertia, as it is necessary in dynamics, Mindlin's Theory regards the normals to the original mid plane to be still straight but no longer normal to the mid-plane after deformation. Additionally, Reissner's theory takes the mid-plane normal stress into account which can be important for special dynamic interaction problems, e.g. sound waves produced in the surrounding medium (air or water) by vibrations of a submerged plate. For such reasons, an extension of Reissner's static theory to dynamic problems is considered in this chapter (as in [7]). The basic equations of motion result to be identical to those of Mindlin's theory with the special shear correction factor $\kappa^2 = 5/6$. Since this is characteristic for Reissner's model, this theory can be called a Reissner-Mindlin Theory.

Although the considered theory is two-dimensional and linear, the analysis of plates involving complex geometries, loading and boundary conditions can only be done by numerical methods. Besides the most widely used Finite Element Method and the Finite Difference Method, during the last decade the Boundary Element Method (BEM) has emerged as an accurate and efficient numerical method for plate analysis, not only in static bending, but also in flexural vibration problems. Basically, there are two approaches for treating static problems by the BEM and three in the case of dynamic problems. These are the direct and the indirect BEM employing the static and the dynamic fundamental solution of the static and the dynamic equations, respectively. Additionally, as a third possibility in dynamics, the direct BEM can be used by employing the static fundamental solution. This creates domain integrals due to the presence of the inertia term in addition to the boundary ones in the integral representation of the solution. Thus, an interior domain discretization is required in addition to the boundary one. For this reason, this approach is called Domain/Boundary Element Method (D/BEM).

But, while within the context of Kirchhoff's model many publications concerning the applications of boundary integrals in all the different versions mentioned before (for a survey in dynamics, see [8]) are available, research work on integral equations for the more refined sixth order plate theory started very late and the number of publications is still rather small. Although a paper by Kalnins [9] concerning the fundamental solutions of Mindlin's theory appeared as early as 1966, it was not untill 1982 that any further research on this field was published. At that time, Vander Weeën [10,11] found the explicit closed analytical forms of the basic fundamental solutions of Reissner's plate model and solved some first test problems using a direct BEM formulation. Then, based on his work, some further developments started.

In static analysis of Reissner-Mindlin plates, there is some work by Antes [12,13] on both, the direct and the indirect method. Moreover, a number of new fundamental solutions concerning the stress functions of single forces and moments and the influence functions of basic geometrical singularities, e.g. of deflection and rotation discontinuities, have also been derived by Antes [14,15]. Also, a few papers reporting on special numerical treatments and applications have recently appeared. In particular, Brebbia and Long [16] discussed the use of discontinuous elements as well as of double nodes to deal with discontinuities at corners. Wang et al. [17] used spline functions of order two and three for interpolating the boundary functions, and analyzed some contact problems. Telles and Karam [18] have solved infinite plate problems by using quadratic isoparametric and, in addition, discontinuous elements. De Barcellos and Monken e Silva [19] have rewritten Vander Weeën's direct BEM formulation for its use on a static Mindlin model. Finally, Constanda [20] published a monograph where by a rigorous mathematical analysis the existence, uniqueness and approximation behaviour of Reissner' plate model solutions by means of boundary integral equations are discussed.

In dynamic analysis, the relevant research work is even less. Irschik, Heuer & Ziegler have published some papers [21, 22] dealing with vibrations of Mindlin plates in the frequency domain via an 'advanced' BEM. However, therein, the higher order Mindlin problem is reduced to two second order Helmholtz-Klein-Gordon boundary value problems for which in the case of rectangular domains a special Green's function can be constructed. Thus, the method is not directly related to the actual topic. To the author's knowledge, till now, only Lei and Huang [7] have published a relevant paper. They used a special direct D/BEM, i.e. fundamental solutions of only the static parts of the Reissner's frequency domain equations. This obvious lack of BEM application to dynamic Reissner-Mindlin plate problems may be due to the fact that the basic dynamic fundamental solutions have been derived only recently by W. Cheng et al. [23, 24].

In the present work, the bending problem of Reissner-Mindlin plates is formulated by the direct and also by the indirect boundary element method where fundamental solutions of both types of singularities, of single forces and moments and of deflection and rotation discontinuities are used. In the dynamic analysis, free and forced flexural vibrations are determined by both, the D/BEM [25] employing the static fundamental solutions of Vander Weeen [10] and the usual direct BEM in a complete boundary integral formulation employing the dynamic fundamental solutions of Cheng et al. [23, 24]. A number of numerical examples for both, static and dynamic problems is presented in order to illustrate the applicability of the different fundamental solutions and formulations.

Integral Formulations for Bending Problems

Consider a plate with constant thickness h where the plane x_1-x_2 is assumed to coincide with the mean surface. It shall be subjected to body forces $F_\alpha(x_1,x_2)$, $(\alpha=1,2)$ and $F_3(x_1,x_2)$ as well as to distributed transverse loads $q(x_1,x_2)$, per unit area. These loadings cause generalized displacements u_i: u_α indicating the rotations ϕ_α, and u_3 the deflection w in the thickness direction x_3. The related strains, the flexural strains $\kappa_{\alpha\beta}$ and the transverse shear strains γ_α can be obtained from the displacements via [11,12]

$$\kappa_{\alpha\beta} = \frac{1}{2}(\phi_{\alpha,\beta} + \phi_{\beta,\alpha}), \tag{1}$$

$$\gamma_\alpha = \phi_\alpha + w_{,\alpha} . \tag{2}$$

The corresponding internal stress-resultants, the bending stress-couples $M_{\alpha\beta}$ and the shear-stress-resultants Q_α are related to these strains through the constitutive equations

$$M_{\alpha\beta} = N(1-\upsilon)\,[\kappa_{\alpha\beta} + \frac{\upsilon}{1-\upsilon}\,\delta_{\alpha\beta}\,\kappa_{\lambda\lambda}] + \frac{\upsilon}{1-\upsilon}\,\delta_{\alpha\beta}\,\lambda^{-2}\,q \tag{3}$$

$$= \hat{M}_{\alpha\beta} + \frac{\upsilon}{1-\upsilon}\,\delta_{\alpha\beta}\,\lambda^{-2}\,q \tag{4}$$

$$Q_\alpha = \lambda^2\,N\,\frac{1-\upsilon}{2}\,\gamma_\alpha, \tag{5}$$

where $N = Eh^3/12\,(1-\upsilon^2)$ denotes the flexural rigidity and $\lambda^2 = 10/h^2$ is a characteristic quantity of Reissner's model.

While the equilibrium at both faces of the plate is satisfied by taking the variation of the normal stress σ_{33} over the plate thickness as

$$\sigma_{33} = 0.25\,(2x_3/h)\,[\,3 - (2x_3/h)^2\,]\,q \quad , \tag{6}$$

i.e. $\sigma_{33} = \pm\, q/2$ for $x_3 = \pm\, h/2$, the equilibrium within the domain Ω of the plate is given by the equations

$$\hat{M}_{\alpha\beta,\beta} - Q_\alpha = -\,p_\alpha = -\,(F_\alpha + \frac{\upsilon}{1-\upsilon}\lambda^{-2}\,q_{,\alpha}) \ , \tag{7}$$

$$Q_{\alpha,\alpha} = -\,p_3 = -\,(F_3 + q) \ . \tag{8}$$

The substitution of the relations (1) to (5) into the Eqs. (7) and (8) yields the equilibrium equations in terms of the rotations $\phi_\alpha = u_\alpha$ and the deflection $w = u_3$:

$$\Delta^*_{ij}\,u_j(x) = -p_i(x) \ , \tag{9}$$

where Δ^*_{ij} denotes the components of Reissner's "Navier" operator:

$$\Delta^*_{\alpha\beta} = 0.5(1-\upsilon)N \left\{ (\Delta-\lambda^2)\delta_{\alpha\beta} + (1+\upsilon)/(1-\upsilon)\partial_{\alpha\beta} \right\} \tag{10}$$

$$\Delta^*_{\alpha 3} = -\,\Delta^*_{3\alpha} = -\,0.5(1-\upsilon)N\,\lambda^2\partial_\alpha \tag{11}$$

$$\Delta^*_{33} = 0.5(1-\upsilon)N\,\lambda^2\Delta \tag{12}$$

The Direct Method Employing Static Fundamental Solutions

In the so-called direct derivation of boundary integral equations starting from the expression of the double internal deformation energy, in a mixed formulation, Stokes' theorem yields [12]:

$$\int_\Omega \left\{\phi_{\alpha,\beta}\hat{M}_{\alpha\beta} + (\phi_\alpha + w_{,\alpha})Q_\alpha\right\}d\Omega = \oint_\Omega \left\{\phi_\alpha(Q_\alpha - \hat{M}_{\alpha\beta,\beta}) - w\,Q_{\alpha,\alpha}\right\}d\Omega$$

$$+ \oint_\Gamma \left\{\phi_n\,\hat{M}_{nn} + \phi_t\hat{M}_{nt} + w\,Q_n\right\} d\Gamma \ , \tag{13}$$

where the geometric and the static boundary values on the boundary Γ with the outer normal vector n_α and the tangential vector s_α are defined as

$$\phi_n = \phi_\alpha n_\alpha \ , \qquad \phi_t = \phi_\alpha s_\alpha \qquad \text{and} \qquad w, \tag{14}$$

$$M_{nn} = M_{\alpha\beta} n_\alpha n_\beta \ , \quad M_{nt} = M_{\alpha\beta} n_\alpha s_\beta \ \text{ and } \ Q_n = Q_\alpha n_\alpha \ . \tag{15}$$

The deformation energy is a symmetric form. Thus, the relation (13) yields Betti's reciprocal theorem for two Reissner' states. If one state consists of the known and unknown state variables of the given problem, and the second state represents the fundamental solution $\phi_\alpha^{(k)}(\mathbf{x},\xi)$, $w^{(k)}(\mathbf{x},\xi)$ due to unit loadings at the point ξ of an infinite plate, i.e. the solutions of

$$\hat{M}_{\alpha\beta,\beta}(\phi_\rho^{(k)},w^{(k)}) - Q_\alpha(\phi_\rho^{(k)},w^{(k)}) = -\delta(\mathbf{x}-\xi)\,\delta_\alpha^k \ , \qquad k = 1,2,3 \tag{16}$$

$$Q_{\alpha,\alpha}(\phi_\rho^{(k)},w^{(k)}) = -\delta(\mathbf{x}-\xi)\,\delta_3^k \ , \tag{17}$$

this reciprocal theorem leads to the following integral equations:
(k = 1,2,3)

$$\begin{aligned} \phi_\alpha(\xi)\delta_\alpha^k + w(\xi)\delta_3^k = & \int_\Omega \left\{p_\alpha(\mathbf{x})\phi_\alpha^{(k)}(\mathbf{x},\xi) + p_3(\mathbf{x})w^{(k)}(\mathbf{x},\xi)\right\}d\Omega_\mathbf{x} \\ & + \oint_\Gamma \left\{\hat{M}_{nn}(\mathbf{x})\Phi_n^{(k)}(\mathbf{x},\xi) + \hat{M}_{nt}(\mathbf{x})\phi_t^{(k)}(\mathbf{x},\xi) + Q_n(\mathbf{x})w^{(k)}(\mathbf{x},\xi)\right\}d\Gamma_\mathbf{x} \\ & - \oint_\Gamma \left\{\phi_n(\mathbf{x})\hat{M}_{nn}^{(k)}(\mathbf{x},\xi) + \phi_t(\mathbf{x})\hat{M}_{nt}^{(k)}(\mathbf{x},\xi) + w(\mathbf{x})Q_n^{(k)}(\mathbf{x},\xi)\right\}d\Gamma_\mathbf{x} . \end{aligned} \tag{18}$$

Since the boundary conditions for stress couples prescribe values for M_{nn} but not for $\hat{M}_{nn}$ (note that $\hat{M}_{nt} = M_{nt}$), the respective boundary integral has to be transformed:

$$\begin{aligned} \oint_\Gamma \hat{M}_{nn}(\mathbf{x})\phi_n^{(k)}(\mathbf{x},\xi)\,d\Gamma_\mathbf{x} = & \\ = & \oint_\Gamma M_{nn}(\mathbf{x})\phi_n^{(k)}(\mathbf{x},\xi)d\Gamma_\mathbf{x} - \frac{\upsilon}{1-\upsilon}\frac{1}{\lambda^2}\oint_\Gamma q(\mathbf{x})\phi_\alpha^{(k)}(\mathbf{x},\xi)\,n_\alpha(\mathbf{x})d\Gamma_\mathbf{x} \\ = & \oint_\Gamma M_{nn}(\mathbf{x})\phi_n^{(k)}(\mathbf{x},\xi)d\Gamma_\mathbf{x} - \int_\Omega \frac{\upsilon}{1-\upsilon}\frac{1}{\lambda^2}\left[q(\mathbf{x})\,\phi_\alpha^{(k)}(\mathbf{x},\xi)\right]_{,\alpha}d\Gamma_\mathbf{x} . \end{aligned} \tag{19}$$

Finally, after combining the domain integrals, one obtains

$$\phi_\alpha(\xi)\delta^k_\alpha + w(\xi)\delta^k_3 = \int_\Omega \Big\{ F_\alpha(x)\Phi^{(k)}_\alpha(x,\xi) + F_3(x)w^{(k)}(x,\xi) + $$
$$+ q(x)[w^{(k)}(x,\xi) - \frac{\upsilon}{1-\upsilon}\frac{1}{\lambda^2}\phi^{(k)}_{\alpha,\alpha}(x,\xi)]\Big\}d\Omega_x$$
$$+ \oint_\Gamma \Big\{M_{nn}(x)\phi^{(k)}_n(x,\xi) + M_{nt}(x)\phi^{(k)}_t(x,\xi) + Q_n(x)w^{(k)}(x,\xi)\Big\}\, d\Gamma_x$$
$$- \oint_\Gamma \Big\{\phi_n(x)\hat{M}^{(k)}_{nn}(x,\xi) + \phi_t(x)\hat{M}^{(k)}_{nt}(x,\xi) + w(x)Q^{(k)}_n(x,\xi)\Big\}d\Gamma_x\,. \quad (20)$$

By using these equations (20), $k = 1,2,3$, the rotations $\phi_\alpha(\xi)$ and the deflection $w(\xi)$ can be determined at any arbitrary point ξ in the interior of the plate Ω, when all unknown boundary reactions have been determined before. The boundary integral equations, necessary for their determination, are gained by locating the singular point ξ on the boundary Γ. This yields (body forces are neglected)

$$c_{\beta\alpha}(\xi)\phi_\alpha(\xi) = \int_\Omega q(x)\, [w^{(\beta)}(x,\xi) - \frac{\upsilon}{1-\upsilon}\frac{1}{\lambda^2}\phi^{(\beta)}_{\gamma,\gamma}(x,\xi)]\, d\Omega_x$$
$$+ \oint_\Gamma \Big\{ M_{nn}(x)\phi^{(\beta)}_n(x,\xi) + M_{nt}(x)\phi^{(\beta)}_t(x,\xi) + Q_n(x)w^{(\beta)}(x,\xi) \Big\}\, d\Gamma_x$$
$$- \oint_\Gamma \Big\{ \phi_n(x)\hat{M}^{(\beta)}_{nn}(x,\xi) + \phi_t(x)\hat{M}^{(\beta)}_{nt}(x,\xi) + w(x)Q^{(\beta)}_n(x,\xi) \Big\}\, d\Gamma_x \quad (21)$$

$$c(\xi)w(\xi) = \int_\Omega q(x)\, [w^{(3)}(x,\xi) - \frac{\upsilon}{1-\upsilon}\frac{1}{\lambda^2}\phi^{(3)}_{\gamma,\gamma}(x,\xi)\,]d\Omega_x$$
$$+ \oint_\Gamma \Big\{ M_{nn}(x)\phi^{(3)}_n(x,\xi) + M_{nt}(x)\phi^{(3)}_t(x,\xi) + Q_n(x)w^{(3)}(x,\xi) \Big\}\, d\Gamma_x$$
$$- \oint_\Gamma \Big\{ \phi_n(x)\hat{M}^{(3)}_{nn}(x,\xi) + \phi_t(x)\hat{M}^{(3)}_{nt}(x,\xi) + w(x)Q^{(3)}_n(x,\xi) \Big\}\, d\Gamma_x, \quad (22)$$

where $c_{\beta\alpha}(\xi) = 0.5\ \delta_{\beta\alpha}$ and $c(\xi) = 0.5$ on smooth curves (see ref. [10] otherwise). Besides, in order to have a complete natural component formulation (i.e. $\phi_n(\xi)$ and $\phi_t(\xi)$ also on the left-hand side) both sides of Equ. (21) have to be multiplied with $n_\beta(\xi)$ and $s_\beta(\xi)$, respectively.

The relevant singular solutions of the Eqs. (16,17) are [10,12,18]:

$$\phi^{(\beta)}_\alpha = \frac{1}{8\pi N}\{[\ \frac{8}{1-\upsilon}B(z) - \ln(z^2) + 1\ ]\ \delta_{\alpha\beta} - [\ \frac{8}{1-\upsilon}A(z) + 2\ ]\ r_{,\alpha}r_{,\beta}\} \quad (23)$$

$$w^{(\beta)} = -\phi_\beta^{(3)} = \frac{1}{8\pi N} r\, r_{,\alpha} (\ln(z^2) - 1) \tag{24}$$

$$w^{(3)} = \frac{1}{16\pi N} \frac{1}{\lambda^2} \{ [z^2 - \frac{8}{1-\upsilon}] \ln(z^2) - 2z^2 \} \tag{25}$$

where

$$A(z) = K_0(z) + \frac{2}{z} [K_1(z) - \frac{1}{z}] \quad \text{and} \quad B(z) = K_0(z) + \frac{1}{z} [K_1(z) - \frac{1}{z}] \tag{26}$$

contain the modified Bessel functions $K_0(z)$ and $K_1(z)$ with the argument $z=\lambda r$. A(z) is continuous while B(z) has the singularity ln(z) [10].

The couples $M_{nn}^{(k)}$, $M_{nt}^{(k)}$ and the shear stress resultants $Q_n^{(k)}$ can be obtained using the relations (1) to (5) [13]:

$$Q_n^{(\beta)} = Q_\alpha^{(\beta)} n_\alpha(x) = \frac{\lambda^2}{2\pi} [B(z)\, n_\beta(x) - A(z) r_{,\beta} r_{,n}] \tag{27}$$

$$Q_n^{(3)} = Q_\alpha^{(3)} n_\alpha(x) = -\frac{1}{2\pi} \frac{1}{r} r_{,n} \tag{28}$$

$$\hat{M}_{nn}^{(\beta)} = \frac{1}{2\pi} \frac{1}{r} \{ [z\, A'(z) - \frac{1-\upsilon}{2}]\, 2 r_{,s} r_{,n} e_{\beta\rho} r_{,\rho} + [\, 2A(z)(r_{,n}^2 - r_{,s}^2) - \frac{1+\upsilon}{2}\,]\, r_{,\beta} \} \tag{29}$$

$$\hat{M}_{nn}^{(3)} = -\frac{1}{8\pi} \{ (1+\upsilon) \ln z^2 + (1-\upsilon)(r_{,n}^2 - r_{,s}^2) \} \tag{30}$$

$$\hat{M}_{nt}^{(\beta)} = \frac{1}{\pi} \frac{1}{r} \{ r_{,s}^2 (z\, A'(z) - \frac{1-\upsilon}{2})\, e_{\beta\rho} r_{,\rho} + 2A(z) r_{,n} r_{,s} r_{,\beta} \} \tag{31}$$

$$\hat{M}_{nt}^{(3)} = -\frac{(1-\upsilon)}{4\pi} r_{,n} r_{,s} \tag{32}$$

where $e_{\alpha\beta}$ is the permutation tensor, $r_{,n} = r_{,\alpha} n_\alpha(x)$ and $r_{,s} = r_{,\alpha} s_\alpha(x)$ and

$$A'(z) = \partial A(z)/\partial z = -\frac{2}{z} K_0(z) - K_1(z) - (\frac{2}{z})^2 [K_1(z) - \frac{1}{z}] \,. \tag{33}$$

Finally, it should be mentioned that in the case of uniform load $q(x)=q_0$, the domain integrals in Eqs. (21, 22) are convertible to boundary integrals by using the following solutions [10,12]

$$v^{(\alpha)} = \frac{r^3}{128\pi N} r_{,\alpha} (2 \ln z^2 - 5) \tag{34}$$

$$v^{(3)} = \frac{r^2}{256\pi N} \{ [r^2 - \frac{32}{\lambda^2(1-\upsilon)}] \ln z^2 + \frac{64}{\lambda^2(1-\upsilon)} - 3r^2 \}, \tag{35}$$

of the Poisson equation $\Delta v^{(k)} = w^{(k)}$. Then, the divergence theorem yields:

$$q_o \int_{\Omega} [w^{(k)} - \frac{\upsilon}{1-\upsilon} \lambda^{-2} \phi^{(k)}_{\alpha,\alpha}] d\Omega = q_o \oint_{\Gamma} [v^{(k)}_{,\alpha} - \frac{\upsilon}{1-\upsilon} \lambda^{-2} \phi^{(k)}_{\alpha}] n_\alpha d\Gamma . \qquad (36)$$

The Indirect Method With Static and Geometric Fundamental Solutions

The basic idea of this method is well known [e.g. 26]. The solution of the boundary value problem is reduced to the determination of layers of fictitious, in general, singular quantities on a boundary Γ enclosing the real body Ω^+. Their unknown intensities are determined in such a way that the resulting states on the real boundary Γ^+ are equal to the prescribed boundary values (see Fig. 1). When the source boundary Γ remains separated with a certain distance from the real boundary Γ^+, all such integral equations (also those with higher order singularities) remain regular.

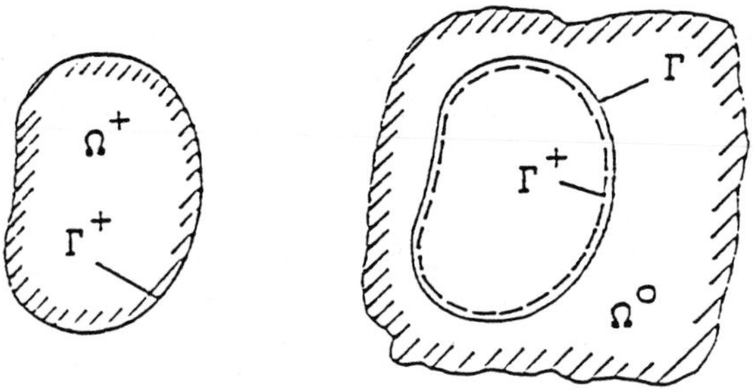

Figure 1: Real plate Ω^+ with real boundary Γ^+ and basic infinite plate Ω^0 with fictitious boundary contour Γ

So-called influence functions represent the connecting links between the state variables describing an elastic state and the singularities generating this state in the infinite domain Ω^0. Except at the source point ξ of the singularity, such functions have to satisfy homogeneous equilibrium equations (7) and (8), the constitutive equations (3) and (5), and, moreover, the homogeneous compatibility conditions [12]

$$0.5\, e_{\beta\rho} \left\{ \kappa_{\alpha\beta,\rho} - \kappa_{\alpha\rho,\beta} + \gamma_{\rho,\alpha\beta} \right\} = D_\alpha , \qquad (37)$$

where $e_{\beta\rho}$ is the permutation tensor. For $D_\alpha = 0$, these Eqs. (37) are identically satisfied by virtue of the relations (1) and (2). Since influence functions are transformed via the same relations as the corresponding state variables, the knowledge of one influence function of a certain type - for a statical and a geometrical singularity, respectively - is sufficient for the calculation of the other ones.

The basic types of statical singularities are the single forces (per unit length). Their displacement reactions at a field point $\mathbf{x}$, the rotations $\phi_\alpha(\mathbf{x})$ and the deflection $w(\mathbf{x})$ due to unit single forces $p_k = \delta(\mathbf{x}-\xi)\delta_k^i$ acting at a point ξ of the infinite plate Ω^0 in a direction i are

$$\phi_\alpha(\mathbf{x}) = (\phi p)_{\alpha.k}(\mathbf{x},\xi)\; p_k(\xi) \quad \text{and} \quad w(\mathbf{x}) = (wp)_{.k}(\mathbf{x},\xi)\; p_k(\xi) \tag{38}$$

where the influence functions are given by (23) to (25), i.e.

$$(\phi p)_{\alpha.k} \triangleq \phi_\alpha^{(k)} \qquad \text{and} \qquad (wp)_{.k} \triangleq w^{(k)} \quad . \tag{39}$$

The influence functions describing the behaviour of the stress couples $\hat{M}_{nn}$ and $\hat{M}_{nt}$ as well as the stress resultant Q_n have also been given before by (27) to (32):

$$(\hat{M}p)_{nn.k} \triangleq \hat{M}_{nn}^{(k)} \;,\; (\hat{M}p)_{nt.k} \triangleq \hat{M}_{nt}^{(k)} \quad \text{and} \quad (Qp)_{n.k} \triangleq Q_n^{(k)} \;. \tag{40}$$

The basic geometrical singularities of Reissner' plates are the so-called twist disclination D_α and the screw dislocation (see Figures 2). Mathematically, these singular states are discontinuities of the rotations ϕ_α and of the deflection w, respectively. The influence functions $(\phi D)_{\alpha.\beta}$ and $(wD)_{.\beta}$, describe the "displacements" at the observation point $\mathbf{x}$ due to a unit rotation discontinuity D_β at ξ, and are fundamental solutions of the compatibilty conditions (37). They have been found [15, 27] to be

$$(\phi D)_{\alpha.\beta} = e_{\beta\rho}\Big\{ e_{\alpha\rho}[2B(z)-2A(z)r_{,\alpha}^2 + \tfrac{1-\upsilon}{2}r_{,\rho}^2 + \tfrac{1+\upsilon}{4}\ln(z^2)]\delta_{\alpha\beta}$$
$$[\, e_{\rho\mu} r_{,\rho} r_{,\mu}(2A(z)+ \tfrac{1-\upsilon}{2}) - \varphi \,] \Big\}/2\pi \tag{41}$$

$$(wD)_{.\beta} = r\, e_{\rho\beta}\Big\{ e_{\mu\rho} r_{,\mu}(1+\upsilon)[\,\ln(z^2)-2\,] - 4r_{,\rho}\varphi \Big\}/8\pi \tag{42}$$

Due to the behaviour of the functions A(z) and B(z), the influence functions $(\phi D)_{\alpha.\beta}$, $\alpha\neq\beta$, are weakly singular while the others are regular, but, because of the inverse circular tangent $\varphi = \arctan(r_{,1}/r_{,2})$, they are multivalued and thus discontinuous.

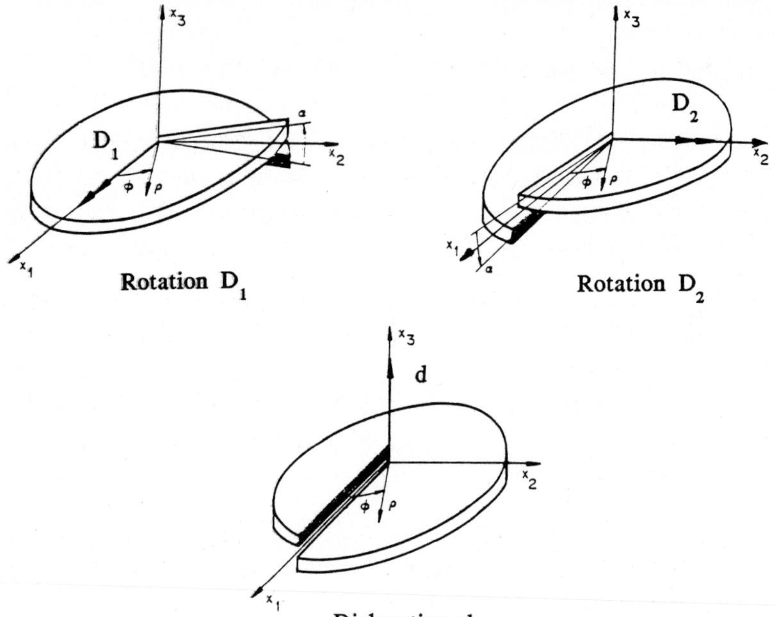

Figure 2: Disclinations and Dislocations in a plate

Since the screw dislocation d may also be interpreted as a dipole of two opposite disclinations D_β [15], its influence functions are to obtain by differentiation of (41) and (42) with respect to the source point coordinates ξ. The result is simply [15]

$$(\phi d)_{\beta.} = e_{\beta\rho} r_{,\rho} r^{-1} [\, 1 - zK_1(z) \,]/2\pi \quad \text{and} \quad (wd)_{.} = \varphi/2\pi \tag{43}$$

These influence functions are strongly singular and discontinuous, respectively. As stated above, we obtain the influence functions of the corresponding strains and stresses by using the adequate relations (1) to (5). Herein, the expressions for the "stresses" only due to singular twist disclinations D_ρ are given, because some influence functions of the screw dislocation d have a r^{-2} singularity and need for this reason a special handling, e.g. a regularization.

$$\hat{(MD)}_{\alpha\beta.\rho} = N(1-\upsilon)r^{-1}\Big\{ [r_{,\alpha}\delta_{\beta\rho}+r_{,\beta}\delta_{\alpha\rho}][zA'(z)+\tfrac{1+\upsilon}{2}] - r_{,\rho}\delta_{\alpha\beta}[2A(z)+\tfrac{3+\upsilon}{2}]$$
$$+\, 2r_{,\rho}r_{,\alpha}r_{,\beta}[2A(z) - zA'(z) + \tfrac{1-\upsilon}{2}] \Big\} /2\pi \tag{44}$$

$$(QD)_{\alpha.\rho} = N(1-\upsilon)\lambda^2 \left\{ B(z)\delta_{\alpha\rho} - A(z)r_{,\alpha}r_{,\rho} \right\} / 2\pi \tag{45}$$

For an actual boundary value problem, any of these singularities - either static or geometric ones, or a combination of both - can be used. The only condition to observe is that one has to employ the same three different singularity layers with unknown intensity - the three orthogonal components of the singular "forces", for example, - in formulating the three integral equations for the three prescribed boundary values. When, for example, the bending stress-couple $\hat{M}_{nn}(s)$ is prescribed along some part of the plate boundary, the three layers can be those of the mentioned three components of the singular forces $p_k(\xi)$. Then, refering to natural co-ordinates both in the source point $\bar{s}$ ($\triangleq$ ξ) and in the observation point s ($\triangleq$ x), one gets, if the fictitious boundary Γ^+ coincides with the real boundary Γ

$$\hat{M}_{nn}(s) = \frac{1}{2}p_n(s) + \oint_\Gamma \left\{ (\hat{(Mp)}_{nn.\bar{n}}(s,\bar{s})\ p_{\bar{n}}(\bar{s}) + \hat{(Mp)}_{nn.\bar{t}}(s,\bar{s})\ p_{\bar{t}}(\bar{s}) + \right.$$

$$\left. + \hat{(Mp)}_{nn.3}(s,\bar{s})\ p_3(\bar{s}) \right\} d\bar{s} \tag{46}$$

where, for example, as easily can obtained from (29)

$$\hat{(Mp)}_{nn.\bar{n}} = r^{-1} \left\{ 2r_{,\bar{s}}r_{,s}r_{,n} \left[\frac{1-\upsilon}{2} - zA'(z)\right] + \right.$$

$$\left. + r_{,\bar{n}} \left[2A(z)(r^2_{,n} - r^2_{,s}) - \frac{1+\upsilon}{2}\right] \right\} / 2\pi \tag{47}$$

The decision about, which combination of singularity layers may be optimal, is not easy. Based on investigations of the spectra of integral operators, some criteria for the choice of the singularities, and thus, of adequate integral equations, are known in the case of plane elastostatics [28], but not, as yet, for the present Reissner' equations. Therefore, herein, the only fact which is generally correct will be used as a criterion: The numerical solution of integral equations of the first kind can be problematic.

Case Studies of Bending Problems

As it is generally not possible to compute the boundary integrals as well as to solve the boundary integral equations analytically, a numerical approach has to be adapted. Recent advances, such as the use of isoparametric elements and the careful analytical treatment of singular cases, have had a major impact on the competitiveness of the boundary element method (BEM) in routine two-dimensional static or three-dimensional dynamic analyses. Those developments, aimed at establishing the BEM as a general engineering tool, have been collated and described by Banerjee and Butterfield [30], and Banerjee and Mukherjee [31], for example.

In this paper, the numerical solution of a problem follows the usual and, moreover, simplest procedures of the BEM:

- The boundary is discretized into elements using piecewise polynominal approximations of the boundary geometry as well as of the prescribed and the unknown boundary values,
- Point collocations are done at the nodes of the shape functions,
- The boundary element integrals are numerically evaluated by Gaussian quadrature.

Since this is assumed to be well known, the details of the procedure to form a linear system of algebraic equations for the unknown nodal values will be omitted here.

Regular Direct BEM Solutions

In almost all papers [16,17,18] presenting BEM solutions of Reissner' plate bending problems the singular version, i.e. point collocation at the boundary nodes is used. Therefore, herein, the regular BEM is applied. Besides, since its validity for rectangular plates has already been tested [12], the more complicated example of a thin (h=0.01a) rhomboidal plate, clamped all around, with skew angles α (see Figure 3) is analyzed.

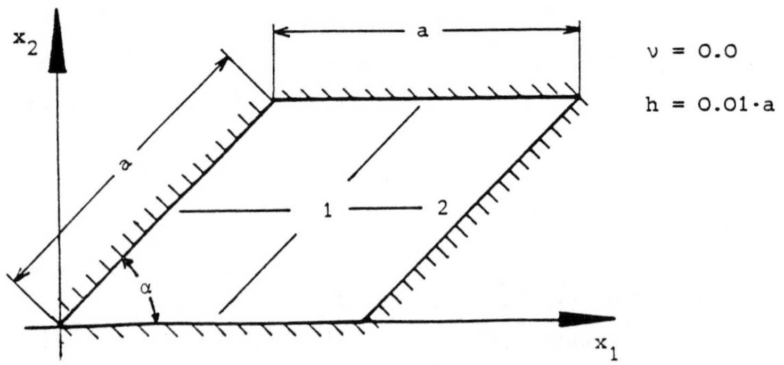

Figure 3: Geometry of the skew rhomboidal plate

Brebbia and Long [16] have solved the same problem by the singular version of the above procedure, but, unfortunately, only relative errors are presented there.

The boundary of the skew plates is discretized by N equal elements. The collocation points are chosen to be located (see [12]) on the outer normal at the nodes in an element-length distance.

N	$w(1)$ $\cdot 10^{-4} qa^4/N$	$M_{11}(1)$ $\cdot 10^{-2} qa^2$	$M_{22}(1)$ $\cdot 10^{-2} qa^2$	$M_{12}(1)$ $\cdot 10^{-2} qa^2$	$M_{nn}(2)$ $\cdot 10^{-2} qa^2$
		skew plate angle $\alpha = 60^0$			
20	7.725	1.201	1.509	-26.71	-3.268
44	7.701	1.200	1.511	-26.92	-3.199
[36]	7.698	1.201	1.512	-26.93	-3.175
		skew plate angle $\alpha = 45^0$			
20	3.777	70.11	1.165	-23.20	-1.593
44	3.776	69.34	1.167	-23.71	-1.663
[36]	3.774	69.34	1.169	-23.76	-1.658
		skew plate angle $\alpha = 30^0$			
20	1.137	26.99	70.33	-12.48	-56.73
40	1.085	26.87	69.89	-12.38	-63.08
[36]	1.084	26.73	70.05	-12.51	-63.18

The listed values [35] of the deflection and the stress couples at the center of the skew plate, as well as the bending couple at the middle of an edge show an excellent agreement with those of a FEM Kirchhoff' plate solution [36].

An Indirect BEM Application

In order to show the applicability of the indirect BEM and, at the same time, the correctness of the influence functions of the geometrical singularities, a simply supported circular plate under a uniform vertical loading q_0 is considered. For this case, the exact solution is known such that exact errors can be measured.

In the general case, where non-zero loadings p_α and/or p_3 are prescribed, the problem can be splitted into a summation problem (A) and a pure boundary value problem (B). First, for solving the problem (A), a particular solution to the equations (9) has to be sought. For not overly complicated distributions p_k, this can be done by guessing. For example, in the case of a constant normal loading (p_α=0, p_3=q_0) we can take

$$\phi_\alpha^A = -q_0 r\, r_{,\alpha} [\, r^2 + \frac{16}{1-\upsilon}\lambda^{-2} \,]/16N \qquad \text{and} \qquad w^A = q_0 r^4/64N. \tag{48}$$

Then, the boundary conditions of the remaining pure boundary value problem (B) has to be altered: in the case considered here,

$$w^B(s) = -w^A(s) \; ; \; \hat{M}^B_{nn}(s) = -\hat{M}^A_{nn}(s) \; ; \; \hat{M}^B_{nt}(s) = -\hat{M}^A_{nt}(s) \; . \tag{49}$$

When layers of single forces, i.e. the influence functions (39) or (23) to (25) are used, the first of these conditions yields an integral equation of the first kind. But the boundary value $w^B(s)$ can be replaced easily by its derivatives with respect to s [29]:.

$$\begin{aligned} w^{B\prime}(s) &= \partial w^B(s)/\partial s = w^B_{,\alpha} s_\alpha \\ w^{B\prime\prime}(s) &= \partial^2 w^B(s)/\partial s^2 = w^B_{,\alpha\beta} s_\alpha s_\beta + \kappa\, w^B_{,\alpha} n_\alpha \,, \end{aligned} \tag{50}$$

where κ represents the curvature of the boundary Γ. For these state variables there exist some strongly singular influence functions, e.g.

$$(w'p)_{.3} = s_\alpha \partial_\alpha (wp)_{.3} = r^{-1} r_{,s} [\, \tfrac{1}{4} r^2 \ln(z^2) - h^2/5(1-\upsilon)]/2\pi N \tag{51}$$

$$(w'd)_{.} = s_\alpha \partial_\alpha (wd)_{.} = r^{-1} r_{,n}/2\pi \tag{52}$$

$$\begin{aligned} (w''D)_{.\alpha} = {} & r^{-1}\Big\{2r_{,n}[n_\alpha-(1-\upsilon)e_{\alpha\beta}r_{,\beta}r_{,s}] -(1+\upsilon)r_{,s}s_\alpha\Big\}/4\pi \\ & - \kappa \Big\{ (1+\upsilon)n_\alpha \ln(z^2) + 4s_\alpha\varphi + 2(1-\upsilon)e_{\alpha\rho}r_{,\rho}r_{,s}\Big\}/8\pi \,. \end{aligned} \tag{53}$$

In spite of its singularity, $(w'p)_{.3}$ leads to a vanishing non-integral term, i.e. to an integral equation of the first kind. Layers of screw dislocations $d(\bar{s})$ produce stress couples with a r^{-2} singularity which means that the influence functions $\hat{(Md)}_{\alpha\beta.}$ are applicable only when certain regularizations are done. For these reasons, the last of the above influence functions is used, and, in the whole, the Reissner' plate problem with simply supported boundaries is solved by employing layers of fictitious forces $p_{\bar{n}}(\bar{s})$, $p_{\bar{t}}(\bar{s})$ and of twist disclinations $D_{\bar{n}}(\bar{s})$:

$$\hat{M}^B_{nn}(s) = \tfrac{1}{2}p_n(s) + \oint_\Gamma \Big\{ \hat{(Mp)}_{nn.\bar{n}}(s,\bar{s})\, p_{\bar{n}}(\bar{s}) + \hat{(Mp)}_{nn.\bar{t}}(s,\bar{s})\, p_{\bar{t}}(\bar{s}) + + \hat{(MD)}_{nn.\bar{n}}(s,\bar{s})\, D_{\bar{n}}(\bar{s}) \Big\}\, d\bar{s} \tag{54}$$

$$\hat{M}^B_{nt}(s) = \tfrac{1}{2}p_t(s) + \oint_\Gamma \Big\{ \hat{(Mp)}_{nt.\bar{n}}(s,\bar{s})\, p_{\bar{n}}(\bar{s}) + \hat{(Mp)}_{nt.\bar{t}}(s,\bar{s})\, p_{\bar{t}}(\bar{s}) + + \hat{(MD)}_{nt.\bar{n}}(s,\bar{s})\, D_{\bar{n}}(\bar{s}) \Big\}\, d\bar{s} \tag{55}$$

$$w^{B,,}(s) = -\tfrac{1}{2}D_n(s) + \oint_\Gamma \Big\{ (w''p)_{.\bar{n}}(s,\bar{s})\, p_{\bar{n}}(\bar{s}) + (w''p)_{.\bar{t}}(s,\bar{s})\, p_{\bar{t}}(\bar{s}) + + (w''D)_{.\bar{n}}(s,\bar{s})\, D_{\bar{n}}(\bar{s}) \Big\}\, d\bar{s} \tag{56}$$

In the Eqs. (54) to (56) we need (40), (44) and (53), and, additionally, the following influence functions:

$$(w''p)_{.\alpha} = r^{-1}\Big\{ r_{,\alpha} - 2r_{,s}r_{,n}e_{\alpha\rho}r_{,\rho}\Big\}/4\pi N + + \kappa \Big\{ r_{,\alpha}r_{,n}[\ln(z^2) + 1] + r_{,s}e_{\alpha\rho}r_{,\rho}[\ln(z^2)-1]\Big\}/8\pi N. \tag{57}$$

After the determination of the boundary layers $p_{\bar{n}}(\bar{s})$, $p_{\bar{t}}(\bar{s})$ and $D_{\bar{n}}(\bar{s})$ via the usual BE approximation procedures, all states in the interior of the plate domain can be computed easily.

Now, consider a simply supported, circular plate with radius R which is subjected to a uniform vertical load of intensity $q_0 = 10^6$ N/m^2. The material data of the plate are taken as: Poisson's ratio $\upsilon = 0.3$ and Young's modulus $E = 2.1 \cdot 10^{11}$ N/m^2.

The boundary of the plate is discretized by only four equal elements and, using the regular version of Eqs. (54) to (56), the collocation points are placed on the outer normal at the nodes of the shape functions in a distance of 0.8 times the element length.

In order to show the higher accuracy of Reissner's theory also for thin plates - the plate thickness is taken as h = 0.01 R - the results are compared, besides to the exact values, to those of a Kirchhoff' model indirect BEM [29]. There, a discretization by 40 elements has been used. And, since the stress couples are more sensitive to numerical errors, their distribution across the circular plate is presented.

position	exact values		Kirchhoff		Reissner	
x_1/R	M_{11}	M_{22}	M_{11}	M_{22}	M_{11}	M_{22}
0.0	20.625	20.625	20.625	20.625	20.625	20.625
0.1	20.419	20.506	20.416	20.505	20.4188	20.5063
0.2	19.800	20.150	19.795	20.151	19.8000	20.1500
0.3	18.768	19.556	18.760	19.562	18.7688	19.5563
0.4	17.325	18.725	17.312	18.736	17.3250	18.7250
0.5	15.469	17.656	15.450	17.675	15.4688	17.6562
0.6	13.200	16.350	13.177	16.377	13.2008	16.3500
0.7	10.519	14.806	10.491	14.844	10.5187	14.8063
0.8	7.425	13.025	7.395	13.076	7.4250	13.0250
0.9	3.919	11.006	3.889	11.072	3.9188	11.0063
1.0	0.000	8.750	0.000	8.866	0.0000	8.7500

Integral Equation Formulations for Vibration Problems

As mentioned before, in this paper, Reissner's theory is extended to dynamic problems. This means that, additionally to the term (6) representing the influence of the transverse load term q, the normal stress σ_{33} has to contain an inertia term due to the acceleration of the deflection w:

$$\sigma_{33} = 0.25(2x_3/h) \left\{ [3-(2x_3/h)^2]\, q - [1-(2x_3/h)^2]\, \rho h\, \ddot{w} \right\} \tag{58}$$

Then, taking Reissner's assumptions concerning the stresses $\sigma_{\alpha\beta}$ and $\sigma_{\alpha 3}$, and his definitions of the rotations ϕ_α and the deflection w [12], the three-dimensional theory equations for the dynamic equilibrium yield straight forward

$$\hat{M}_{\alpha\beta,\beta} - Q_\alpha = - p_\alpha + \rho \frac{h^3}{12} \ddot{\phi}_\alpha \tag{59}$$

$$Q_{\alpha,\alpha} = - p_3 + \rho h \ddot{w} \tag{60}$$

where ρ is the density of the plate material, and the overdots denote the differentiation with respect to time. For loadings p_α and p_3, i.e. transverse loads q varying sinusoidally with time, the internal reactions also vary sinusoidally, and the equations (59/60) take the form

$$\tilde{\hat{M}}_{\alpha\beta,\beta} - \tilde{Q}_\alpha = - \tilde{p}_\alpha - \rho \frac{h^3}{12} \omega^2 \tilde{\phi}_\alpha \tag{61}$$

$$\tilde{Q}_{\alpha,\alpha} = - \tilde{p}_3 - \rho h \, \omega^2 \tilde{w} \tag{62}$$

where "~" denotes the respective vibration amplitudes, and ω is the vibrational circular frequency. If one substitutes the relations (1) to (5) in the equations (61/62), then the equations of motion in terms of $\tilde{u}_j = (\tilde{\phi}_\alpha, \tilde{w})$ will be obtained as

$$\Delta^{*D}_{ij} \, \tilde{u}_j(x) = -\tilde{p}_i(x) \; . \tag{63}$$

There, Δ^{*D}_{ij} denotes the components of the dynamic, frequency domain operator:

$$\Delta^{*D}_{\alpha\beta} = N \frac{1-\upsilon}{2} \left\{ [\, \Delta - \lambda^2 + c(\omega) \,] \, \delta_{\alpha\beta} + \frac{1+\upsilon}{1-\upsilon} \, \partial_{\alpha\beta} \right\} \tag{64}$$

$$\Delta^{*D}_{\alpha 3} = - \Delta^{*D}_{3\alpha} = - N \frac{1-\upsilon}{2} \lambda^2 \, \partial_\alpha \tag{65}$$

$$\Delta^{*D}_{33} = N \frac{1-\upsilon}{2} \lambda^2 \left\{ \Delta + \frac{6}{5} c(\omega) \right\} \tag{66}$$

where the frequency dependent factor $c(\omega)$ is defined as

$$c(\omega) := 2(1+\upsilon) \, \rho \, \omega^2/E \tag{67}$$

The Domain/Boundary Element Method

The static-like form of the equations (61) (see Eqs. (7, 8)) suggests using the integral identities for Reissner' plate statics (as described under 2.1.) in order to achieve an integral representation of the problem. Use of the equations (16) to (20) finally results in the integral representation

$$\tilde{\phi}_\alpha(\xi)\delta^k_\alpha + \tilde{w}(\xi)\delta^k_3 = \int_\Omega \Big\{ \rho h\omega^2[\tfrac{h^2}{12}\,\tilde{\phi}_\alpha(x)\Phi^{(k)}_\alpha(x,\xi) + \tilde{w}(x)w^{(k)}(x,\xi)] + $$
$$+ \tilde{q}(x)\,[\, w^{(k)}(x,\xi) - \tfrac{\upsilon}{1-\upsilon}\,\lambda^{-2}\,\phi^{(k)}_{\alpha,\alpha}(x,\xi)]\Big\}d\Omega_x$$
$$+ \oint_\Gamma \Big\{ \tilde{M}_{nn}(x)\phi^{(k)}_n(x,\xi) + \tilde{M}_{nt}(x)\phi^{(k)}_t(x,\xi) + \tilde{Q}_n(x)w^{(k)}(x,\xi)\Big\}d\Gamma_x$$
$$- \oint_\Gamma \Big\{\tilde{\phi}_n(x)\hat{M}^{(k)}_{nn}(x,\xi) + \tilde{\phi}_t(x)\hat{M}^{(k)}_{nt}(x,\xi) + \tilde{w}(x)Q^{(k)}_n(x,\xi)\Big\}d\Gamma_x \,. \tag{68}$$

There, $\phi^{(k)}_\alpha$ and $w^{(k)}$ as well as the related terms $\hat{M}^{(k)}_{nn}$, $\hat{M}^{(k)}_{nt}$ and $Q^{(k)}_n$ mean the static fundamental solution as defined in (23) to (32), and ξ is located in the interior of the plate domain Ω.

Then, shifting the singular point ξ to a position on the boundary Γ, the above integral equations are changed to

$$c_{\beta\alpha}(\xi)\tilde{\phi}_\alpha(\xi) = \int_\Omega \Big\{ \rho h\omega^2[\tfrac{h^2}{12}\,\tilde{\phi}_\alpha(x)\Phi^{(\beta)}_\alpha(x,\xi) + \tilde{w}(x)w^{(\beta)}(x,\xi)] + $$
$$+ \tilde{q}(x)[w^{(\beta)}(x,\xi) - \tfrac{\upsilon}{1-\upsilon}\,\lambda^{-2}\,\phi^{(\beta)}_{\alpha,\alpha}(x,\xi)]\Big\}d\Omega_x$$
$$+ \oint_\Gamma \Big\{ \tilde{M}_{nn}(x)\phi^{(\beta)}_n(x,\xi) + \tilde{M}_{nt}(x)\phi^{(\beta)}_t(x,\xi) + \tilde{Q}_n(x)w^{(\beta)}(x,\xi)\Big\}d\Gamma_x$$
$$- \oint_\Gamma \Big\{\tilde{\phi}_n(x)\hat{M}^{(\beta)}_{nn}(x,\xi) + \tilde{\phi}_t(x)\hat{M}^{(\beta)}_{nt}(x,\xi) + \tilde{w}(x)Q^{(\beta)}_n(x,\xi)\Big\}d\Gamma_x \,. \tag{69}$$

$$c(\xi)\tilde{w}(\xi) = \int_\Omega \Big\{ \rho h\omega^2[\tfrac{h^2}{12}\,\tilde{\phi}_\alpha(x)\Phi^{(3)}_\alpha(x,\xi) + \tilde{w}(x)w^{(3)}(x,\xi)] + $$
$$+ \tilde{q}(x)[w^{(3)}(x,\xi) - \tfrac{\upsilon}{1-\upsilon}\,\lambda^{-2}\,\phi^{(3)}_{\alpha,\alpha}(x,\xi)]\Big\}d\Omega_x$$
$$+ \oint_\Gamma \Big\{ \tilde{M}_{nn}(x)\phi^{(3)}_n(x,\xi) + \tilde{M}_{nt}(x)\phi^{(3)}_t(x,\xi) + \tilde{Q}_n(x)w^{(3)}(x,\xi)\Big\}d\Gamma_x$$
$$- \oint_\Gamma \Big\{\tilde{\phi}_n(x)\hat{M}^{(3)}_{nn}(x,\xi) + \tilde{\phi}_t(x)\hat{M}^{(3)}_{nt}(x,\xi) + \tilde{w}(x)Q^{(3)}_n(x,\xi)\Big\}d\Gamma_x \,. \tag{70}$$

where the coefficients $c_{\beta\alpha}$ and c of the integral-free terms are defined as in statics.

For the numerical solution of these systems, the boundary integral equations (68) and (69/70), the boundary Γ and the interior domain Ω are both discretized into a number of boundary and interior elements, respectively. Then, via the usual approximation procedures - introduction of appropriate shape functions, point collocation and numerical integration - the discretized versions of these integral equations are obtained, where, in this case, point collocations at both, at boundary and interior nodes has to be done. Finally, the matrix form of both systems, (68) and (69/70), can be written as

$$\begin{bmatrix} (\mathbf{T}^1_{bb} - \omega^2 \mathbf{M}^1_{bb}) & -\mathbf{U}^2_{bb} & -\omega^2 \mathbf{M}_{bi} \\ (\mathbf{T}^1_{ib} - \omega^2 \mathbf{M}^1_{ib}) & -\mathbf{U}^2_{ib} & (\mathbf{I} - \omega^2 \mathbf{M}_{ii}) \end{bmatrix} \bullet \begin{Bmatrix} \mathbf{u}_{1b} \\ \mathbf{t}_{2b} \\ \mathbf{u}_i \end{Bmatrix} =$$

$$\begin{bmatrix} \mathbf{U}^1_{bb} & (\omega^2 \mathbf{M}^2_{bb} - \mathbf{T}^2_{bb}) \\ \mathbf{U}^1_{ib} & (\omega^2 \mathbf{M}^2_{ib} - \mathbf{T}^2_{ib}) \end{bmatrix} \bullet \begin{Bmatrix} \mathbf{t}_{1b} \\ \mathbf{u}_{2b} \end{Bmatrix} + \begin{Bmatrix} \mathbf{q}_b \\ \mathbf{q}_i \end{Bmatrix} \tag{71}$$

where $\mathbf{u}_{1b}$ and $\mathbf{t}_{2b}$ are the vectors of the unknown geometrical and statical nodal boundary variables, respectively, while the vectors $\mathbf{u}_{2b}$ and $\mathbf{t}_{1b}$ contain the known, i.e. prescribed nodal boundary values. Finally, $\mathbf{u}_i$ is the vector of the unknown interior nodal values. The index at the vectors $\mathbf{q}$, and the first of the lower two indices at the boundary element integral matrices $\mathbf{U}$ and $\mathbf{T}$, as well as at the interior element inertia integral matrix $\mathbf{M}$ indicate the location of the collocation point ξ.

For the special case that along the whole boundary Γ all geometric boundary values are prescribed to be zero, i.e. for a clamped plate, the above system can be simplified [8]. In a first step, the unknown boundary reactions $\mathbf{t}_b$ can be expressed by

$$\mathbf{t}_b = - [\, \mathbf{U}_{bb} \,]^{-1} \bullet \left\{ \omega^2 \, [\, \mathbf{M}_{bi} \,] \bullet \mathbf{u}_i + \mathbf{q}_b \right\} \; . \tag{72}$$

Then, by substituting $\mathbf{t}_b$, the remaining equations are reduced to

$$\left\{ \mathbf{I} - \omega^2 \left[\mathbf{M}_{ii} - \mathbf{U}_{ib} \bullet [\, \mathbf{U}_{bb} \,]^{-1} \bullet \mathbf{M}_{bi} \right] \right\} \bullet \mathbf{u}_i = \mathbf{q}_i - \mathbf{U}_{ib} \bullet [\mathbf{U}_{bb}]^{-1} \bullet \mathbf{q}_b \tag{73}$$

Moreover, for the free vibration problem, $\mathbf{q}_i = \mathbf{q}_b = \mathbf{0}$ and the equation (73) reduces to the eigenvalue problem

$$\mathbf{H} \bullet \mathbf{u}_i = \left[\mathbf{M}_{ii} - \mathbf{U}_{ib} \bullet [\ \mathbf{U}_{bb}\ ]^{-1} \bullet \mathbf{M}_{bi} \right] \bullet \mathbf{u}_i = \omega^{-2}\ \mathbf{u}_i\ . \tag{74}$$

The matrix **H** is real and in general non-sparse, non-symmetric and non-positive definite. Solutions of (74) may be accomplished [8] iteratively by the algorithm of Smith et al. [33]. For any harmonic excitation with circular frequency ω, the responses, i.e. the boundary reactions and the interior rotations and deflection, are obtained directly from (71).

When the load $q(\mathbf{x},t)$ has a general transient time variation, use can be made of the Laplace transform with respect to time. For zero initial displacements and velocities, the formulation of the transformed problem is simply obtained by replacing $-\omega^2$ by k^2 where k is the Laplace transform parameter. Then, solving the system (71) with $-\omega^2$ replaced by k^2 for a sequence of values k, a numerical inversion of this transformed solutions can provide the time domain response. The numerical Laplace transform inversion can be done effectively [8] with the algorithm of Durbin [34].

The Dynamic Boundary Element Method

Obviously, in the above D/BEM formulation of the dynamic problem the inertia term domain integrals affect the basic boundary character (similar to the static problem formulation when body forces are taken into account) . The only way to avoid these inertia term domain integrals, is to employ the fundamental solutions of the complete system of dynamic equations (63), i.e. the solution for a dynamic unit point load at an arbitrary point ξ:

$$\Delta^{*D}_{ij}(\tfrac{\partial}{\partial \mathbf{x}})\ \tilde{u}^{(k)}_j(\mathbf{x},\xi) = -\ \delta(\mathbf{x}-\xi)\ \delta^k_i \tag{75}$$

According to Hörmander's theorems [32], this solution is sought in the form

$$\tilde{u}^{(k)}_i(\mathbf{x},\xi) = {}^{\infty}\Delta^{*D}_{ik}(\tfrac{\partial}{\partial \mathbf{x}})\ e(\mathbf{x},\xi)\quad , \tag{76}$$

where ${}^{\infty}\Delta^{*D}_{ik}$ is the matrix of cofactors and $e(\mathbf{x},\xi)$ is a scalar function. Substitution of (76) in equation (75) yields

$$[\det \underline{\Delta}^{*D}(\tfrac{\partial}{\partial \mathbf{x}})]\ e(\mathbf{x},\xi) = -\ \delta(\mathbf{x}-\xi) \tag{77}$$

where det $\underline{\Delta}^{*D}$ denotes the determinant of the matrix $\underline{\Delta}^{*D}$. Using radial symmetry, equation (77) reduces to

$$N^3(\tfrac{1-\upsilon}{2}\lambda)^2 \left\{(\Delta -\lambda^2+c)[\,\Delta^2 + c(\tfrac{1-\upsilon}{2}+\tfrac{6}{5})\Delta + \tfrac{6}{5}\,\tfrac{(1-\upsilon)}{2}c(c-\lambda^2)]\right\} = -\frac{\delta(r)}{2\pi r} \quad (78)$$

or

$$N^3\,(\tfrac{1-\upsilon}{2}\lambda)^2 \left\{(\Delta - a_1)(\Delta - a_2)(\Delta - a_3)\right\} = -\frac{\delta(r)}{2\pi r}\,, \quad (79)$$

where the frequency dependent factors a_1, a_2 and a_3 are given by

$$\begin{aligned} a_1 &= \lambda^2 - c(\omega) \\ a_{2,3} &= \tfrac{1}{2}[-c(\tfrac{1-\upsilon}{2}+\tfrac{6}{5}) \pm \sqrt{c^2(\tfrac{1-\upsilon}{2}-\tfrac{6}{5})^2 + \tfrac{12}{5}(1-\upsilon)c\lambda^2}\,]\,. \end{aligned} \quad (80)$$

As it is shown by Cheng et al. [23, 24], a particular solution of equation (79) can be found if a_1 is positive (then, $a_2>0$ and $a_3<0$ hold), i.e. for frequencies ω in the range $0 < \omega < \lambda\sqrt{E/2(1+\upsilon)\rho}$. It can be given as ($r=|x-\xi|$):

$$e(r) = \frac{1}{2\pi}N^{-3}(\tfrac{1-\upsilon}{2}\lambda)^{-2}\left\{\frac{K_0(\sqrt{a_1}r)}{(a_1-a_2)(a_1-a_3)} + \frac{K_0(\sqrt{a_2}r)}{(a_2-a_1)(a_2-a_3)} + -\frac{\pi}{2}\frac{Y_0(\sqrt{|a_3|}r)}{(a_1-a_3)(a_2-a_3)}\right\}\,, \quad (81)$$

where K_0 and Y_0 is the modified Bessel function of second kind and the Neumann function, respectively.

Hence, the fundamental solution for the Reissner-Mindlin plate frequency domain equations of motion (75) is obtained by merely substituting Equ. (81) into Equ.(76). The components of the resulting singular displacements are determined as the following, rather complicated expressions:

$$\begin{aligned} \tilde{u}_\alpha^{(\beta)} = \frac{1}{2\pi N}\frac{1}{a_2-a_3}\Big\{&(\tfrac{6}{5}cA_0+A_2)\delta_{\alpha\beta} + \frac{1+\upsilon}{1-\upsilon}[(A_2+\tfrac{1}{r}B_2)\delta_{\alpha\beta} - (A_2+\tfrac{2}{r}B_2)r_{,\alpha}r_{,\beta}] \\ &+ \frac{10\lambda^2+(1+\upsilon)c}{5(1-\upsilon)(a_1-a_2)(a_1-a_3)}[\{a_2(A_1+\tfrac{1}{r}B_1)-a_1(A_2+\tfrac{1}{r}B_2)-a_3(C_1+\tfrac{1}{r}C_2)\}\delta_{\alpha\beta} \\ &-\{a_2(A_1+\tfrac{2}{r}B_1)-a_1(A_2+\tfrac{2}{r}B_2)-a_3(C_1+\tfrac{2}{r}C_2)\}r_{,\alpha}r_{,\beta}\Big\} \end{aligned} \quad (82)$$

$$\tilde{u}_\alpha^{(3)} = -\tilde{u}_3^{(\alpha)} = \frac{1}{2\pi N}\frac{1}{a_2-a_3} B_2 r_{,\alpha} \tag{83}$$

$$\tilde{u}_3^{(3)} = \frac{1}{2\pi N}\frac{1}{a_2-a_3} \lambda^{-2}\left\{ \frac{2}{1-\upsilon} A_2 - a_1 A_0 \right\} \tag{84}$$

with

$$\begin{aligned}
A_0 &= K_0(\sqrt{a_2}r) + \frac{\pi}{2} Y_0(\sqrt{|a_3|}r) , \quad A_\alpha = a_\alpha K_0(\sqrt{a_\alpha}r) - a_3 \frac{\pi}{2} Y_0(\sqrt{|a_3|}r) \\
B_\alpha &= \sqrt{a_\alpha} K_1(\sqrt{a_\alpha}r) + \sqrt{|a_3|}\frac{\pi}{2} Y_1(\sqrt{|a_3|}r) , \\
C_1 &= a_1 K_0(\sqrt{a_1}r) - a_2 K_0(\sqrt{a_2}r) , \\
C_2 &= \sqrt{a_1} K_1(\sqrt{a_1}r) - \sqrt{a_2} K_1(\sqrt{a_2}r) .
\end{aligned} \tag{85}$$

The corresponding singular "stresses", i.e. the singular stress couples $\tilde{M}_{\alpha\beta}^{(k)}$ and stress resultants $\tilde{Q}_\alpha^{(k)}$ are even more lengthy; their explicit expressions may be found in [24, 25].

Now, by employing this dynamic fundamental solution the inertia domain integrals can be avoided, and, as easily can be seen from Equ. (69/70), the complete dynamic integral representation of a vibrating Reissner-Mindlin plate is given by

$$\begin{aligned}
c_{\beta\alpha}(\xi)\tilde{\phi}_\alpha(\xi) &= \int_\Omega \left\{ \tilde{q}(x)[\tilde{w}^{(\beta)}(x,\xi) - \frac{\upsilon}{1-\upsilon}\lambda^{-2}\tilde{\phi}_{\alpha,\alpha}^{(\beta)}(x,\xi)]\right\} d\Omega_x \\
&+ \oint_\Gamma \left\{ \tilde{M}_{nn}(x)\tilde{\phi}_n^{(\beta)}(x,\xi) + \tilde{M}_{nt}(x)\tilde{\phi}_t^{(\beta)}(x,\xi) + \tilde{Q}_n(x)\tilde{w}^{(\beta)}(x,\xi)\right\} d\Gamma_x \\
&- \oint_\Gamma \left\{\tilde{\phi}_n(x)\tilde{M}_{nn}^{(\beta)}(x,\xi) + \tilde{\phi}_t(x)\tilde{M}_{nt}^{(\beta)}(x,\xi) + \tilde{w}(x)\tilde{Q}_n^{(\beta)}(x,\xi)\right\} d\Gamma_x .
\end{aligned} \tag{86}$$

$$\begin{aligned}
c(\xi)\tilde{w}(\xi) &= \int_\Omega \left\{ \tilde{q}(x)[\tilde{w}^{(3)}(x,\xi) - \frac{\upsilon}{1-\upsilon}\lambda^{-2}\tilde{\phi}_{\alpha,\alpha}^{(3)}(x,\xi)]\right\} d\Omega_x \\
&+ \oint_\Gamma \left\{ \tilde{M}_{nn}(x)\tilde{\phi}_n^{(3)}(x,\xi) + \tilde{M}_{nt}(x)\tilde{\phi}_t^{(3)}(x,\xi) + \tilde{Q}_n(x)\tilde{w}^{(3)}(x,\xi)\right\} d\Gamma_x \\
&- \oint_\Gamma \left\{\tilde{\phi}_n(x)\tilde{M}_{nn}^{(3)}(x,\xi) + \tilde{\phi}_t(x)\tilde{M}_{nt}^{(3)}(x,\xi) + \tilde{w}(x)\tilde{Q}_n^{(3)}(x,\xi)\right\} d\Gamma_x .
\end{aligned} \tag{87}$$

where $c_{\beta\alpha}(\xi)$ and $c(\xi)$ are defined as before.

Here, the approximation procedure for gaining the discretized version of this system needs point collocations only at the boundary nodes of the shape functions. Thus, in the notation as used before in Equ. (71), the final system of algebraic equations is given as

$$\left[\mathbf{T}^1_{bb} \;\; -\mathbf{U}^2_{bb} \right] \bullet \left\{ \begin{matrix} \mathbf{u}_{1b} \\ \mathbf{t}_{2b} \end{matrix} \right\} = \left[\mathbf{U}^1_{bb} \;\; -\mathbf{T}^2_{bb} \right] \bullet \left\{ \begin{matrix} \mathbf{t}_{1b} \\ \mathbf{u}_{2b} \end{matrix} \right\} + \left\{ \mathbf{q}_b \right\} \tag{88}$$

In this system, only boundary reactions, i.e. $\mathbf{u}_{1b}$ and $\mathbf{t}_{2b}$, are unknown.

A Numerical Check for D/BEM and Dynamic BEM

Consider a simply supported square plate of side length a = 0.2 m whose material properties are taken to be a Poisson's ratio $\upsilon = 0.34$, a Young's modulus $E = 1.02 \bullet 10^{11}$ N/m^2 and mass density $\rho = 8350$ kg/m^3.

In the numerical treatment, a discretization with four elements of equal length $\Delta a = 0.05$ m for each of the four plate edges is taken in the dynamic boundary integral formulation (86/87), and, additionally, sixteen quadrilateral interior elements (of size $\Delta a \bullet \Delta a$) in the case of the domain boundary integral equations (68) to (70). Quadratic and biquadratic shape functions are employed for approximating all the states along the boundary and the "displacements" in the interior, respectively. Thus, point collocation creates the system (88) and (71) with 96 equations and 195 equations, respectively. The harmonic excitation is considered in the range up to $\omega = 200 \,/\, a^2\sqrt{\rho h/N}$, where numerical solutions are evaluated all $\Delta\omega = 1. \,/\, a^2\sqrt{\rho h/N}$.

First, the correctness and applicability of both methods, of the dynamic BEM employing the dynamic fundamental solution (D-F) and of the D/BEM employing the static fundamental solution (S-F), is demonstrated. Figures 4 and 5 depict in dimensionless values the central delection $\bar{w} = w\, \rho h\omega^2/q_0$ versus the excitation frequency $\bar{\omega} = \omega\, a^2\sqrt{\rho h/N}$ in the case of a rather thin plate (h/a = 0.05) and a moderately thick plate (h/a = 0.1). Obviously, in the whole, the agreement is excellent. Differences are found only for frequencies $\bar{\omega}$ higher than 120 with a certain increase in the case of the thicker plate. But, further numerical studies are necessary to decide whether it is caused by the rather coarse grid or it is really due to the use of the different fundamental solutions.

A second study analyses two problems: the importance of using the sixth order Reissner' theory and the effect of the plate thickness. In Figure 6, the central deflection versus frequency is shown for Kirchhoff's theory (h = 0.05 a) and for Reissner's theory (using the dynamic BEM) in the case of two different thicknesses, h = 0.05 a and h = 0.10 a. It becomes apparent that the behavior in the range of low frequencies ($\bar{\omega}$ < 50) is almost identical, but especially the higher natural frequencies are shifted, the more, the thicker the plate and the higher the frequency.

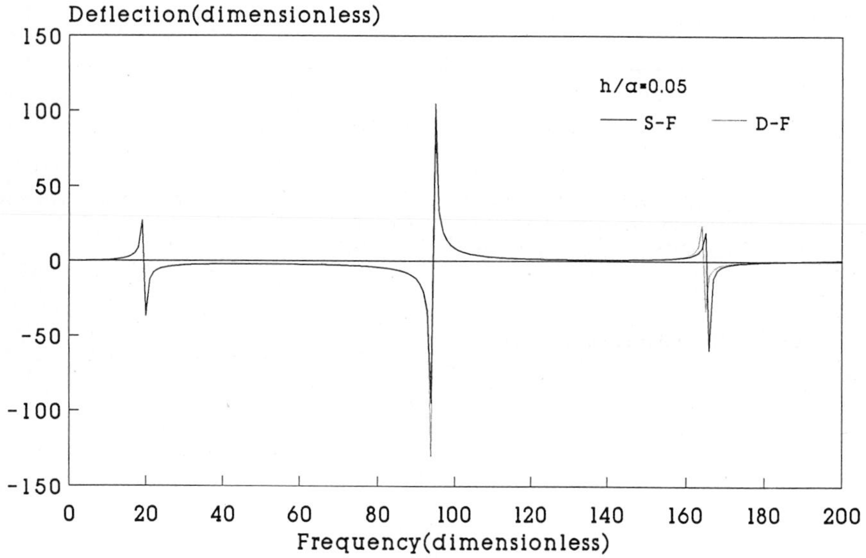

Figure 4: Central deflection (of a simply supported square plate under harmonic uniform load) versus frequency - h = 0.05 a: Comparison of dynamic BEM (D-F) and D/BEM (S-F) solution

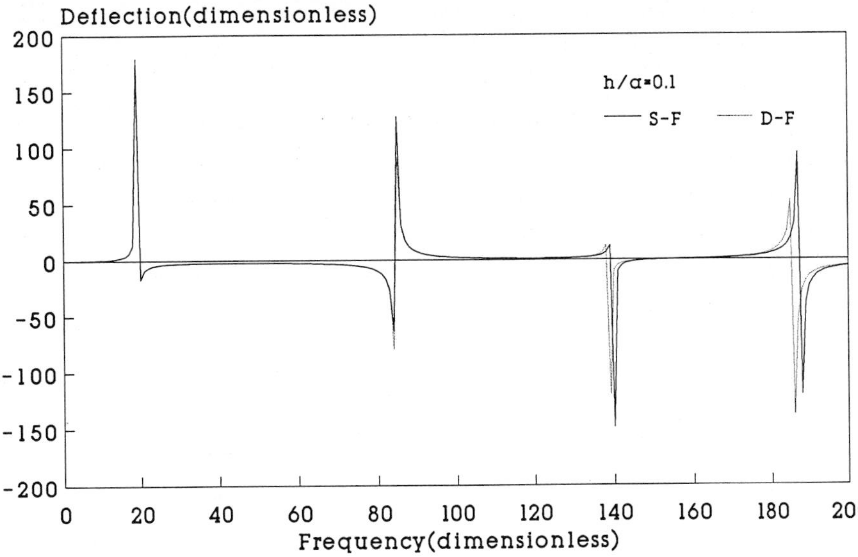

Figure 5: Central deflection (of a simply supported square plate under harmonic uniform load) versus frequency - h = 0.1 a: Comparison of dynamic BEM (D-F) and D/BEM (S-F) solution

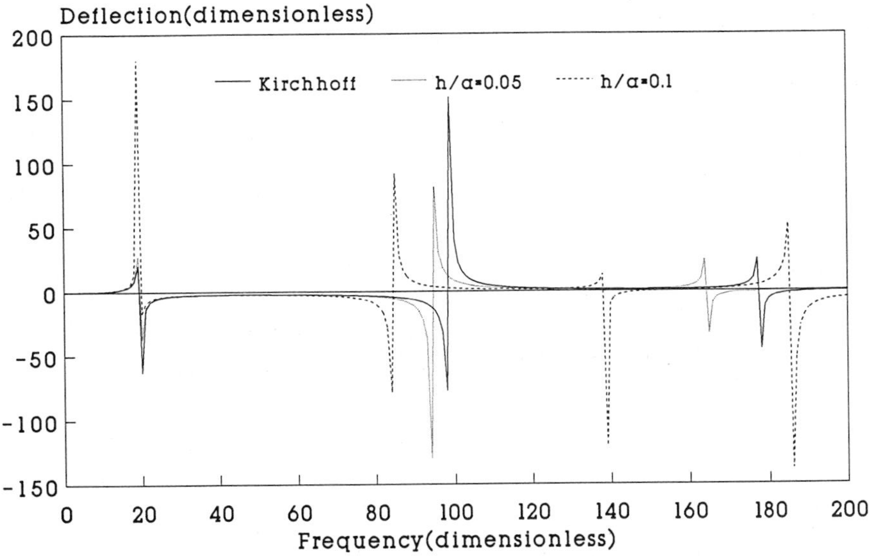

Figure 6: Central deflection (of a simply supported square plate under harmonic uniform load) versus frequency: Comparison of dynamic Kirchhoff' BEM and Reissner' BEM solution

Acknowledgement:

The author likes to acknowledge the financial support of the Deutsche Akademische Austauschdienst grant DAAD 324/306/005/9 which allows W. Cheng to work on Reissner's plate dynamics at the Institut für Angewandte Mechanik, Technische Universität Braunschweig.

References:

[1] Kirchhoff, G.: Über das Gleichgewicht und die Bewegung einer elastischen Scheibe. J. Reine und Angewandte Mathematik **40** (1850) 51-88

[2] Love, A.E.H.: A treatise on the mathematical theory of elasticity, 4th ed., Cambridge Univ. Press, Cambridge 1934

[3] Reissner, E.: The effect of transverse shear deformation on the bending of elastic plates. J. Applied Mechanics **12** (1945) A69-A77

[4] Reissner, E.: Reflections on the theory of elastic plates. Appl. Mech. Revs. **38** (1985) 1453-1464

[5] Hutchinson, J.R.: Vibrations of plates, pp. 415-430 in: Boundary Elements X, Vol. 4: Geomechanics, wave propagation and vibrations (Ed.: C.A. Brebbia) Springer Verlag, Berlin 1988

[6] Mindlin, R.D.: Influence of rotary inertia and shear on flexural motions of isotropic, elastic plates. J. Appl. Mech. **73** (1951) 31-38.

[7] Lei X.-Y. & Huang M.-K.: Mixed method of BIEM and FEM to solve free vibrations of Reissner's plate. pp. 455-460 in: Boundary Elements (Ed.: Q. Du) Pergamon Press, Oxford 1986.

[8] Beskos, D.E.: Dynamic analysis of plates and shallow shells by the D/BEM, pp. 177-196 in: Advances in the Theory of Plates and Shells (Eds.: Voyiadjis, G.Z. & Karamanlidis, D.) Elsevier, Amsterdam 1990.

[9] Kalnins, A.: On fundamental solutions and Green's functions in the theory of elastic plates. J. Appl. Mech. **33** (1966) 31-38.

[10] Wander Weeën, F.: Application of the boundary integral equation method to Reissner's plate model. Int. J. for Numer. Meth. in Engng. **18** (1982) 1-10.

[11] Vander Weeën, F.: Application of the direct boundary element method to Reissner's plate model, pp. 487-499 in: Boundary Element Methods in Engineering (Ed.: C.A. Brebbia) Springer Verlag, Berlin 1982.

[12] Antes, H.: On a regular boundary integral equation and a modified Trefftz method in Reissner's plate theory. Engng. Analysis **1** (1984) 149-153

[13] Antes, H.: An indirectly derived integral equation system for simply supported Reissner plates. Mech. Res. Comm. 13 (1986) 63-69

[14] Antes, H.: The stress functions of point loadings in Reissner's plate theory. Mech. Res. Comm. **11** (1984) 115-120.

[15] Antes, H.: Basic geometrical singularities in Reissner's plate theory. Mech. Res. Comm. **12** (1985) 295-302.

[16] Brebbia, C.A. & Long, S.Y.: Boundary element analysis of plates using Reissner's theory. pp. 3-18 in: Boundary Elements IX Vol. 2: Stress Analysis Applications (Eds.: Brebbia, C.A., Wendland, W.L., Kuhn, G.) Springer 1987

[17] Wang Y., Jiang L. & Wang Z.: Spline boundary element method for Reissner's plate and its application on foundation plates. pp: 111-125 in: Boundary Elements IX, Vol. 2: Stress Analysis Applications (Eds.: Brebbia C.A., Wendland W.L. & Kuhn G.) Springer Verlag, Berlin 1987.

[18] Karam, V.J. & Telles, J.C.F.: On boundary elements for Reissner's plate theory. Engineering Analysis **5** (1988) 21-27.

[19] De Barcellos, C.S. & Monken e Silva, L.H.: A boundary element formulation for the Mindlin's plate model, pp. 123-130 in: Boundary Element Techniques: Applications in Stress Analysis and Heat Transfer (Eds.: C.A. Brebbia & W.S. Venturini) Comp. Mech. Publ., Southampton 1989.

[20] Constanda, C.: A mathematical analysis of bending of plates with transverse shear deformation. Pitman Longman, Harlow U.K. 1990.

[21] Irschik, H., Heuer, R. & Ziegler, F.: Free and forced vibrations of polygonal Mindlin-plates by an advanced BEM. Proc. IUTAM Conf. on Advanced Boundary Element Methods, Springer Verlag, Berlin 1987.

[22] Irschik, H., Heuer, R. & Ziegler, F.: Dynamic analysis of polygonal Mindlin plates on two-parameter foundations using classical plate theory and an advanced BEM. Comp. Mech. **4** (1989) 293-300.

[23] Cheng, W.: Die Schallabstrahlung einer schwingenden Reissnerplatte. PhD Thesis (in preparation).

[24] Cheng, W. & Antes, H.: The dynamic fundamental solution of the Reissner-Mindlin plate theory. (in preparation).

[25] Cheng, W. & Antes, H.: Vibrations of Reissner plates by boundary-interior elements. Proc. Int. Conf. on Comp. Engng. Science - ICES'91, Patras, April 1991.

[26] Zastrow, U.: Numerical plane stress analysis by integral equations based on the singularity method. Solid Mechanics Arch. **10** (1985) 187-221.

[27] Antes, H.: Influence functions of statical and geometrical singularities in Reissner' plates (in german). Z. angew. Math. Mech. **67** (1987) T174-176

[28] Heise, U.: The spectra of some integral operators for plane elastostatical boundary value problems. J. of Elasticity **8** (1985) 47-79.

[29] Glahn, H.: Eine Integralgleichung zur Berechnung gelenkig gelagerter Platten bei krummen Rand. Ingenieur-Archiv **44** (1975) 189-198.

[30] Banerjee, P.K. & Butterfield,R.: Boundary element methods in engineering science. McGraw Hill, London 1981.

[31] Banerjee, P.K.. & Mukherjee, R.: Developments in boundary element methods, Vol.3. Elsevier, London 1981.

[32] Hörmander, H.: Linear partial differential operators. Springer Verlag, Berlin 1963.

[33] Smith, B.T., Boyle, J.M., Dongarra, J.J., Garbow, B.S., Ibeke, Y., Klema, V.C. & Moler, C.B.: Matrix eigen-system routines - EISPACK guide, Springer Verlag, Berlin 1976.

[34] Durbin, F.: Numerical inversion of Laplace transform: an efficient improvement to Dubner and Abate's method. Computer J. **17** (1974) 371-376.

[35] Enders, U.: Analysis of skew plates by BEM (in German). Master Thesis, Ruhr-Universität, Bochum 1986.

[36] Böge, G.: Beitrag zur Berechnung schiefwinkliger Platten. PhD Thesis, Techn. Universität, Berlin 1969.

Analysis of Plates and Shells by Boundary Collocation

J.R. HUTCHINSON

Civil Engineering Department
University of California, Davis CA, 95616, USA

Summary

The purpose of this chapter is to explain the technique and to review the past research on the boundary collocation method applied to the solution of bending, buckling and vibration of plates and shells. Boundary collocation is the method by which a sum of exact solutions to the governing differential equation is used, and boundary conditions are satisfied in a point-wise sense on the boundary. The method is extremely simple and when it works, it works exceedingly well. As with all methods, it does have certain drawbacks. An attempt is made in this chapter not only to explain the details of the method, but to clearly point out both its advantages and disadvantages.

Introduction

The boundary collocation method (BCM) is closely allied to the boundary element method (BEM) which has been the primary focus of this book. Both the BCM and the BEM use exact solutions of the governing differential equations so that the approximations can be restricted to the boundary. This allows solutions for domains of arbitrary shape with arbitrary boundary conditions. The BEM is restricted to use of the fundamental solution; whereas, the BCM can employ any solution forms which satisfy the governing differential equations. Approximation of the boundary conditions in the BCM is usually accomplished at discrete points on the boundary; while, the BEM requires integration around the boundary.

The boundary collocation method (BCM) is among the simplest methods of solving partial differential equations, both from a conceptual point of view, as well as, a computational point of view. The solution is expressed as a sum of known solutions of the governing differential equation, and boundary conditions are satisfied at selected collocation points on the boundary. When this process is completed, the solution represents an exact solution to the approximate problem. An estimation of the error of approximation can be found by simply checking the boundary conditions at points other than the collocation points. The method is easily applied to irregular domains with arbitrary boundary conditions. A recent and fairly comprehensive review of boundary collocation methods in mechanics of continuous media has been compiled by Kolodziej [1]. The references in this chapter will therefore concentrate primarily on the applications to plates and shells and the reader can refer to reference [1] for important allied problems.

Past research will be described first for the bending of thin plates, next for the buckling and vibration of thin plates, then for vibration and buckling of thick plates, and finally for research involving shells. The method of boundary collocation was first applied by Barta [2] in 1937 to the bending of a thin square clamped plate for both a uniform load and a concentrated load. He showed that the method using 16 collocation points (really only 3 points because of symmetry) around the boundary produced a central deflection within 8% of the actual, and maximum moments within 12.9% for the uniform load case. In 1952 Thorne [3] solved the same problem as Barta with a different choice of solution forms. It is of interest to note that Thorne didn't present his work as a means of approximating boundary conditions, but rather, as what he considered the more practical problem, that of plates actually fixed at a number of isolated points on the boundary. The solution for the bending of a plate with arbitrary outer boundary and a circular hole was developed in 1955 by Sekiya [4]. In that paper Sekiya satisfied the boundary conditions at the interior hole identically and the outer boundary conditions by collocation. His numerical example was for a uniformly loaded clamped square plate. Conway's [5] 1960 paper used a similar formulation to Barta's [2] but considered applications to equilateral triangles and regular hexagons as well as square plates. In a discussion of Conway's paper Deverall [6] noted a major problem with the method. The problem is that as two boundary points get closer and closer together the two linear equations resulting from these points have nearly the same coefficients and this can lead to ill-conditioned matrices. In a 1961 paper Conway [7] considered not only bending of polygon plates but buckling and vibration as well. Leissa and Niedenfuhr [8,9] considered some problems of the bending of square plates in 1962 and 1963. In 1965 Leissa, Lo and Niedenfuhr [10] treated uniformly loaded clamped and simply supported plates of regular polygon shape. The paper of Leissa, Lo and Niedenfuhr was criticized by Rao and Rajaiah [11] because the choice of boundary conditions lead to poorly converging solutions and an erroneous conclusion, which was, that in the limit as the number of sides of the simply supported polygon increased the solution approached that of a simply supported plate. A fuller description of this seeming paradox will be treated in the section on boundary conditions. In 1967 both Conway and Farnham [12] and Leissa and Clausen [13] presented results for circular plates having mixed boundary conditions. Figure 1 shows the three types of problems solved by Conway and Farnham.

Leissa and Clausen solved only the problems shown in Figures 1a and 1b while Conway and Farnham solved all three. Their conclusions were much the same, that is, for the clamped-simply supported (C-S) case (Figure 1a) the BCM results are good, but for the simply supported-free (S-F) case (Figure 1b) and the clamped-free (C-F) case (Figure 1c) the results were poor. Also in 1967 Lo and Leissa [14] considered the same problem as Sekiya [4] as well as the problem of an infinite plate having equally spaced circular holes. The plate was loaded by its own weight and supported at points equidistant from the hole centers. In 1969 Leissa, Clausen, Hulbert and Hopper [15] compared nine distinct procedures for solving plate bending problems. Of the methods considered in that paper BCM came out among the top rated methods. Hoffman and Ariman [16] considered the thermal bending of plates with circular holes in 1970. The 1985 paper by Burgess and Mahajerin [17] was the first to use the fundamental solution as basis functions in the BCM. Burgess and Mahajerin illustrate their method with 5 separate examples, and claim that the method produces equivalent accuracy of a BEM solution with half the number of collocation points and with a reduction in computer execution time by a factor of 350. The 1987 paper by Johnson [18] also makes use of the fundamental solution but in a different way than Burgess and Mahajerin.

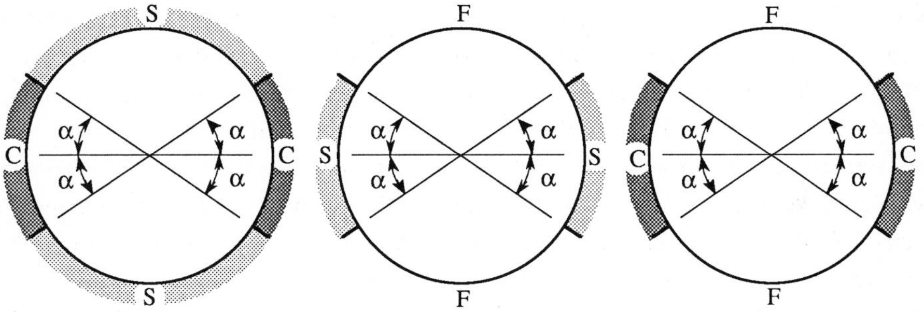

(a) C-S Plate (b) S-F Plate (c) C-F Plate

Figure 1. Circular Plates with Mixed Boundary Conditions

Use of the BCM for buckling and vibration of thin plates was considered first by Conway and Leissa [19] in 1960. They gave results for buckling caused by a uniform compressive stress in clamped square and equilateral-triangular plates. The 1961 paper of Conway [7] extended the previous results to polygonal plates and the fundamental frequencies for equilateral-triangular and square and hexagon simply supported plates were also computed. In 1975 Hegarty and Ariman [20] computed natural frequencies for square plates with circular holes. They presented curves of frequency versus the ratio of hole size to plate length for both clamped and simply supported plates. In the 1985 paper by Akkari and Hutchinson [21] straight BCM was used and compared to a line element method. Examples were given for trapezoidal and elliptical plates as well as circular and rectangular plates. Where possible, solutions were compared with exact solutions and shown to converge very well. In reference [21] solution forms in Cartesian coordinates were used. In 1987 Akkari and Hutchinson [22] used the polar coordinate solutions which most of the previous researchers had used and found that for most problems, the polar formulation worked better. Akkari and Hutchinson [23] in 1988 studied the vibrations of Mindlin thick plates. Comparisons with results using other solution techniques showed the method to produce excellent results except in cases involving free boundaries.

There have been very few applications of the BCM to shells. One such application is the 1962 paper of Conway and Leissa [24] in which it is applied to shallow spherical shells with some success. A 1990 application of BCM to the free vibration of solids of revolution by Houmat and Hutchinson [25] was applied to some thick shell problems. While this formulation was for any arbitrary solid of revolution, it is also completely applicable to any shell of revolution. Some new results applying this method to thin shells are shown later in this chapter.

There are a number of additional papers [26-32] in which the BCM was applied to problems involving plates. These papers, for the most part, satisfy some of the boundary conditions exactly. While this method of partial satisfaction of the boundary conditions leads to rapid convergence, it also requires a very specific boundary. Since one of the main advantages of the BCM is to be able to handle arbitrary boundaries, the method of partial satisfaction precludes this major advantage.

A method which is very similar to the BCM is the edge function method (EFM) which was introduced by Quinlan [33] in 1962 for the bending of skew plates. In this method the solution forms of the governing differential equations are restricted to forms which decay away from each of the straight-line boundary elements. Approximations of the boundary conditions could be accomplished by collocation but are more usually accomplished by orthogonalization along each of the boundary elements. The method was applied to the bending of rectangular plates by Quinlan [34] in 1965. In 1977 the EFM was applied to the determination of natural frequencies and mode shapes for thin plates and shallow shells by Nash, Tai, O'Callaghan and Quinlan [35]. In 1985 the method was applied to free vibrations of thin orthotropic plates by O'Callaghan and Studdert [36]. The 1988 review paper by Quinlan [37] is also partly concerned with thin plate problems. It is also pointed out in reference [37] that where actual singularities exist it is imperative to include them in the solution forms along with the edge functions.

An author who has solved a number of plate problems by a very similar method to the BCM and EFM methods is Nagaya [38-40]. Nagaya's method also makes use of solutions of the differential equations, but instead of satisfying the boundary conditions at discrete collocation points, Nagaya uses a Fourier expansion on the entire boundary. This method, although it works well, is much more complicated both analytically and numerically than the BCM. It should also be mentioned that there have been a number of plate solutions using interior collocation techniques such as the paper of Ng and Sa [41]. These techniques are effective but need to be reformulated for each different shape of plate.

Some authors such as Herrera [42,43] refer to the BCM method as Trefftz method. Trefftz [44] in 1926 proposed a method for solution of the Dirichlet problem in which he used known solutions of the differential equation; however, he satisfied boundary conditions by minimizing a potential around the boundary. Morley [45] in 1956 extended Trefftz method to plates. Leissa et al. [15], however, classify the Trefftz-Morley method as a completely separate method of solution from the BCM. This author agrees with Leissa that the BCM does seem to be sufficiently different from the Trefftz-Morley method to be given a separate name. In the sixties the term "point matching" was coined to describe the BCM, but the more recent preference (see for example reference [1]) is for the method to be referred to as the BCM.

The previously mentioned work of Herrera [42,43] shows the mathematical approach to BCM as does the work of Wendland [46].

The next section will describe the general method of approach for the BCM. This will be followed by sections on the specifics of how the method has been applied to (a) thin plate bending, (b) thin plate buckling, (c) thin plate vibrations, (d) thick plate vibration, (e) bending of shallow spherical shells and (f) vibration of thick shells.

General Description of the Method

The method will be described in terms of the more general weighted residual method WRM (see for example reference [47]). For the boundary value problem (e.g., plate bending) it is necessary to solve

$$Lw(\mathbf{x}) = f(\mathbf{x}) \quad \text{in} \quad \Omega \tag{1}$$

$$B_n w(\mathbf{x}) = g_n(\mathbf{x}) \quad \text{on} \quad \Gamma \quad n = 1,2...,N \tag{2}$$

where L and B_n are known linear differential operators, $f(\mathbf{x})$ and $g_n(\mathbf{x})$ are known functions and $w(\mathbf{x})$ is an unknown function. N is the number of boundary conditions that must be specified at each point on the boundary. If L is a fourth order operator as in thin plate bending then $N = 2$. If L is a sixth order operator as in thick plate bending and shallow spherical shell theory then $N = 3$. In the WRM w is approximated by an expansion in the form

$$\hat{w}(\mathbf{x}) = \sum_{j=1}^{J} a_j \phi_j(\mathbf{x}) \tag{3}$$

where $\phi_j(\mathbf{x})$ are prescribed trial functions and a_j are unknown parameters. The approximate algebraic equations are found by writing the weighted residual forms

$$\int_{\Omega} \mathrm{v}_i (L\hat{w} - f)\, d\Omega + \sum_{n=1}^{N} \int_{\Gamma} \bar{\mathrm{v}}_{in} (B_n \hat{w} - g_n)\, d\Gamma = 0 \quad i = 1,2,...,J \tag{4}$$

where v_i and $\bar{\mathrm{v}}_{in}$ are appropriate weighting functions. If the expansion has the form

$$\hat{w}(\mathbf{x}) = w_p(\mathbf{x}) + \sum_{j=1}^{J} a_j \phi_j(\mathbf{x}) \tag{5}$$

where $w_p(\mathbf{x})$ is an appropriate particular solution of the nonhomogeneous equation (1), and the trial functions $\phi_j(\mathbf{x})$ are chosen to satisfy the homogeneous equation obtained from (1), then only the boundary conditions need to be considered. This requires that

$$\sum_{n=1}^{N} \int_{\Gamma} \bar{v}_{in} (B_n \hat{w} - g_n) \, d\Gamma = 0 \qquad i = 1,2,\ldots,I \tag{6}$$

Further, if the weighting functions are chosen in the form of Dirac delta functions at discrete points $\mathbf{x}_i$ on the boundary then the weighted residual method becomes the boundary collocation method in which the boundary conditions (2) are satisfied at the discrete points $\mathbf{x}_i$. This leads to a system of simultaneous equations which can be written in matrix form as

$$\mathbf{H}\ \mathbf{a} = \mathbf{b} \tag{7}$$

For $N = 1$ the coefficients are

$$h_{ij} = B_1\, \phi_j(\mathbf{x}_i) \tag{8}$$

$$b_i = g_1(\mathbf{x}_i) - B_1\, w_p(\mathbf{x}_i) \tag{9}$$

For $N = 2$ the matrices **H** and **B** can be partitioned as shown below

$$\begin{bmatrix} h_{ij} \\ h_{i+I,j} \end{bmatrix} \{a_j\} = \begin{Bmatrix} b_i \\ b_{i+I} \end{Bmatrix} \tag{10}$$

The coefficients of these partitioned matrices are

$$h_{ij} = B_1\, \phi_j(\mathbf{x}_i) \tag{11}$$

$$h_{i+I,j} = B_2\, \phi_j(\mathbf{x}_i) \tag{12}$$

$$b_i = g_1(\mathbf{x}_i) - B_1\, w_p(\mathbf{x}_i) \tag{13}$$

$$b_{i+I} = g_2(\mathbf{x}_i) - B_2\, w_p(\mathbf{x}_i) \tag{14}$$

For $N = 3$, as in thick plate and shallow spherical shell problems, the matrices **H** and **B** can simply be partitioned again.

For the non-eigenvalue problems such as plate bending it is simply a matter of solving equation (7) for the unknown a_j. The approximate solution is then given by equation (3). This approximate solution can be viewed as an exact solution of an approximate problem since the differential equation has been identically satisfied. The approximation is to the boundary conditions at points other than those identically satisfied. A measure of the accuracy of the solution is in how well the true boundary conditions have been satisfied at points other than the collocation points.

When dealing with eigenvalue problems such as those represented by buckling and vibration of plates the right hand side of equation (7) will be zero. The coefficients of the matrix **H** will, however, be functions of the eigenvalue. The solution process is then to search for the eigenvalues which make the determinant of **H** go to zero. On finding the eigenvalues, equation (7) can be solved for the relative values of a_j and the mode shapes can be evaluated from equation (5). For these straight forward procedures it is necessary that the number of collocation points I and the number of terms in the series J be such as to produce a square matrix **H**. For $N = 1$ this would mean the same number of collocation points as terms in the series, that is, $I = J$. For $N = 2$ if one chose to satisfy both boundary conditions at each point, as has been most often done, then the number of terms in the series would have to be twice the number of collocation points, that is, $J = 2I$.

As an alternative to the insuring that the matrix **H** is square by a proper choice of terms and boundary conditions, one can go to the process known as overdetermined collocation or more simply as over-collocation. In over-collocation more collocation points are chosen than are necessary. Equation (7) then contains more equations than unknowns. The procedure for solving equation (7) in a least squares sense (e.g., reference [48]) is accomplished as follows: Consider a trial solution $\tilde{\mathbf{a}}$ then equation (7) can be written as

$$\mathbf{H}\,\tilde{\mathbf{a}} - \mathbf{b} = \mathbf{e} \tag{15}$$

where **e** represents the error. The sum of the squares of the error is $\mathbf{e}^T\,\mathbf{e}$ and minimizing that error gives

$$\mathbf{H}^T\,\mathbf{H}\,\tilde{\mathbf{a}} = \mathbf{H}^T\,\mathbf{b} \tag{16}$$

The matrix $\mathbf{H}^T\,\mathbf{H}$ is square and positive definite. The solution steps are the same as those outlined above when **H** is square. One drawback to the implementation of this least squares process in eigenvalue problems is that the search for zeros of the determinant of a square matrix **H** involves searching for crossings, whereas the search for the zeros of the determinant of $\mathbf{H}^T\,\mathbf{H}$ involves searching for minima because the determinant (in theory) is always positive.

Thin Plate Bending

The equation for thin plate bending corresponding to equation (1) is

$$D\nabla^4 w = q \tag{17}$$

where w is the transverse displacement (in the z direction), q is the applied force per unit area and ∇^2 is the Laplacian operator. Both w and q are functions of the in-plane coordinates. The flexural rigidity D is defined as,

$$D = \frac{Eh^3}{12(1 - \nu^2)} \tag{18}$$

where h is the thickness of the plate and ν is Poisson's ratio. Boundary conditions are expressed in terms of the displacement w, the normal slope $w_{,n}$, the bending moment M_n and the effective shear V_n where n and s represent the outward normal and the tangential coordinates at the boundary respectively as shown in Figure 2.

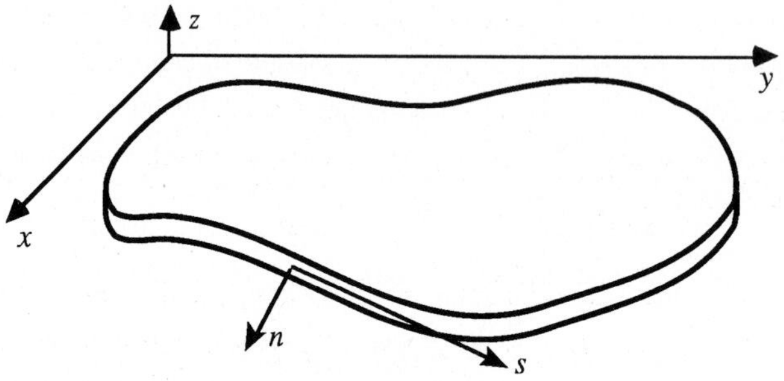

Figure 2. Coordinates of the Plate

The notation $w_{,n}$ means the partial derivative of w with respect to n. The bending moment M_n and effective shear V_n are defined as follows:

$$M_n = -D(w_{,nn} + \nu w_{,ss}) \tag{19}$$

$$V_n = -D[w_{,nnn} + (2 - \nu)w_{,sns}] \tag{20}$$

Usual boundary conditions are specified by equating to zero two of the four functions w, $w_{,n}$, M_n *and* V_n. Usual boundary conditions are

Clamped (C):	$w = 0;$	$w_{,n} = 0$	(21)
Simply Supported (S):	$w = 0;$	$M_n = 0$	(22)
Free (F):	$M_n = 0;$	$V_n = 0$	(23)

Of course, other boundary conditions such as guided edges or various types of elastic support are possible but seldom encountered. When dealing with free corners it is also necessary to specify a zero corner load. This is equivalent to specifying a zero twisting moment, where the twisting moment is defined as

$$M_{ns} = -D(1 - \nu)w_{,ns} \tag{24}$$

There have been many choices made for the basis functions of equation (5) these basis functions all satisfy the homogeneous equation (17) (i.e., q = 0). The most popular has been the form that will be referred to as the variables separable solution in polar coordinates (VSP). It is

$$\begin{Bmatrix} r^n \\ r^{-n} \\ r^{n+2} \\ r^{-n+2} \end{Bmatrix} \begin{Bmatrix} \sin n\theta \\ \cos n\theta \end{Bmatrix} \quad \begin{matrix} n = 1,2,\ldots,\infty \text{ for sin terms} \\ n = 0,1,\ldots,\infty \text{ for cos terms} \end{matrix} \tag{25}$$

For $n = 0$ replace r^{-n} with $\ln r$ and r^{-n+2} with $r^2 \ln r$

For $n = 1$ replace r^{-n+2} with $r \ln r$

Each term in the left set of braces times each term in the right set of braces represents a solution form. Of course, in dealing with solid plates with a centrally placed origin the singular solutions ($\ln r$, $r^2 \ln r$, and r to any negative power) are omitted. References [2 and 4-16] have all used this form, and have all used a single centrally located origin.

A second form which has been used for basis solutions are polynomial forms. The real and imaginary part of any analytic function of z where $z = x + iy$ satisfies the harmonic equation. A harmonic function w_h also satisfies the biharmonic equation as does $x\, w_h$, $y\, w_h$ and $r^2\, w_h$. It is, therefore, simple to create a series of polynomial solutions to use as basis functions ϕ. This procedure was used in references [3] and [26].

A third form will be referred to as the variables separable form in Cartesian coordinates (VSC). Those solution forms are

$$\begin{Bmatrix} \sinh \alpha y \\ \cosh \alpha y \\ \alpha y \sinh \alpha y \\ \alpha y \cosh \alpha y \end{Bmatrix} \begin{Bmatrix} \sin \alpha x \\ \cos \alpha x \end{Bmatrix} \quad \text{and} \quad \begin{Bmatrix} \sinh \beta x \\ \cosh \beta x \\ \beta x \sinh \beta x \\ \beta x \cosh \beta x \end{Bmatrix} \begin{Bmatrix} \sin \beta y \\ \cos \beta y \end{Bmatrix} \tag{26}$$

This form was used for plate bending only in reference [26]. However, it was also used for the plane stress problem in reference [49]. In that reference the α's were chosen as $n\pi/a$ and the β's as $n\pi/b$ where a and b are as defined in Figure 3. In reference [49] a few polynomial solutions were also included to help describe the overall behavior and thus increase convergence.

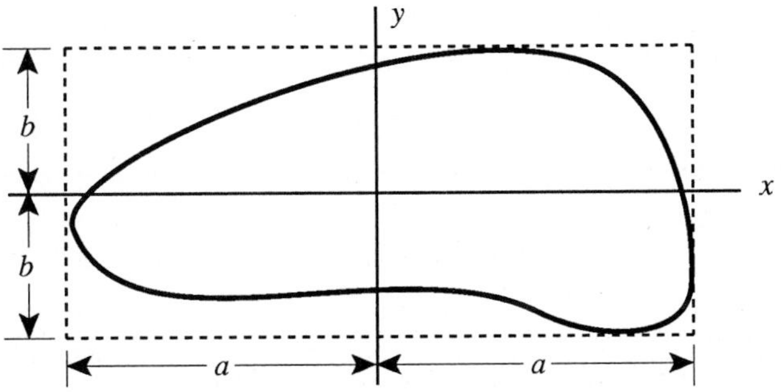

Figure 3. Coordinate system and dimensions for arbitrary domain.

The VSC form can also be written using exponential forms instead of the hyperbolic forms as follows

$$\left\{\begin{array}{c} e^{\alpha(b-y)} \\ e^{-\alpha(b-y)} \\ \alpha(b-y)\, e^{\alpha(b-y)} \\ \alpha(b-y)\, e^{-\alpha(b-y)} \end{array}\right\} \left\{\begin{array}{c} \sin \alpha x \\ \cos \alpha x \end{array}\right\} \quad \text{and} \quad \left\{\begin{array}{c} e^{\beta(a-x)} \\ e^{-\beta(a-x)} \\ \beta(a-x)\, e^{\beta(a-x)} \\ \beta(a-x)\, e^{-\beta(a-x)} \end{array}\right\} \left\{\begin{array}{c} \sin \beta y \\ \cos \beta y \end{array}\right\} \tag{27}$$

Each of these terms can also be considered as being edge functions along each of the four sides of the rectangle shown as a dashed line in Figure 3. For instance, the edge functions corresponding to the line $x = a$ are

$$\left\{\begin{array}{c} e^{-\beta(a-x)} \\ \beta(a-x)\, e^{-\beta(a-x)} \end{array}\right\} \left\{\begin{array}{c} \sin \beta y \\ \cos \beta y \end{array}\right\} \tag{28}$$

These forms decrease as x diminishes into the interior from the line $x = a$. It can be seen that if one were solving in a rectangular region the edge function and standard BCM would be completely equivalent. In the edge function method the edge functions are the VSC forms for a local coordinate system as shown in Figure 4.

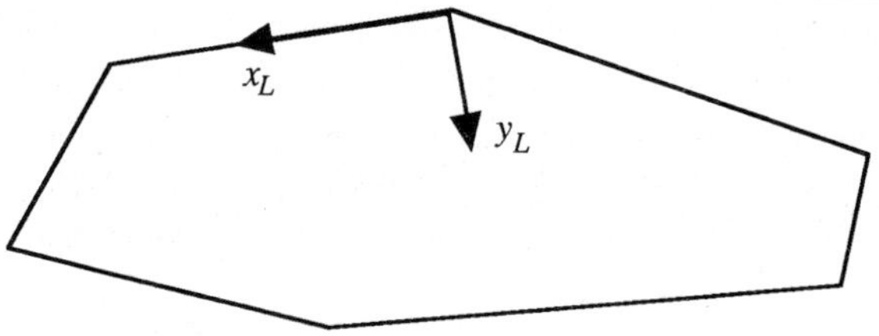

Figure 4. Local coordinates for Edge Function Method

The solution forms in terms of these local coordinates is

$$\left\{\begin{array}{c} e^{-\alpha y_L} \\ \alpha y_L\, e^{-\alpha y_L} \end{array}\right\} \left\{\begin{array}{c} \sin \alpha x_L \\ \cos \alpha x_L \end{array}\right\} \tag{29}$$

A fourth form that has been used in references [17,18] is the fundamental solution. In this form the solution is centered outside the region at a number of source points. The BCM in this form becomes very similar to the indirect BEM. The major difference is that in the BCM, boundary conditions are satisfied only at discrete points; whereas, in the BEM the boundary conditions are satisfied in an integrated sense. In reference [17] the solution $r^2 \ln r$ was used and twice as many source points as boundary collocation points were required. In reference [18] the solution forms were chosen as $r^2 \ln r$, $x \ln r$, $y \ln r$, and $\ln r$. By a unique choice of boundary conditions the same number of boundary collocation points as source points were accommodated.

The loading used by most of the researchers [2-18] was a uniform load for which the particular solution used was

$$w_p = q\, r^4 / 64\, D \tag{30}$$

Barta [2] also solved for the concentrated load at the center of the plate for which the particular solution is

$$w_p = \frac{P\, r^2 \ln r/a}{8\, \pi\, D} \tag{31}$$

Johnson [18] considered the uniformly varying load whose particular solution is

$$w_p = \frac{q_0}{8D}\, x^2\, y^2 + \frac{q_x}{24D}\, x^3\, y^2 + \frac{q_y}{24D}\, x^2\, y^3 \tag{32}$$

Both Johnson [18] and Burgess and Mahajerin [17] discuss the general loading method but since it requires subdividing the domain they do not implement it. Burgess and Mahajerin [17] do introduce an approximate method of treating more general loading cases by making a "polar triangle" subdivision which makes analytical integration possible if the load intensity on each polar triangle is approximated by an average constant intensity.

The boundary conditions that have been applied have not always been simply those listed in equations (21-24). For instance, in the works of Conway [7], because only straight line boundaries were considered, Conway chose to satisfy w and $\nabla^2 w = 0$ rather than w and $M_n = 0$ for the simply supported boundaries. This is a legitimate choice because if one considers $w = 0$ on a straight line boundary then all of the derivatives of w in the tangential direction must also be zero so that $w_{,ss}$ in equation (19) is zero and the imposed boundary condition can be expressed as $\nabla^2 w = 0$ (i.e., $M_n + M_s = 0$). In reference [8] Leissa and Niedenfuhr represented a concentrated load at a free corner by setting the twisting moment M_{ns} equal to half the concentrated load at the corner. Leissa, Lo and Niedenfuhr [10] also investigated plates of regular polygon shapes with simple supports. They used $M_n = 0$ instead of $\nabla^2 w = 0$ and came to the erroneous conclusion that as the number of sides increases the solution will approach that of a simply supported plate. Since, $\nabla^2 w = 0$ is a legitimate boundary condition for the simply supported plate with straight boundaries, the solution must be independent of Poisson's ratio, but the simply supported plate solution is a function of Poisson's ratio. Therefore, the simply supported polygon plate solution cannot approach the simply supported circular plate solution as the number of sides increases. The paper by Rao and Rajaiah [11] showed that the reason for Leissa et al. [10] coming to the wrong conclusion is that the BCM is slow converging to the correct answer if one uses $M_n = 0$ instead of $\nabla^2 w = 0$ for simple supports along straight boundaries. Of course, for curved boundaries the correct choice is $M_n = 0$.

Johnson [18] used a unique set of boundary conditions. For clamped boundaries he used $w = 0$ $w_{,x} = 0$, $w_{,y} = 0$, and $w_{,ss} = 0$, and for simply supported plates he used $w = 0$ $w_{,s} = 0$, $w_{,ss} = 0$, and $M_{,n} = 0$ at the collocation points. These would at first appear to be an over specification, however, if one considers that the conditions are being met at only separate points, then they make sense as a means of arriving at the same number of collocation points as source points. Johnson notes that his solution is very sensitive to the offset distance of the source points from the boundary.

It was drawn to my attention in reading the paper by Burgess and Mahajerin [17] that they had trouble in evaluating the exact solution for an S-F-S-C uniformly loaded plate using the series expression given on page 208 of Timoshenko and Woinowsky-Krieger [50]. Burgess and Mahajerin pointed out that Wu and Altiero [51] had apparently incorrect answers for the same "exact" solution that they used for comparison to a BEM solution. Burgess and Mahajerin tried to correct the problem by calculating the bending moments from differences in the displacement function. The problem, however, is in the formulation given in Timoshenko and Woinowsky-Krieger. The formulation is not incorrect mathematically but leads to just the type of poor convergence found in [17 and 51]. Timoshenko and Woinowsky-Krieger used the coordinate system shown in Figure 5a and used hyperbolic terms in the y direction. As the terms in the series increase the hyperbolic functions will all be small at y = 0 and large at y = b leading to extreme numerical difficulties. If they had used the coordinate system shown in Figure 5b with the same hyperbolic expansion the numerical difficulties would disappear. As an alternative the coordinate system shown in Figure 5a with the solution form shown below could be used.

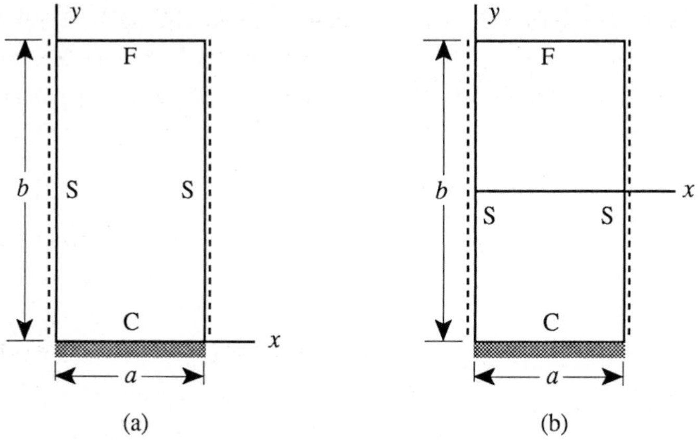

Figure 5. SCSF Plate with different origins.

$$w = \frac{4qa^4}{\pi^5 D} \sum_{n=1,3,5,\ldots}^{\infty} \left[\frac{1}{n^5} + A_n\, e^{-\alpha y} + B_n\, \alpha y e^{-\alpha y} + C_n\, e^{-\alpha(b-y)} + D_n\, \alpha y e^{-\alpha(b-y)} \right] \sin \alpha x \qquad (33)$$

where $\alpha = n\pi/a$. Applying the boundary conditions leads to the a four by four system of equations for the constants A_n, B_n, C_n, and D_n. The deflections are found by summing equation (33) and the moments are found by summing the proper derivatives of equation (33).

There are no convergence problems in carrying out this procedure. Numerical results are shown in Table 1. The columns marked exact are the series solutions, the columns marked B-M are the "exact" solutions from the Burgess and Mahajerin paper and the columns marked FCM are the Burgess and Mahajerin solutions applying their fundamental collocation method.

Table 1. Comparison of exact solution with the "exact" (B-M) and BCM (FCM) solutions of Burgess and Mahajerin [17] (a = 10; b = 20; q = 1)

Fig 4a		Dw			M_x			M_y		
x	y	FCM	B-M	Exact	FCM	B-M	Exact	FCM	B-M	Exact
9.5	1.5	1.6360	1.7939	1.7939	0.2027	0.1742	0.1751	-0.6191	-0.5194	-0.5189
9.5	10.0	16.2859	16.9512	16.9524	2.0326	2.0390	2.0565	0.8129	0.7777	0.7827
9.5	18.5	21.9331	21.7858	21.8034	2.3835	1.6199	2.3703	0.3354	-1.8711	0.3718
7.5	5.0	43.1655	43.1779	43.1780	4.7971	4.7959	4.7953	2.4414	2.4404	2.4407
7.5	10.0	75.1312	75.6906	75.6910	7.9379	7.9328	7.9357	3.1340	3.1288	3.1297
7.5	15.0	87.5561	88.2418	88.2382	8.9045	8.9135	8.9024	2.5964	2.6002	2.5970
5.0	0.0	-0.7051	0.0000	0.0000	-3.8605	-3.7407	-3.7400	-12.5910	-12.4689	-12.4666
5.0	2.5	24.0013	23.8947	23.8947	1.7238	1.7420	1.7426	-0.6559	-0.6644	-0.6633
5.0	6.5	78.2583	78.2201	78.2203	7.9080	7.9171	7.8999	3.9561	4.0123	3.9603
5.0	10.0	105.8086	106.0516	106.0510	10.4650	10.4705	10.4651	4.2024	4.2000	4.1981
5.0	13.5	119.3286	119.7705	119.7722	11.5730	11.5590	11.5714	3.7857	3.7739	3.7778
5.0	17.5	131.0191	131.8763	131.8700	12.2516	12.5138	12.2468	2.4090	3.1975	2.4039
5.0	20.0	148.8957	149.2819	149.4910	13.0470	13.1337	13.0529	0.0030	0.0000	0.0000

It can be seen from this table that the true exact solutions are in better agreement with the BCM (FCM) solutions than were the "exact" solutions of Burgess and Mahajerin. This observation is particularly noticeable in the cases where the moments for B-M and FCM have the greatest discrepancy. The FCM solution of Burgess and Mahajerin is, therefore, even better than they had thought.

Buckling of Thin Plates

The equation for the buckling of thin plates under two dimensional hydrostatic loading is

$$D\nabla^4 w + P\nabla^2 w = 0 \tag{34}$$

where P is the inplane load per unit length. The solution forms which have been used for this problem [7,19] are

$$\begin{Bmatrix} J_n(kr) \\ Y_n(kr) \\ (kr)^n \\ (kr)^{-n} \end{Bmatrix} \begin{Bmatrix} \sin n\theta \\ \cos n\theta \end{Bmatrix} \tag{35}$$

where J_n and Y_n are n^{th} order Bessel functions of the first and second kinds, respectively and k is defined as $k^2 = P/D$. The boundary conditions used in [7] were $w = 0$ and $\nabla^2 w = 0$ since the applications were to simply supported polygon plates. In reference [19] the boundary conditions were clamped. No one has solved buckling problems using a variables separable form in Cartesian coordinates nor the fundamental solution form.

Vibration of Thin Plates

The equation for vibration of thin plates is

$$D\nabla^4 w + m\frac{\partial^2 w}{\partial t^2} = q \tag{36}$$

where m is the mass per unit area of the plate. For the eigenvalue problems that will be considered here, the transverse load q will be taken as zero. The motion is considered as sinusoidal with time so that

$$w(x,y,t) = w(x,y) \sin \omega t \tag{37}$$

where ω is the frequency of vibration. The VSP solution forms, as used in references [7,19,20,22], are

$$\begin{Bmatrix} J_n(\lambda r) \\ Y_n(\lambda r) \\ I_n(\lambda r) \\ K_n(\lambda r) \end{Bmatrix} \begin{Bmatrix} \sin n\theta \\ \cos n\theta \end{Bmatrix} \quad \begin{matrix} n=1,2,\ldots,\infty & \text{for } \sin n\theta \text{ terms} \\ n=0,1,\ldots,\infty & \text{for } \cos n\theta \text{ terms} \end{matrix} \tag{38}$$

where λ is defined from $\lambda^4 = m\omega^2/D$. J_n and Y_n are the nth order Bessel functions of the first and second kind respectively and I_n and K_n are the nth order modified Bessel functions of the first and second kind respectively. In dealing with problems where the origin is within the plate the Y_n and K_n Bessel functions are omitted because they are singular at the origin. The VSC solution forms that were used in [21] were

$$\begin{Bmatrix} \sinh \beta_n y \\ \cosh \beta_n y \\ \sinh \gamma_n y \\ \cosh \gamma_n y \end{Bmatrix} \begin{Bmatrix} \sin \alpha_n x \\ \cos \alpha_n x \end{Bmatrix} \quad \text{and} \quad \begin{Bmatrix} \sinh \kappa_n x \\ \cosh \kappa_n x \\ \sinh \lambda_n x \\ \cosh \lambda_n x \end{Bmatrix} \begin{Bmatrix} \sin \delta_n y \\ \cos \delta_n y \end{Bmatrix} \tag{39}$$

where

$$\beta_n^2 = \alpha_n^2 + \bar{\omega} \tag{40}$$

$$\kappa_n^2 = \delta_n^2 + \bar{\omega} \tag{41}$$

$$\gamma_n^2 = \alpha_n^2 - \bar{\omega} \tag{42}$$

$$\lambda_n^2 = \delta_n^2 - \bar{\omega} \tag{43}$$

and

$$\bar{\omega}^2 = \omega^2\, m/D \tag{44}$$

the terms α_n and δ_n were chosen as

$$\alpha_n = n\pi/a \tag{45}$$

$$\delta_n = n\pi/b \tag{46}$$

where a and b are defined as in Figure 3. In reference [21] a line element method was also introduced whereby the boundary conditions were satisfied along boundary lines instead of just at collocation points. Instead of using the Dirac delta function as the weighting function a constant weighting function was used along each line segment. By treating each line segment as a straight line the integrations in equation (6) were easily evaluated analytically. The results showed improvement in convergence with very little additional analytical or numerical effort.

Edge functions are based on the same VSC forms shown in equation (39) except that exponential forms are substituted for the hyperbolic forms. In terms of the local coordinates shown in Figure 4 the solution forms are

$$\begin{Bmatrix} e^{-\beta_n y_L} \\ e^{-\gamma_n y_L} \end{Bmatrix} \begin{Bmatrix} \sin \alpha_n x_L \\ \cos \alpha_n x_L \end{Bmatrix} \tag{47}$$

where β and γ are defined in equations (40) and (42) respectively. It should be noted that the γ in equation (42) can become imaginary so that the exponential form switches to sinusoidal form when this occurs. The same comment holds in the general VSC solution in equation (39) for both the γ and λ terms.

No one has apparently used the fundamental solutions in the BCM for the plate vibration problems, but the method is completely feasible and might lead to improved results.

Thick Plate Vibrations

Thick plate solutions by the BCM have not received much attention. The only reference I could find to thick plate bending was the paper by Le Fort [32]. It was so specifically oriented to solving the bending of perforated plates with square penetration patterns that a full description is not possible here. The only BCM paper on thick plate vibration is by Akkari and Hutchinson [23]. The Mindlin plate theory [52] was employed in that paper. In the Mindlin plate theory the assumption is that normals to the midplane remain straight but not normal to the midplane after deformation, so that

$$u_r = z\Psi_r(r,\theta\, t) \tag{48}$$

$$u_\theta = z\Psi_\theta(r,\theta\, t) \tag{49}$$

$$u_z = w(r,\theta\, t) \tag{50}$$

where u_r, u_θ *and* u_z are the displacements in the r, θ and z directions respectively, w is the midplane displacement, Ψ_r is the rotation which produces radial displacement and Ψ_θ is the rotation which produces tangential displacement. The dynamic equilibrium equations in terms of the displacement functions (w, Ψ_r, Ψ_θ) are

$$\frac{D}{2}[(1 - \nu)\nabla^2\Psi_r + (1 + \nu)\Phi_{,r}] - \kappa^2 Gh(\Psi_r + w_{,r}) = \frac{\rho h^3}{12}\Psi_{r,tt} \tag{51}$$

$$\frac{D}{2}[(1 - \nu)\nabla^2\psi_\theta + (1 + \nu)\Phi_{,\theta}] - \kappa^2 Gh(\Psi_\theta + w_{,\theta}) = \frac{\rho h^3}{12}\Psi_{\theta,tt} \tag{52}$$

$$\kappa^2 Gh(\nabla^2 w + \Phi) = \rho h w_{,tt} \tag{53}$$

where

$$\Phi = \Psi_{r,r} + \frac{1}{r}\Psi_{\theta,\theta} \tag{54}$$

G is the shear modulus, ρ is the density and κ^2 is the shear coefficient which in reference [23] was taken as $5/(6-\nu)$. Instead of combining equations (51)-(53) to give a single governing equation in w, Mindlin employed a reduction procedure to obtain the following simplified set of equations,

$$(\nabla^2 + \delta_1^2)\, W_1 = 0 \tag{55}$$

$$(\nabla^2 + \delta_2^2)\, W_2 = 0 \tag{56}$$

$$(\nabla^2 + \delta_3^2)\, W_3 = 0 \tag{57}$$

where;

$$\delta_1^2 = \delta_0^4\{R + S + [(R - S)^2 + 4\delta_0^{-4}]^{1/2}\} / 2 \tag{58}$$

$$\delta_2^2 = \delta_0^4\{R + S - [(R - S)^2 + 4\delta_0^{-4}]^{1/2}\} / 2 \tag{59}$$

$$\delta_3^2 = 2(R\delta_0^4 - S^{-1}) / (1 - \nu) \tag{60}$$

$$R = h^2 / 12, \quad \delta_0^4 = \rho\omega^2 h / D, \quad \text{and} \quad S = D / \kappa^2 Gh \tag{61}$$

where R and S represent the effects of rotary inertia and shear deformation respectively, and ω is the angular frequency. W_1 and W_2 are components of displacements perpendicular to the middle surface and W_3 is the potential function which allows for the twist about the normal to the plane of the plate. Once the solution to equations (55)-(57) is found then the displacement functions are given by

$$\Psi_r = (\sigma_1 - 1)\, W_{1,r} + (\sigma_2 - 1)\, W_{2,r} + \frac{1}{r} W_{3,\theta} \tag{62}$$

$$\Psi_\theta = (\sigma_1 - 1)\, W_{1,r} + \frac{1}{r}(\sigma_2 - 1)\, W_{2,\theta} + W_{3,r} \tag{63}$$

$$w = W_1 + W_2 \tag{64}$$

where

$$\sigma_1 = \delta_2\, [R\delta_0^4 - S^{-1}]^{-1} \tag{65}$$

$$\sigma_2 = \delta_1\, [R\delta_0^4 - S^{-1}]^{-1} \tag{66}$$

Solution forms for W_1, W_2, and W_3 are

$$\begin{Bmatrix} J_n(\delta_1 r) \\ Y_n(\delta_1 r) \end{Bmatrix} \begin{Bmatrix} \cos n\theta \\ \sin n\theta \end{Bmatrix} \quad \text{for } W_1 \tag{67}$$

$$\begin{Bmatrix} J_n(\delta_2 r) \\ Y_n(\delta_2 r) \end{Bmatrix} \begin{Bmatrix} \cos n\theta \\ \sin n\theta \end{Bmatrix} \quad \text{for } W_2 \tag{68}$$

$$\begin{Bmatrix} J_n(\delta_3 r) \\ Y_n(\delta_3 r) \end{Bmatrix} \begin{Bmatrix} \sin n\theta \\ \cos n\theta \end{Bmatrix} \quad \text{for } W_3 \tag{69}$$

In the Mindlin theory three boundary conditions are specified at each point. Appropriate boundary conditions for the various cases are specified as follows:

Clamped:

$$w = 0 \tag{70}$$

$$\Psi_r = 0 \tag{71}$$

$$\Psi_\theta = 0 \tag{72}$$

Simply supported:

$$w = 0 \tag{73}$$

$$M_n = M_r \cos^2(\phi-\theta) + M_\theta \sin^2(\phi-\theta) + 2M_{\theta r} \sin(\phi-\theta) \cos(\phi-\theta) = 0 \tag{74}$$

$$M_{ns} = (M_\theta - M_r) \sin(\phi-\theta) \cos(\phi-\theta) + M_{\theta r}[\cos^2(\phi-\theta) - \sin(\phi-\theta)] = 0 \tag{75}$$

Free:

$$M_n = 0 \tag{76}$$

$$M_{ns} = 0 \tag{77}$$

$$Q_n = Q_r \cos(\phi-\theta) + Q_\theta \sin(\phi-\theta) = 0 \tag{78}$$

where the angles ϕ and θ are as described in Figure 6.

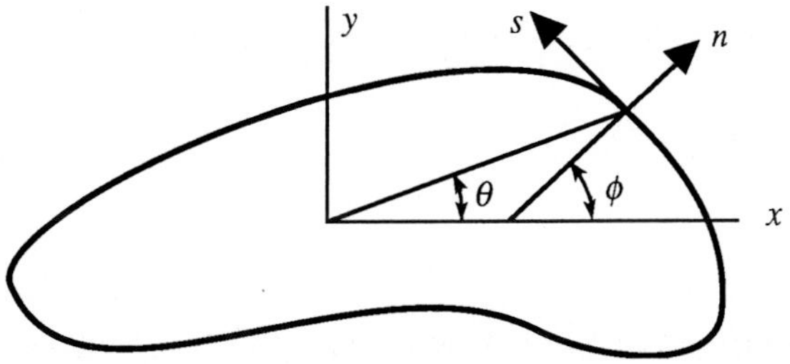

Figure 6. Circular coordinates for an arbitrary domain

Table 2 from reference [23] is a very interesting comparison of a number of different solutions for the simply supported square plate. The thin plate solution can be found in the monograph by Leissa [53]. The boundary conditions allow an exact solution of the three dimensional elasticity equations as shown by Levinson [54]. The Mindlin solution is also easily found for the simply supported boundary conditions as was done in Levinson's paper [54]. All three methods are compared with the BCM method using 24 collocation points around the boundary. It can be seen that these fundamental frequencies for the elasticity solution the Mindlin solution and the BCM method agree reasonably well while the thin plate theory diverges as the thickness to width ratio increases. The lengths a and b are as defined in Figure 3.

Table 2. Comparison of the fundamental frequency parameters $\omega(\rho/Dh^3)^{1/2}$ of a simply supported thick square plate with various thickness ratios. ($a = b = 1$; $\nu = 0.3$).

$\frac{h}{2a}$	Thin Theory	Elasticity Method	Mindlin Theory	BCM Method
0.05	0.493	0.486	0.491	0.489
0.10	0.987	0.951	0.953	0.954
0.20	1.974	1.752	1.742	1.752
0.40	3.948	2.788	2.749	2.784
0.60	5.922	3.339	3.270	3.332
0.80	7.896	3.648	3.555	3.636
1.00	9.870	3.833	3.724	3.817

In reference [23] all comparisons with known solutions involving simply supported and clamped plates showed the same good results, but for problems involving free edges, difficulties were encountered. For other than free circular plates ill-conditioning of the matrices occurred and the results were poor.

Shallow Spherical Shells

Conway and Leissa [24] solved problems of shallow spherical shells by the BCM in 1962. They used Reissner's [55] shallow spherical shell equations which are

$$\nabla^4 F - (hE/R)\nabla^2 w = 0 \tag{79}$$

$$\nabla^4 w + [1/(RD)]\nabla^2 F = q/D \tag{80}$$

where w is the radial deflection in a direction of a normal exterior to the shell, R is the radius of the spherical shell and F is a stress function for the membrane forces as follows

$$N_r = \frac{1}{r} F_{,r} + \frac{1}{r^2} F_{,\theta\theta} \tag{81}$$

$$N_\theta = F_{,rr} \tag{82}$$

$$N_{r\theta} = -\left(\frac{1}{r} F_{,\theta}\right)_{,r} \tag{83}$$

Taking the Laplacian of equation (80) and substituting for $\nabla^4 F$ from equation (79) gives

$$\nabla^6 w + [hE/(R^2 D)]\nabla^2 w = \nabla^2 q/D \tag{84}$$

Solution forms for these equations where $s = x/l$ are

$$\left\{\begin{matrix} \mathrm{ber}_n\, s \\ \mathrm{bei}_n\, s \\ \mathrm{ker}_n\, s \\ \mathrm{kei}_n\, s \\ s^n \\ s^{-n} \end{matrix}\right\}\left\{\begin{matrix} \sin n\theta \\ \cos n\theta \end{matrix}\right\} \qquad \begin{matrix} n = 1,2,...,\infty \text{ for sin terms} \\ n = 0,1,...,\infty \text{ for cos terms} \end{matrix} \tag{85}$$

For $n = 0$ replace s^{-n} with $\ln s$

The functions ber_n, bei_n, ker_n and kei_n are the Kelvin functions of order n. The stress function F, of course, can be expressed in a similar way to the expression for w. Conway and Leissa applied this formulation to a uniformly loaded spherical shell clamped on a square base as shown in Figure 7. The mean radius of the shell was 90 inches and the thickness was 3 inches. They satisfied the boundary conditions at $\theta = 0$, 22.5° and 45° the rest being satisfied by symmetry. The boundary conditions Conway and Leissa used for this problem were $w = w_{,r} = 0$ and zero tangential strain ($N_\theta - \nu N_r = 0$). They also solved the shallow spherical shell with a radially loaded elliptical insert. Reasonable solutions resulted in both cases.

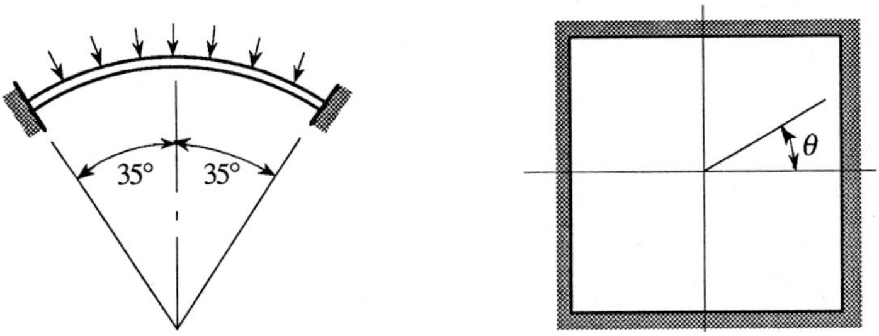

Side view Top view

Figure 7. Uniformly loaded spherical shell clamped on a square base. From Conway and Leissa [24].

In 1977 Nash, Tai, O'Callaghan and Quinlan [35] used the edge function method for determination of the natural frequencies of a shallow spherical shell. The shell was similar to that shown in Figure 7. It was simply supported at the square boundary which had a length of 12.0 inches on each side. The radius of curvature was 30.0 inches and the shell thickness was 0.05 inches. The first four natural frequencies were found, and the first second and fourth frequencies were shown to be in good agreement with previously published results.

Thick Shells of Revolution

In the recent paper of Houmat and Hutchinson [25] the BCM method was applied to the solution of free vibrations of solids of revolution. In that paper solution forms which satisfy the three dimensional equations of linear elasticity were used to solve problems with arbitrary shape as shown in Figure 8.

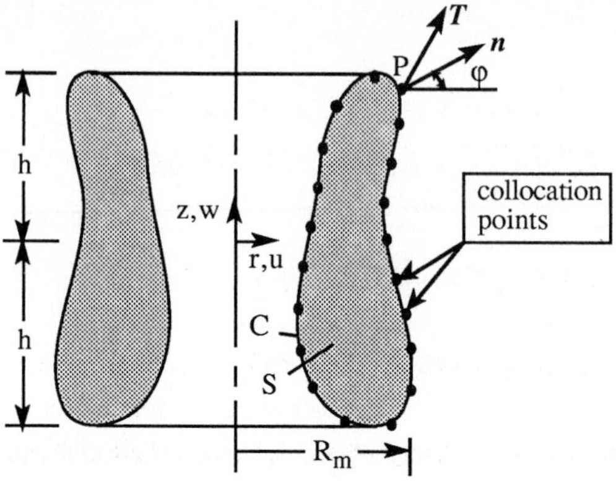

Figure 8. Coordinates and characteristic dimensions of an arbitrary outline of a solid of revolution

The solution forms that were used are the variables separable form in cylindrical coordinates that are shown in Table 3

Table 3. Solutions of the governing differential equations in cylindrical coordinates. J_n is the nth order Bessel function of the first kind. Primes denote differentiation with respect to the argument.

$\alpha^2 + \delta^2 = \frac{(1-2\nu)}{2(1-\nu)}\omega^2$; $\alpha^2 + \beta^2 = \omega^2$; ν is Poisson's ratio .

	Form 1	Form 2	Form 3
u	$\delta J_n'(\delta r)\begin{Bmatrix}\cos(\alpha z)\\ \sin(\alpha z)/\alpha\end{Bmatrix}\cos(n\theta)$	$-\beta J_n'(\beta r)\begin{Bmatrix}\cos(\alpha z)\\ \alpha\sin(\alpha z)\end{Bmatrix}\cos(n\theta)$	$-nJ_n(\beta r)/r\begin{Bmatrix}\cos(\alpha z)\\ \sin(\alpha z)/\alpha\end{Bmatrix}\cos(n\theta)$
v	$-nJ_n(\delta r)/r\begin{Bmatrix}\cos(\alpha z)\\ \sin(\alpha z)/\alpha\end{Bmatrix}\sin(n\theta)$	$nJ_n(\beta r)/r\begin{Bmatrix}\cos(\alpha z)\\ \alpha\sin(\alpha z)\end{Bmatrix}\sin(n\theta)$	$\beta J_n'(\beta r)\begin{Bmatrix}\cos(\alpha z)\\ \sin(\alpha z)/\alpha\end{Bmatrix}\sin(n\theta)$
w	$J_n(\delta r)\begin{Bmatrix}-\alpha\sin(\alpha z)\\ \cos(\alpha z)\end{Bmatrix}\cos(n\theta)$	$\beta^2 J_n(\beta r)\begin{Bmatrix}-\sin(\alpha z)/\alpha\\ \cos(\alpha z)\end{Bmatrix}\cos(n\theta)$	0

In Table 3 u, v and w refer to the radial tangential and axial displacements as defined in Figure 8. There is another set of solution forms which is found simply by changing the J's to Y's. The stress components can be found by applying the strain-displacement relations and Hooke's law to the displacement forms (stress forms were also tabulated in reference [25]). Three boundary conditions must be specified at each point on the boundary. The boundary conditions were specified as follows

$$u = 0 \quad \text{or} \quad T_r = 0 \tag{86}$$

$$v = 0 \quad \text{or} \quad T_\theta = 0 \tag{87}$$

$$w = 0 \quad \text{or} \quad T_z = 0 \tag{88}$$

T_r, T_θ, and T_z are the components of the traction vector $\boldsymbol{T}$ at the boundary point P along the r, θ, and z directions respectively, and are given by

$$T_r = \sigma_{rr} \cos \varphi + \tau_{rz} \sin \varphi \tag{89}$$

$$T_\theta = \tau_{r\theta} \cos \varphi + \tau_{\theta z} \sin \varphi \tag{90}$$

$$T_z = \tau_{rz} \cos \varphi + \sigma_{zz} \sin \varphi \tag{91}$$

φ is the angle that the unit normal vector $\boldsymbol{n}$ at the boundary point P makes with the r axis, as shown in Figure 8. Figure 9 shows the various shapes which were considered in that work. Comparisons were made with solutions from the educational version of the commercial finite element package ANSYS (Swanson Analysis Systems Inc., Houston). For all of these cases an 8 node solid structural element was used. The case of the hollow very thick cylinder with free boundaries was also compared with the highly accurate solutions obtained by Hutchinson and El-Azhari [56] by a series method. Comparisons with the accurate series solution showed that frequencies using 18 collocation points in the BCM were more accurate than the ANSYS solution using 32 elements.

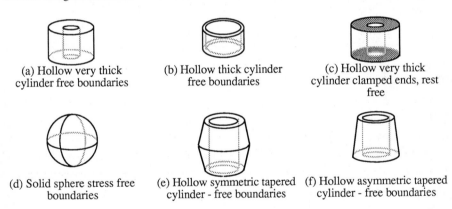

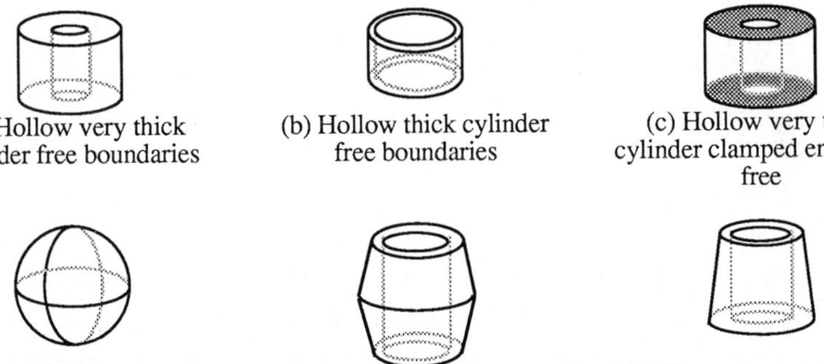

(a) Hollow very thick cylinder free boundaries

(b) Hollow thick cylinder free boundaries

(c) Hollow very thick cylinder clamped ends, rest free

(d) Solid sphere stress free boundaries

(e) Hollow symmetric tapered cylinder - free boundaries

(f) Hollow asymmetric tapered cylinder - free boundaries

Figure 9. Shapes considered in reference [25]

None of the above shapes are thin shells so new results for thin shells were generated. Table 4 shows these new results for a thin cylindrical shell with stress free boundaries. The thickness is one hundredth of the outer radius and the height is equal to the outer radius. The notation used in Table 4 is NT is the number of terms in each series, NP is the number of collocation points and NE is the number of 8 node elements used in ANSYS. The dimensionless frequency ω is the actual frequency multiplied by the outer radius and divided by the shear velocity. It can be seen in this table that it was impossible to get four of the frequency values using the BCM for n = 0 and n = 1. This was not at all the case for any of the shapes shown in Figure 9. Even with the missing frequencies it still must be concluded that the BCM gives very reasonable results for thin as well as thick shells using this formulation.

Table 4. Comparison of the lowest four even and odd frequencies ω from BCM, and ANSYS. Circumferential wave numbers n = 0, 1, 2, 3, and 4.
BCM : Row 1 : NT = 7 , NP = 14
Row 2 : NT = 9 , NP = 18
ANSYS : NE = 20

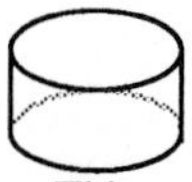

Thin Cylindrical Shell

n	Method	Even				Odd			
		1	2	3	4	1	2	3	4
0	BCM	1.577	1.619	1.620	1.676	1.612	1.620	1.646	1.686
		1.578	1.619	-	1.676	1.612	-	1.646	-
	ANSYS	1.577	1.618	1.625	1.660	1.613	1.621	1.637	1.699
1	BCM	1.416	1.587	1.634	-	1.250	1.547	1.621	1.670
		1.416	1.587	1.637	1.787	1.250	1.547	1.608	1.621
	ANSYS	1.416	1.584	1.643	1.751	1.250	1.546	1.613	1.688
2	BCM	0.013	1.000	1.466	1.608	0.017	1.304	1.542	1.637
		0.013	1.000	1.466	1.608	0.017	1.301	1.525	1.680
	ANSYS	0.013	1.000	1.463	1.595	0.017	1.303	1.533	1.654
3	BCM	0.037	0.664	1.298	1.532	0.043	1.065	1.432	1.592
		0.037	0.661	1.300	1.532	0.041	1.069	1.457	1.630
	ANSYS	0.037	0.665	1.295	1.520	0.044	1.063	1.425	1.605
4	BCM	0.071	0.457	1.120	1.438	0.079	0.845	1.305	1.528
		0.071	0.458	1.120	1.441	0.078	0.849	1.301	1.570
	ANSYS	0.071	0.457	1.118	1.430	0.079	0.843	1.298	1.543

Discussion

In the great majority of papers cited in this chapter the BCM has been shown to give excellent results with a minimum of analytic and computational effort. The method is both easy to understand and easy to apply yet it is one of the least used methods today. Perhaps the reason for its unpopularity is that the flaws in the method are also extremely evident. One of the most obvious flaws is the one pointed out by Deverall [6], which is, that as two boundary points get closer and closer together the two linear equations resulting from these points have nearly the same coefficients and this can lead to ill-conditioned matrices. It is interesting that none of the researchers noted ill-conditioning because of proximity of collocation points as a problem.

The poor results of Conway and Farnham [12] and Leissa and Clausen [13] for circular plates having the mixed boundary conditions shown in Figures 1b and 1c does not appear to be from ill-conditioning because of two points being close together. It is more likely that the solution forms are not able to represent the deflected form near the junction between the free edge and the simply supported or clamped edge. There is probably some type of singular behavior taking place at that point. In reference [22] it was found that for cantilever trapezoidal plates the corner between the fixed and free edges could best be matched by applying only one boundary condition at that point. The condition that w is zero.

True singular behavior cannot be expected to be represented by either of the variables separable type of formulations because all of those solutions are very smooth. For instance in reference [57] it was found when investigating the vibration of membranes that the L shaped membrane gave severe problems. The L shaped membrane has a reentrant corner and in certain modes such as the fundamental mode a singularity exists at the reentrant corner. Using a variables separable solution form centered at the point A as shown in Figure 10a, the fundamental solution could not be found. By subdividing the domain and using solution forms centered at A and B shown in Figure 10b, and matching conditions along the dashed subdivision line, the fundamental frequency could be found. No one has reported trying the L shaped plate but it should lead to the same difficulties as L shaped membrane for the variables separable approach. It is possible however that the fundamental solution approach as reported by Burgess and Mahajerin [17] and Johnson [18] would take care of this problem.

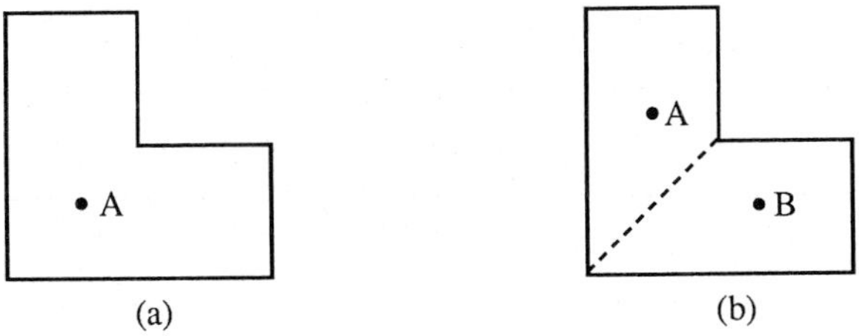

Figure 10. L Shaped Membrane

It has been suggested that one could actually include a singularity at the place one is known to occur, such as, a singular solution placed at the reentrant corner in Figure 10. This, of course, means that one would have to have pre-knowledge of the type of singularity that exists. It would also remove some of the automatic process of simply being able to describe the placement of points around the boundary. At the same time, the ability to be able to include such singularities can be considered a major advantage of the method.

The line element method used by Akkari and Hutchinson [21] appears to have some real merit. The use of constant weighting functions along straight line segments made the integrations easy to evaluate analytically. The results showed improvement in convergence over the BCM with very little additional analytical or numerical effort. This process can, of course, be carried to the extreme as in the solutions of Nagaya [38-40] in which a Fourier series of weighting functions is used and numerical integration is carried out around the entire boundary. Nagaya's process, because it involves the numerical integration, would seem to greatly decrease the computational efficiency of the solution process as well as possibly increase the chance of round-off error.

The edge function method has been shown to be an effective variation of the BCM in references [33-37]. It appears that in all the applications of this process straight line elements were used. This limits the boundary to being polygonal. It occurs to me that the process could be applied to a more general curved boundary by defining the edge functions along a superscribed polygon and satisfying boundary conditions at collocation points along the actual curved boundary. Of course this would negate the use of orthogonalization along the straight line elements, as is most commonly done, but it would provide greater flexibility in the boundary shape.

The use of the least squares approach was reported in three of the BCM plate references [15,20,22]. The method has been shown to be very valuable in interior collocation as reported by Ng and Sa [41]. For boundary collocation Hegarty and Ariman [20] indicate that they got the best results by using a ratio of equations to unknowns of 2. Akkari and Hutchinson [22] showed similar improvement with least squares implementation; however, they found that in certain problems some of the natural frequencies were actually missing. Further, the matrix multiplication represented $\mathbf{H}^T \mathbf{H}$ in equation (16) coupled with the complication of searching for minimums of $|\mathbf{H}^T \mathbf{H}|$ instead of crossings of $|\mathbf{H}|$ made the implementation sufficiently more difficult computationally to be hardly worth the effort. Leissa et al. [15] note that, "the least squares procedures are known to generate ill-conditioned matrices on occasion." The advantage of the least squares implementation is that the solution is less dependent on the problem solver's ability to choose point locations judiciously, but this hardy seems to outweigh the disadvantages when dealing with boundary collocation, particularly in eigenvalue problems.

Conclusions

The boundary collocation method is by far the simplest method both conceptually and numerically for solving the linear partial differential equations that arise in many plate and shell problems. It is also the most under-utilized method. Some of its advantages and disadvantages are listed below.

Advantages

- It is easy to understand and program.
- It is easily programmed for arbitrary shape and arbitrary boundary conditions.
- A small number of unknowns produce excellent results.
- Analytic treatment of singularities can be included.
- The solution appears as a closed form for the whole region.

Disadvantages

- It is limited to linear problems.
- A complete set of solutions to the differential equations must be known.
- Matrices are full and sometimes ill-conditioned.

There is much need for future research in the boundary collocation method. It has been shown to be a very effective means of solution for many of the practical problems involving plates and shells and yet has not reached the general popularity of many of the more difficult solution procedures. The major drawback seems to be with the belief that the BCM produces ill-conditioned matrices. While this is sometimes the case, it is hoped that future research can alleviate this drawback.

Acknowledgment

The author wishes to thank Abderrahim Houmat for computing the frequencies for thin cylindrical shells shown in Table 4.

References

1. Kolodziej, J.A., Review of Application of Boundary Collocation Methods in Mechanics of Continuous Media, *Solid Mechanics Archives*, **12**, 1987, pp. 187-231.

2. Barta, J., Über die näherungsweise Lösung einiger zweidimensionaler Elastizitätsaufgaben, *Zeitschrift fur angewandte Mathematik und Mechanik.*, **7**, 1937, pp. 184-185.

3. Thorne, C.J., Square Plate Fixed at Points, *Journal of Applied Mechanics*, **70**, 1948, pp. 73-79

4. Sekiya, T., An Approximate Solution in the Problems of Elastic Plates with Arbitrary External Form and a Circular Hole, *Proceedings of the 5th Japan National Congress for Applied Mechanics*, 1955, pp. 95-98

5. Conway, H.D., The Approximate Analysis of Certain Boundary-Value Problems, *Journal of Applied Mechanics*, **27**, 1960, pp. 275-277.

6. Deverall, L.I., Discussion of: The Approximate Analysis of Certain Boundary-Value Problems, *Journal of Applied Mechanics*, **28**, 1961, pp. 156-157.

7. Conway, H.D., The Bending, Buckling, and Flexural Vibration of Simply Supported Polygonal Plates by Point-Matching, *Journal of Applied Mechanics*, **28**, 1961, pp. 288-191.

8. Leissa, A.W. and Niedenfuhr, F.W., A Study of the Cantilevered Square Plate Subjected to Uniform Loading, *Journal of the Aerospace Sciences*, **29**, 1962, pp. 162-169.

9. Leissa, A.W. and Niedenfuhr, F.W., Bending of a Square Plate With Two Adjacent Edges Free and the Others Clamped or Simply Supported, *AIAA Journal*, **1**, 1963, pp. 116-120.

10. Leissa, A.W. , Lo C.C. and Niedenfuhr F.W., Uniformly Loaded Plates of Regular Polygonal Shape, *AIAA Journal*, **3**, 1965, pp. 566-567.

11. Rao, A.K. and Rajaiah, K., Polygon-Circle Paradox of Simply Supported Thin Plates under Uniform Pressure, *AIAA Journal*, **6**, 1968, pp. 155-156.

12. Conway, H.D. and Farnham, K.A., Deflections of Uniformly Loaded Circular Plates with Combinations of Clamped, Simply Supported and Free Boundary Conditions, *International Journal of Mechanical Sciences*, **9**, 1967, pp. 661-671.

13. Leissa, A.W. and Clausen, W.E., Deflection of a Circular Plate Having Mixed Boundary Conditions, *AIAA Journal*, **4**, 1967, pp. 2287-2289.

14. Lo, C.C. and Leissa A.W., Bending of Plates With Circular Holes, *Acta Mechanica*, **4**, 1967, pp. 64-78.

15. Leissa, A.W., Clausen W.E., Hulbert L.E. and Hopper A.T., A Comparison of Approximate Methods for the Solution of Plate Bending Problems, *AIAA Journal*, **7**, 1969, pp. 920-928.

16. Hoffman, R.E. and Ariman, T., Thermal Bending of Plates with Circular Holes, *Nuclear Engineering and Design*, **14**, 1970, pp. 231-238.

17. Burgess G. and Mahajerin, E., A Numerical Method for Laterally Loaded Thin Plates, *Computer Methods in Applied Mechanics and Engineering*, **49**, 1985, pp. 1-15.

18. Johnson, D., Plate Bending by a Boundary Point Method, *Computers and Structures*, **26**, 1987, pp. 673-680.

19. Conway, H.D. and Leissa, A.W., A Method for Investigating Certain Eigenvalue Problems of the Buckling and Vibration of Plates, *Journal of Applied Mechanics*, **27**, 1960, pp. 557-558.

20. Hegarty, R.F. and Ariman, T., Elasto-Dynamic Analysis of Rectangular Plates with Circular Holes, *International Journal of Solids and Structures*, **11**, 1975, pp. 895-906.

21. Akkari, M.M. and Hutchinson, J.R., An Alternative BEM Formulation Applied to Plate Vibrations, *Boundary Elements VII*, Eds. Brebbia, C.A. and Maier, G., Springer-Verlag, Berlin, **1**, 1985, pp. 6-111 - 6-126.

22. Akkari, M.M. and Hutchinson, J.R., An Improved Boundary Method for Plate Vibrations, *Boundary Element Techniques: Applications in Stress Analysis and Heat Transfer*, Eds. Brebbia, C.A. and Venturini, W.S., Computational Mechanics Publications, Southampton, 1987, pp. 89-103.

23. Akkari, M.M. and Hutchinson, J.R., Boundary Point Collocation Method for the Vibration of a Mindlin Thick Plate, *Boundary Elements X*, Ed. Brebbia, C.A., Springer-Verlag, Berlin, **3**, 1988, pp. 465-476.

24. Conway, H.D. and Leissa, A.W., Application of the Point Matching Method to Shallow-Spherical Shell Theory, *Journal of Applied Mechanics*, **29**, 1962, pp. 745-747.

25. Houmat, A. and Hutchinson, J.R., A Boundary Method for Free Vibration of Solids of Revolution, *Advances in Boundary Elements Methods in Japan and USA*. Eds. M. Tanaka, C.A. Brebbia and R. Shaw, Computational Mechanics Publications, 1990, pp. 121-135.

26. Nash, W.A., Several Approximate Analyses of the Bending of a Rectangular Cantilever Plate by Uniform Normal Pressure, *Journal of Applied Mechanics*, **19**, 1952, pp. 33-36.

27. Conway, H.D., On Some Systems of Equations Encountered in Thin Plate and Elasticity Theory, *Journal of Applied Mechanics*, **28**, 1961, pp. 143-144.

28. Conway, H.D., Triangular Plates Analyzed by Point Matching, *Journal of Applied Mechanics*, **29**, 1962, pp. 755-756.

29. Warren, W.E., Bending of Rhombic Plates, *AIAA Journal*, **2**, 1964, pp. 166-168.

30. Sattinger, S.S. and Conway H.D., The Solution of Certain Isoscelles-Triangle and Rhombus Torsion and Plate Problems, *International Journal of Mechanical Sciences*, **7**, 1965, pp. 221-228.

31. Conway, H.D. and Farnham K.A., The Free Flexural Vibrations of Triangular, Rhombic and Parallelogram Plates and Some Analogies, *International Journal of Mechanical Sciences*, **7**, 1965, pp. 811-816.

32. Le Fort, P., Bending of Perforated Plates with Square Penetration Patterns, *Nuclear Engineering and Design*, **12**, 1970, pp. 122-134.

33. Quinlan, P.M., The λ-method for Skew Plates, *Proceedings of the Fourth U.S. National Congress of Applied Mechanics*, 1962, pp. 733-750.

34. Quinlan, P.M., The λ-method for Rectangular Plates, *Proceedings of the Royal Society of London*, Series A, **288**, 1965, pp. 371-395.

35. Nash, W.A., Tai, I.H., O'Callaghan, M.J.A. and Quinlan, P.M., Statics and Dynamics of Elastic Bodies - A New Approach, *International Symposium on Numerical Analysis in Applied Engineering Science*, Eds. T.A. Cruse et al., CETIM, Senlis, France, 1977, pp. 8-3 - 8-8.

36. O'Callaghan, M.J.A. and Studdert, R.P., The Edge Function Method for the Free Vibration of Thin Orthotropic Plates, *Boundary Elements VII*, Eds. Brebbia, C.A. and Maier, G., Springer-Verlag, Berlin, 1985, 6-37 - 6-53.

37. Quinlan, P.M., The Edge Function Method (EFM) for 2-D Regions with Arbitrary Boundaries, in Fracture Elastodynamics, Thin Plates and Laplace/Poisson Problems, *Boundary Elements X*, Ed. Brebbia, C.A., Springer-Verlag, Berlin, **1**, 1988,

38. Nagaya, K., Dynamics of Viscoelastic Plate with Curved Boundaries of Arbitrary Shape, *Journal of Applied Mechanics*, **45**, 1978, pp. 629-635.

39. Nagaya, K., Dynamic Response of a Plate with Arbitrary Shape, *Journal of Applied Mechanics*, **47**, 1980, pp. 620-625.

40. Nagaya, K., Simplified Method for Solving Problems of Vibrating Plates of Doubly Connected Arbitrary Shape, *Journal of Sound and Vibration*, **74**, 1981, pp. 543-551.

41. Ng, S.F. and Sa, T.A., A Collocation Approach to Plate Vibration, *Journal of Structural Mechanics*, **12**, 1984, pp. 43-57.

42. Herrera, I., **Boundary Methods An Algebraic Theory**, Pitman Publishing Co., London, 1984.

43. Herrera, I., Trefftz Method, *Progress in Boundary Element Research*, Ch. 10, Ed. Brebbia, C.A., Springer-Verlag, Berlin, 1984, pp. 225-253.

44. Trefftz, E., Ein Gegenstück zum Ritzschen Verfahren, *Proceedings II International Congress of Applied Mechanics*, 1926, pp. 131-137.

45. Morley, L.S.D., The Approximate Solution of Plate Problems, *Proceedings of the Ninth International Congress for Applied Mechanics*, Brussels, **6**, 1956, pp. 22-29.

46. Wendland, W.L., Asymptotic Accuracy and Convergence of Point Collocation Methods, *Topics in Boundary Element Research*, Brebbia, C.A., Springer-Verlag, Berlin, **2**, 1985, pp. 230-257.

47. Finlayson, B.A., **The Method of Weighted Residuals, and Variational Principles**, Academic Press, New York, 1972.

48. Eason, E.D., A Review of Least-Squares Methods for Solving Partial Differential Equations, *International Journal for Numerical Methods in Engineering*, **10**, 1976, pp. 1021-1046.

49. Hutchinson, J.R., An Alternative BEM Formulation with Application to Plane Elasticity Problems, *Boundary Elements*, Eds. Brebbia, C.A., Futagami, T. and Tanaka, M., Springer-Verlag, Berlin, 1983, pp. 407-416.

50. Timoshenko, S. and Woinowsky-Kreiger, S., **Theory of Plates and Shells**, McGraw-Hill, New York, Second Edition, 1959.

51. Wu, B.C. and Altiero, N.J., A Boundary Integral Method Applied to Plates of Arbitrary Plan Form and Arbitrary Boundary Conditions, *Computers and Structures*, **10**, 1979, pp. 703-707.

52. Mindlin, R.D., Influence of Rotatory Inertia and Shear on Flexural Motions of Isotropic Elastic Plates, *Journal of Applied Mechanics*, **73**, 1951, pp. 31-38.

53. Leissa, A.W., **Vibration of Plates**, NASA SP-160, 1969.

54. Levinson, M., Free Vibration of a Simply Supported Rectangular Plate: Exact Elasticity Solution, *Journal of Sound and Vibration*, **98**, 1985, pp. 289-298.

55. Reissner, E., Stresses and Small Displacements of Shallow Spherical Shells, *Journal of Mathematics and Physics*, **25**, 1946, p. 80 and 26, 1947, p. 279.

56. Hutchinson, J.R. and El-Azhari, S.A., Vibrations of Free Hollow Circular Cylinders, *Journal of Applied Mechanics*, **53**, 1986, pp. 641-646.

57. Hutchinson, J.R., An Alternative BEM Formulation Applied to Membrane Vibrations, *Boundary Elements VII*, Eds. Brebbia, C.A. and Maier, G., **1**, Ch.6, Springer-Verlag, 1985, pp. 6-13 - 6-25.